D0487107

✓ BIOTECHNOLOGY

Present Position & Future Development

Martina Newell McGloughlin & James I. Burke

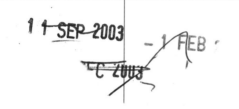
ROYAL AGRICULTURAL COLLEGE LIBRARY
CIRENCESTER

This book should be returned to the Library
not later than the date stamped below

1 1 SEP 2003   - 1 FEB

C 2003

Teagasc
AGRICULTURE AND FOOD DEVELOPMENT AUTHORITY

First published in 2000 by:

Teagasc, 19 Sandymount Avenue, Ballsbridge, Dublin 4, Ireland.

© Teagasc, 2000.

All rights reserved. No part of this publication may be reproduced,
stored in a retrieval system, or transmitted in any form without the
written permission of the publisher.

ISBN 1 84170 122 X

CONTENTS

List of Tables

List of Figures

ACKNOWLEDGMENTS

The authors would like to thank Dr Liam Downey, Director, Teagasc (Agriculture and Food Development Authority) who initally suggested the publication and provided the resources which made this book possible. We would also like to express our appreciation to the many people who provided authoritative and refreshing insights to the various topics. To Prof. P.J. Dix, Biology Department, National University of Ireland, Maynooth, Co. Kildare, Ireland, Dr. Ed Re, CEPRAP, University California Davis, USA and T.M. Thomas, Head of Centre, Teagasc, Crops Research Centre, Oak Park, Carlow, Ireland we express particular thanks.

The assistance of John Keating and Charles Godson, Teagasc, Information and Public Relations Department in preparing the book for printing is gratefully acknowledged. We are also indebted to Ms. Connie Conway, Teagasc, Oak Park for expert secretarial assistance.

Finally, thanks is also extended to Ed, Mila, Tomas and Kathleen, Dara, Eimear, Mary, James and Dearbhla for their patience and encouragement during the time spent preparing this book.

Martina Newell Mc.Gloughlin and James I Burke,

September 2000

PREFACE

This book focuses on the applications of biotechnology, describes the technologies involved, explains the progress made to-date and outlines the future of the technology for each application. The main areas covered include:

▶ Crop production

▶ Animal biotechnology

▶ The environment

▶ Industrial biotechnology

▶ Animal and human health.

Sections are also included which cover:

▶ Regulation and

▶ Intellectual property issues.

Considerable attention is devoted to developments in new platform technologies including genomics, proteomics and bioinformatics along with the implications of high throughput analytical techniques including microarrays. New developments in imaging and optical biology are dealt with in detail, while the impact of biosensors, bioelectronics and bionetworks are discussed.

In considering the likely impact of genomics research, the authors conclude that this area of research will be the most fruitful to the acquisition of new information in basic and applied biology in the coming decades. The genomes of microbes, plants, and mammals will be sequenced, and much will be learned about the functions of genes and the means by which they are regulated. Genomics research will have major impact, yielding new insights into fundamental processes such as cell division, differentiation, transformation, the development and reproduction of organisms and the diversity of populations. Other complimentary disciplines, such as proteomics and bioinformatics, will make genomics research even more rewarding.

In addition to the benefits from investing in new overarching platform technologies, investment in applied biology also includes the promise of new approaches to the genetic improvement of plants, particularly disease resistance, pest resistance, better nutrient content and reduced risk of pesticide residues. The authors conclude that the key factors which make biotechnology particularly relevant to the Agri-Food sector are:

Consumer interest in the relationship between food and health (both positive and negative) which has grown dramatically in recent decades. It will remain a major market determinant, with the incidence of food pathogens, and of other contaminants of increasing concern to the consumer and to the industry alike. Biotechnology offers solutions in identifying the organisms involved, analysing the mechanisms of infection and developing safer procedures.

Crops, animals and foodstuffs are biological materials and therefore amenable to bio-modification for nutritional, economic and other benefits.

The international competitiveness of the food processing industry depends on the ability to innovate and diversify into new product lines/ sectors and away from the price-supported commodities on which many European countries now significantly depend. Biotechnology is a means of achieving rapid high-tech expansion into value added novel foods and processes.

The ways in which biotechnology can make a major contribution in all of these areas are discussed. So also are the impacts on medicine and health care, for humans and animals in providing improved approaches to the diagnosis, treatment, and prevention of disease.

Databases are giving way to 'knowledge bases' and researchers are shifting from 'genes' to 'gene systems.' Advances in this field and in such areas as biomaterials and tissue engineering are providing hope for conditions once thought irresolvable.

The emergence of biotechnology has raised many questions of enormous public interest, including the safety of genetically modified organisms (GMOs) in food, the effects of GMOs on the environment and the application of biotechnology in new methods of medical therapy. In the absence of independent scientific information on biotechnology, the general public is not given the opportunity to gain an understanding of, and make informed decisions on the use of biotechnology in the agricultural, industrial and health care sectors.

This book highlight the many promising avenues of research and technological development offered by biotechnology and pinpoints where investment in research can make major contributions to economic growth in Ireland in the 21st century.

INTRODUCTION

INTRODUCTION

In the simplest and broadest sense, Biotechnology is a series of enabling technologies, which involves the manipulation of living organisms or their sub-cellular components to develop useful products, processes or services. Many millennia ago, people discovered that microorganisms could be used in fermentation processes, to make bread, brew alcohol, and produce cheese. Through mutation and selection processes, use of microorganisms as process tools became more and more sophisticated as time went by, and this ability took on another dimension with the advent of recombinant DNA technology in the early 1970s. Our resulting capacity to manipulate the genetic makeup of living organisms with complexity and precision has become one of the cornerstones of modern biotechnology.

It enables us to enhance the ability of an organism to produce a particular chemical product (e.g. penicillin from fungus), to prevent it producing a product (e.g. polygalacturanase in plant cells) or to enable an organism to produce an entirely new product (e.g. insulin in microorganisms).

The steps required to achieve these goals can be simply summarised as follows:

1) **Identification of the gene that directs the production of the desired substance**

2) **Isolation of the gene using restriction enzymes**

3) **Placing the gene with appropriate expression signals on a suitable DNA molecule for transformation**

4) **Transfer the recombined DNA into the appropriate host organism**

5) **Selection and multiplication of the individuals containing the recombinant DNA.**

To date the greatest impact of biotechnology has been in the medical and pharmaceutical arena. Over 200 million people worldwide have benefited from the hundreds of diagnostics, therapeutics and vaccines produced by the $25 billion biomedical biotechnology industry. Medications developed through biotechnological techniques have been approved for use in patients who have cancer, diabetes, cystic fibrosis, haemophilia, multiple sclerosis, hepatitis B, and Karposi's sarcoma. Drugs developed through the technology are used to treat invasive fungal infections, pulmonary embolisms, ischemic strokes, kidney transplant rejection, infertility, growth hormone deficiency, and other serious disorders. Medications have also been developed to improve the health of animals. Scientists are currently investigating applications of advanced gene therapy, a technology that may one day be used to pinpoint and rectify hereditary disorders.

Many of the products we eat and wear are, or can be, made using the tools of biotechnology. It is possible to enhance the nutritional content, texture, colour, flavour, growing season, yield, disease or pest resistance, and other properties of production crops. Transgenic techniques can be applied to farmed animals to improve their growth, fitness, and other qualities. Enzymes produced using recombinant DNA methods are used to make cheese, keep bread fresh, produce fruit juices, wines, treat fabric for blue jeans and other denim clothing. Other recombinant DNA enzymes are used in laundry and automatic dishwashing detergents.

We can also engineer microorganisms to improve the quality of our environment. In addition to the opportunities for a variety of new products, including biodegradable products, bioprocessing using engineered microbes offers new ways to treat and use wastes and to use renewable resources for materials and fuel. Instead of depending on non-renewable fossil fuels we can engineer organisms to convert maize and cereal straw, forest products and municipal waste and other biomass to produce fuel, plastics and other useful commodities. Naturally occurring microorganisms are being used to treat organic and inorganic contaminants in soil, groundwater, and air. This application of biotechnology has created an environmental biotechnology industry important in water treatment, municipal waste management, hazardous waste treatment, bioremediation, and other areas.

Used effectively, biotechnology has enormous potential to improve the quality of our life and our environment.

Chapter 1

OVERARCHING PLATFORM TECHNOLOGIES

OVERARCHING PLATFORM TECHNOLOGIES

Most of the fundamental technologies that fall within the broad rubric of biotechnology are well known and will not be covered here however, there are a number of novel "platform technologies" that are revolutionising biotechnology research across all disciplines.

Genomics, Proteomics and Bioinformatics

The future of biological research will be shaped in part by using computer systems to find ever more effective methods to analyse genetic information. The other side of the coin is that computer scientists will look to biology for methods to overcome the limitations of integrated circuits, leading to the development of massive parallel processing and networking capabilities, and ultimately the simulation of higher functions and artificial intelligence.

The complexity of biological systems, coupled with the explosion in gene sequence information mandates the need for multidimensional methods for gene expression analysis. These are the key to "functional genomics", an area in which research institutions must have strong capabilities to be competitive in the next 10-20 years. Although applications in medicine have been the main thrust of this development, this technology is now having a major impact in agricultural biotechnology, and most specifically plant biotechnology research. Plant genome scientists will increasingly employ DNA chips in their research, and functional analysis of the genome through such approaches as gene knockout will be employed. Such tools are essential for genome researchers to move beyond sequencing and into the next phase of research where they conduct enormously large-scale gene discovery surveys and gene expression analyses.

Definitions

Genomics is the discovery and study of many genes simultaneously. Three overlapping areas have been described: structural genomics which is primarily concerned with the determination of genome structure at the sequence level; comparative genomics which involves the molecular basis of differences between organisms at a variety of taxonomic levels; and, functional genomics which focuses on the function of genes. Outgrowths of functional genomics have been termed proteomics and metanomics, which are the global studies of gene expression at the protein and metabolite levels respectively. The study of the integration of information flow within an organism is emerging as the field of systems biology. Bioinformatics is the acquisition, curation and interrogation of large collections of complex biological data.

Structural genomics

Advances in analytical tools, automation, computational power and algorithms have revolutionised our ability to generate and analyse immense amounts of DNA sequence and genotype information. The complete genomes of a number of microorganisms have now been determined, and those of more complex organisms including human, mouse and the plants, *Arabidopsis thaliana* and rice, will be determined within the next few years. The latest facilities that are just becoming operational will be able to sequence up to 10 Mb per day. This will make it possible to sequence whole microbial genomes within a day. Bioinformatics is playing an increasing role in structural genomics. There is currently a vast amount of DNA sequence data in the public domain and an even greater amount in private databases. The potential of this data has only just begun to be exploited. A rate-limiting step is the need for semi-intelligent algorithms to manage and mine the data.

Comparative genomics

Only a finite number of chromosomal rearrangements have occurred during the evolution of mammals and angiosperm plants. Therefore, large blocks of genetic material are collinear in many higher animal and plant genomes. Synteny is becoming increasingly well-documented between mammals as well as monocot plant species and preliminary data indicates significant synteny between monocot and dicot species. Extensive synteny is also evident among related microbes, for example between gram-negative eubacteria such as *Escherichia coli* and *Hemophilus influenzae*, and between the fungi *Saccharomyces cerevisiae* and *Candida albicans*. As several animal and plant species are sequenced, it is becoming possible to predict genes present in each part of the genome, once the extent and pattern of synteny has been established for a particular species.

Synteny raises several interesting questions and opportunities. What are the minimum numbers of building blocks that comprise one species in terms of intensively characterised (model) species and what are the evolutionary forces driving such rearrangements? What are the exceptions to synteny and what is the evolutionary and functional significance of the large differences in genome size? What are the phenotypes determined by orthologous genes and how do they account for differences between species? There is the growing realisation that genome projects encompassing animals, plants or microbes from numerous taxa enable powerful inferences to be made among species.

Comparative genomics also provides information on allelic variation for genes controlling traits of medical, economic and agricultural importance. This will be important for structure-function studies as well as critical to understanding why one species or genotype performs better than another and hence is integral to molecular improvement strategies.

Figure 1: Advanced genomics will accelerate discovery of next generation products.

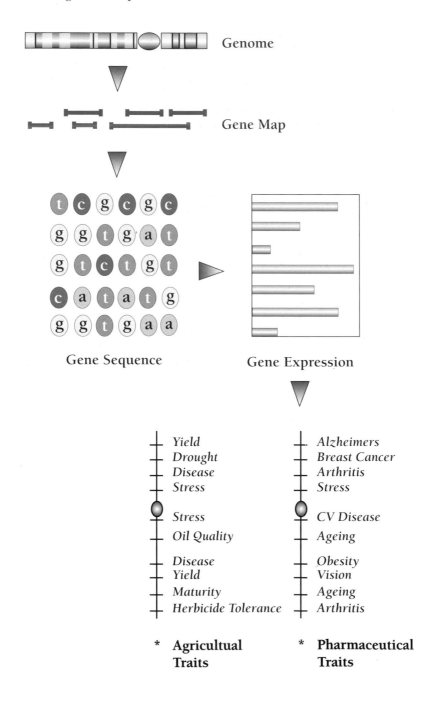

Functional genomics, proteomics and systems biology

A major revolution is occurring in our ability to determine information on gene expression patterns and protein function. This is particularly being driven by global analyses of gene expression and inferences derived from DNA sequence data. In the area of proteomics, the methods for analysis of protein profiles and cataloguing protein-protein interactions on a genome-wide scale are technically more difficult but improving rapidly, especially for microbes. These approaches generate vast amounts of quantitative data. The amount of expression data becoming available in the public and private sectors is already increasing exponentially. Gene and protein expression data will rapidly dwarf the DNA sequence data and it will be considerably more difficult to manage and exploit.

The next hierarchical level of phenotype considers how the proteome within and among cells cooperates to produce the biochemistry and physiology of individual cells and organisms. Several authors have tentatively offered "physiomics" as a descriptor for this approach. The final hierarchical levels of phenotype include anatomy and function for cells and whole organisms. The term "phenomics" has been applied to this level of study. Functional genomics as a means of assessing phenotype differs from more classical approaches primarily with respect to the scale and degree of automation of biological investigations. Modern functional genomics approaches will examine how 1,000 to 10,000 genes are expressed as a function of development. Major advances in several different areas of analytical chemistry, analytical biochemistry, image analysis, robotics and process automation have led to an abundance of effective approaches for the very large scale tasks of functional genomics.

Functional genomics will impact most areas of biology, from fundamental biochemistry to improvement of quality, and agronomic traits in crops, improved protection against pathogenic microbes, and improved exploitation of beneficial microbes. Strain collections encompassing insertions or deletions in every potential gene will be available for testing of phenotypes in model species. Catalogues of all expressed genes will soon be available and we will have the ability for global analysis of all genes expressed under different conditions, in different organs, or in different individuals. Proteomic catalogues of, for example, all phosphorylated proteins or all pair-wise protein-protein interactions, will become available. Such large-scale approaches will provide new opportunities for defining targets for manipulation. Gene discovery will be much faster and cheaper. The rate-limiting steps will be confirming gene function of candidate genes and characterising the roles and interactions of large numbers of genes, particularly at the whole organism level.

Informatics

The inevitable consequence of the breadth and scale of research efforts in structural and functional genomics is a very large quantity of data, which is not easily examined or understood. Given the sequence of the human genome, for example, it is an immense task to identify individual genes. Similar problems exist for a wide variety of topics in both structural and functional genomics, primarily due to the scale and parallel nature of these approaches. One of the consequences is that databases themselves become the target of research opportunity, especially at the beginning or initial stages of biological research.

The acquisition of relational databases, as well as the development of efficient methods for searching and viewing these data, constitutes a new discipline called "bioinformatics". In a broader view, bioinformatics contains computational or algorithmic approaches to the production of information from large amounts of biological data, and this might include prediction of protein structure, dynamic modelling of complex physiological systems or the statistical treatment of quantitative traits in populations in order to determine the genetic basis for these traits. Unquestionably, bioinformatics will be an essential component of all research activities utilising structural and functional genomics approaches. There will be demand for life scientists who actively incorporate the use of bioinformatics tools into their work, at the sequence level, in structure modelling, and in modelling, linking and simulating complex higher level structures such as neurological pathways.

Some industrial activities in genomics and screening are outlined in Table 1.

Directed Evolution

Genetic diversity is generated through two natural processes: metagenesis, the spontaneous mutation of genes from one generation to another, and sexual recombination in which genes from two different organisms combine to produce offspring with characteristics of each. Natural selection ensures that only organisms with traits suited to their environment live long enough to reproduce – meaning only the 'fittest' progeny survive into the next generation. Directed evolution uses the same strategy when applying new methods of generating increased genetic variability to accelerate the rate of new product discovery and development. For example the company Diversa employs "directed evolution" and "gene reassembly" approaches to optimise target compounds for use in specific applications. Another company Maxygen uses "DNA shuffling" technology to accelerate the creation of new gene sequences with the intent of producing new genes which yield improved traits such as higher yields, improved stress tolerance, and better nutritional characteristics. This approach mimics the natural process of evolution and brings together advances in molecular biology and classical breeding, while capitalising on the large amount of genetic information being generated through genome analysis.

Table 1:   Genomic and screening programmes of selected agrochemical and pharmaceutical companies in agbiotech

COMPANY	PROGRAMME
BASF (Ludwigshafen, Germany)	Functional genomics of plants
Bayer (Leverkusen, Germany)	Target screening in model organisms
Dow Chemical (Midland, MI)	Functional genomics of plants
DuPont (Wilmington, DE)	Genomics and target screening
Monsanto (St. Louis, MO)	Combinatorial screening and plant genomics
Novartis (Basel, Switzerland)	Functional genomics and combinatorial screening
Rhône-Poulenc (Lyon, France)	Functional genomics of plants
Rohm and Haas (Philadelphia, PA)	Gene switching and plant genomics
Zeneca (Wilmington, DE)	Combinatorial screening and plant genomics

Source: Adapted from Thayer, A.M. Chem. Eng. News, April 1999, p. 21

Just as environmental pressures act to select or reject certain characteristics in natural evolution, Maxygen has developed a range of screening technologies to allow the rapid selection of candidates that contain the desired traits and characteristics. These include flexible assay systems, which measure the production of small molecules in culture without significant purification steps or specific assay reagents. In addition to these colourmetric, fluorimetric, and high-throughput physical assays, the company is developing cell-based screening technologies and technologies that can be used in the DNA shuffling culture itself.

To date the company has achieved some success in:

▶ **Increasing biological activity of various cytokines and immunomodulators**

▶ Improving specific pathways for production of chemicals and pharmaceutical intermediates

▶ Evolving novel viral host tropisms

▶ Improving expression levels and binding affinities of antibodies

▶ Increasing specific activity of novel enzymes.

High Throughput Analysis

Nucleic acids

New chemical methods and instrumentation are leading to ever more rapid mechanisms for performing basic procedures, leading to an explosion in the rate of acquisition of data. Examples include capillary based sequencing as in Molecular Dynamics MegaBASE systems and Perkin Elmer Biosystems Genetic Analyser; realtime quantitative PCR using Frequency resonance energy transfer (FRET), and Roche's Lightcycler rapid thermocycler. Craighead and his team at Cornell University are working on a "biochip" - an "artificial gel" made of silicon - that could replace cumbersome organic polymers to speed DNA sequencing. Electrophoresis gels consist of a maze of interlocking polymer molecules that leave many tiny openings through which moving DNA molecules must navigate. Using the same techniques used to make electronic circuits, tiny passageways can be carved on a silicon chip. An advantage of these artificial gels is that its openings are of uniform size and distribution, rather than random as in organic gels. This makes it possible to measure the velocity with which molecules of varying sizes move and compare the results with theoretical predictions.

To parallel the instrumentation, newly evolving methodologies enable the rapid isolation, cloning, expression and detection of genes and gene pathways derived directly from raw environmental samples. Using a combination of novel assays and ultra high-throughput screening technologies, scientists at companies like Diversa, Millennium, Aurora, NCE are able to efficiently isolate and express genes encoding novel biomolecules, and then screen for activity at a rate of up to 1 billion clones per day. Utilising this approach, over 1000 novel recombinant enzymes have been identified and sequenced by Diversa.

Gene expression

There are currently four commonly used approaches to high throughput, comprehensive analysis of relative transcript expression levels:

▶ **The enumeration of expressed sequence tags (ESTs) from representative cDNA libraries**

‣ The enumeration of serially concentrated 9-11 base tags from specially prepared cDNA libraries

‣ The quantitation of gene-specific sequence-delimited fragments by differential display and variations of differential display

‣ Array-based hybridisation.

These approaches are under development and use in both non-profit and for-profit concerns.

Microarrays

DNA chips or microarrays facilitate high throughput analysis of thousands of genes simultaneously, and are thus potentially very powerful tools for gaining insight into the complexities of higher organisms including analysis of gene expression, detecting genetic variation, making new gene discoveries, fingerprinting strains and developing new diagnostic tools. These technologies permit scientists to conduct large-scale surveys of gene expression in organisms, thus adding to our knowledge of how they develop over time or respond to various environmental stimuli. The new techniques will be especially useful in gaining an integrated view of how multiple genes are expressed in a coordinated manner.

In the days before positive selection vectors, a researcher might have screened thousands of clones by hand with an oligonucleotide just to find one elusive insert. Today's DNA array technology reverses that approach. Instead of screening an array of unknowns with a defined probe, each position or "probe cell" in the array is occupied by a defined DNA fragment, and the array is probed with the unknown sample. The typical array may contain all possible combinations of oligonucleotides (8-mers, for example) that occur as a "window" is tracked along a DNA sequence. It might contain longer oligonucleotides designed from all the open reading frames identified from a complete genome sequence, or it might contain cDNAs-of known or unknown sequence-or PCR products.

These DNA arrays, or biochips, represent a blossoming field, estimated to be worth $40 million a year and expected to grow to 10 times that over the next few years. Two principal types of DNA chips now available are based on the principle of hybridisation in which nucleotides on complementary nucleic acid strands recognise each other through base pairing. Only tiny amounts of DNA and chemical reagents are needed and sample preparation effort is minimal.

To produce a 'synthesised' DNA chip, a huge number of oligonucleotide probes are synthesised directly on a glass surface or silicon wafer using a process called photolithography. More than 400,000 such probes can be placed on a single chip measuring 1.28cm X 1.28 cm.

Next, a fluorescent labelled target nucleic sequence is hybridised to the probes on the chip, and the resulting fluorescent image is scanned by a laser beam and analysed by a computer. The intensity of fluorescent light varies with the strength of the hybridisation thus providing a quantitative 'snapshot' of the gene expression. Even very rare mRNA species (1 in 300,000) can be detected by this approach thus making it possible to detect 'hard-to-find' genes. The process is automated and now commercially available. Affymetrix, a company located in Santa Clara, California manufactures five to ten thousand DNA chips per month and is targeting applications such as screening for human immunodeficiency virus or genes associated with cancer, and gene resequencing. The company is also getting into plant applications, it is working on an *Arabidopsis* chip and already is supplying Pioneer Hi Bred with custom DNA chips for monitoring maize gene expression. Affymetrix has established programmes where academic scientists can use company facilities at a reduced price and they are also setting up 'user centres' at selected universities.

A related but less complex technology called DNA microarray or 'spotted' DNA chips involves precisely spotting very small droplets of genomic or cDNA clones or PCR samples on a microscope slide. The process uses a robotic device with a print head bearing fine "repeatograph" tips that work like fountain pens to draw up DNA samples from a 96-well plate and spot tiny amounts on a slide. Up to 10,000 individual clones can be spotted in a dense array within one square centimetre on a glass slide. After hybridisation with a fluorescent target mRNA, signals are detected by a custom scanner. This is the basis of the systems used by Molecular Dynamics and Incyte (who acquired this technology when it took over Synteni). A description of DNA microarray technology, including short videos of the arrayer and scanner in action and a picture of the complete yeast genome on a single chip, can be viewed at http://cmgm.stanford.edu/pbrown/array.html.

Regardless of how they are made, DNA arrays are put to a number of uses that can be loosely divided into two groups: genotyping and gene expression. Genotyping arrays are designed to examine DNA at the sequence level. DNA arrays for examining gene expression can more correctly be called "gene chips" because they can involve longer fragments of synthetic or complementary DNA. Clontech's Atlas arrays are designed to detect expression of a specific gene. Atlas arrays are available for a range of genes of ongoing or current research interest, including those encoding cytokines, transcription factors, and cell-cycle regulators. Display Systems Biotech's Display ARRAY membranes can be used either to study expression patterns within a variety of gene families or to search for new homologous genes.

Genosys Biotechnologies' Panorama gene arrays, the first of their kind, contain DNA representative of the entire *E. coli* genome, represented by 4,290 PCR-amplified open reading frames. Probing these arrays is a simple way to quantify expression levels from all 4,290 *E. coli* genes under any growth conditions. It seems likely that as more genomes are sequenced and analysed, similar arrays will become available for a wide variety of organisms. NEN, in collaboration with AlphaGene, will soon be providing slides spotted with arrays of 2,400 known human genes. Other defined arrays include Research Genetics' high-density arrays of human and yeast genes and Vysis' GenoSensor arrays, which make use of comparative genomic hybridisation to correlate gene expression with disease states.

However, from a high throughput perspective there are question marks over microarrays. Mark Benjamin, senior director of business development at Rosetta Inpharmatics (Kirkland, WA), is sceptical about the long-term prospects for standard DNA arrays in high-throughput screening as the first steps require exposing cells and then isolating RNA, which is something that's very hard to do high-throughput. Another drawback is that most of the useful targets are likely to be unknown (particularly in the agricultural sciences where genome sequencing has only just got underway), and DNA arrays that are currently available test only for previously sequenced genes. Indeed, some argue that current DNA arrays may not be sufficiently sensitive to detect the low expression levels of genes encoding targets of particular interest. And the added complication of the companies' reluctance to provide raw data means that derived data sets may be created with less than optimal algorithims, thereby irretrievably losing potentially valuable information from the starting material.

High throughput protein analysis

Several technologies now make it feasible to perform mass screening of proteins and are revolutionising the field of proteomics. These include:

▶ Advanced 2D electrophoresis

▶ Mass spectrometry, especially: MS-MS (Tandem mass spec analysis), LC/MS/MS (liquid chromatography mass spectrometry/mass spectrometry) and MALDI-TOF-MS (Matrix Assisted Laser Desorption/Ionisation-Time of Flight Mass Spectrometry)

▶ Protein Affinity Chromatography.

2D gels can now be transformed into high resolution digital protein maps using staining, imaging, and bioinformatics software. Individual proteins can then be excised from 2D gels, split into polypeptide fragments, and sequenced using mass spectrometry.

Protein identification based on partial sequence obtained from mass spectral analysis and/or peptide mass mapping is becoming increasingly valuable with the availability of genomic databases. Mass spectrometry analysis is critical for determining proper expression and folding and for analysis of post-translational modification. MALDI-TOF MS has brought great advances to the field of proteomics. It has many advantages over existing systems such as:

▶ **It is more sensitive than Edman sequencing and avoids interference from N-terminal blocked ends**

▶ **It identifies proteins from sub-picomole quantities**

▶ **Researchers can start from a variety of sample preparations: pure proteins, bands from SDS-PAGE gels, or even crude samples are acceptable**

▶ **There is an exceedingly fast turnaround of between 2 to 5 days**

▶ **The sub-picomole protein identification by MALDI-TOF MS coupled with advanced protein affinity chromatography provides a powerful functional genomics platform for the identification of protein-protein interactions.**

Proteomics technology is advancing by leaps and bounds, but the hurdles are greater than anything molecular biology has yet had to overcome: DNA can be amplified, while proteins can't; DNA is a simple linear code, while proteins fold in complex ways and interact unpredictably; DNA is basically static, while proteins change in myriad ways even in an individual cell over a short period of time. Despite these difficulties, many predict that proteomics will eventually replace nucleic acid based systems, but until proteomics technology catches up to the vision, this scientific revolution will be on hold.

Imaging/optical biology

In vivo analysis systems are also benefiting from these technological advances. For example in a recent issue of Science, Ng and colleagues show how a combination of two advanced imaging methods, fluorescence resonance energy transfer (FRET) and fluorescence lifetime imaging microscopy (FLIM), may revolutionise the way immunofluorescence is performed. In their study, the authors use these fluorescence microscopy techniques to acquire a spatial map of the distribution of the activated form of the enzyme, protein kinase C (PKC) in intact cells.

Technologies in optical biology will enable high-speed, quantitative phenotyping both *ex vivo* and *in vivo*. The data derived from these analyses will be entered into a relational database to establish correlations between specific numbers of phenotypically distinct populations and their *in vivo* micro-environments that they alter in development, differentiation and disease. In addition, *in situ* morphometrics will quantify the critical number of cells and their products associated with a specific phenotype, necessary to manifest the complex biological response or behaviour. In this manner the complexity of the functional genome can be dissected with multiplicity, instead of going one gene at a time. Research institutions need to strengthen the existing core in optical biology and complement it with the most advanced *in situ* morphometric capabilities to establish a ground-breaking core in targeted phenotyping. The informatics derived from these applications will form the foundation for true functional genomics i.e. quantifying the numbers of cells and their products with specific phenotypes necessary to predict and/or change the outcome of a biological response.

The future: Nanotechnology, biosensors, bioelectronics and bionetworks

Two new sensor technologies allow hitherto unimaginable access to the inside workings of the cell. Researchers at the University of Michigan research have created PEBBLEs (Probes Encapsulated By BioListic Embedding), an innovative method for monitoring the biochemistry of living cells. These polymer-based sensors work inside mammalian cells where they can detect subtle changes in concentrations of ions and small molecules. PEBBLEs are self-contained sensors powerful enough to detect even slight changes in cell biochemistry, but small enough to avoid damaging the cell.

The other innovation, developed by a team of chemists and physiologists at the University of Illinois involves a new measurement technique that can simultaneously identify and measure more than 30 compounds found in a single cell. The method combines nanoliter sampling, capillary electrophoresis and fluorescence spectroscopy for direct, convenient and highly sensitive measurements. It allows complete identification and measurement of biologically important compounds in individual cells without performing any chemical reactions to make the compounds detectable.

Bioelectronics is an emerging technology that employs biological molecules instead of inorganic materials in conventional integrated-circuit technology or in applications involving unconventional architectures, such as optical processors. The driving force for this research is the possibility of constructing devices on the molecular level and thereby achieving extremely high densities of data storage sites and nano-sized computers. Biological systems are capable of storing and processing information at the molecular level. Although biological processes function more slowly than do conventional solid-state devices, this penalty is more then offset by a huge increase in the density of operating units. Various biomimetic or biologically based materials, such as the protein bacteriorhodopsin, are being evaluated for use in bioelectronics.

In living things, data processing is achieved by arrays of neurons. Although the operation of single neurons is well understood, the operation of biological neural networks remains largely unexplored. Recent achievements in the culturing of a monolayer of neurons on a micro-electrode array promise to provide some insight into the operation of neuron arrays. Although neuron devices - bionetworks - would not operate on a molecular scale, they have the potential to form the basis for new computer architectures, including parallel processors.

One of the givens of the new century is that computing will merge not only with communications and machinery but also with biological processes, raising such possibilities as hardware implants, smart tissues, intelligent machines, true living computers, and man-machine hybrids. Molecular techniques also show promise in creating micromachines that move and exert force. An added advantage is that traditional etching techniques can be used to build these devices. Such micromachines may eventually be able to assemble molecular- or atomic-scale components.

Biotechnology research has moved a long way from the basic *in vivo* and *in vitro* systems familiar to all molecular biologists. We have now entered an era where *in silico* and *ex machina* approaches are dominating the drive for investigations in this field and leading to advances not dreamed of just a few short years ago.

Implications for Ireland

Microtechnology is having a major impact on the development of investigative tools and analytical instruments for molecular science. In just the past five years, several key capabilities have been realised through the application of microfabrication processes that were developed by the integrated circuits manufacturing industry. Examples include gene chip arrays (Affymetrix), capillary electrophoresis arrays and portable PCR instruments (Lawrence Livermore National Laboratory). These success stories have created an explosion of research activity in the applications of microtechnology to molecular science research, gene sequencing, drug discovery and biochemical analysis. The technology and tools under development have many different labels indicating the diversity of application: lab-on-a chip, gene chips, biochips, microarrays, microfluidics, and bioMEMS (biomedical Microelectromechanical Systems). This is a multidisciplinary field where engineering and molecular science must team together for a successful outcome. It is appropriate that a new, forward looking, Irish Research Initiative should be undertaken in this area.

Appropriate State investments to address key research questions could help make Ireland a world leader in this promising new arena. The major technical obstacle to development of practical bioelectronic devices lies in determining how to preserve and control the properties of the active state when the bioactive species is immobilised in an artificial membrane. Research to explore the fundamental process of biological self-assembly, a capability inherent in biological molecules such as lipids, DNA, and proteins, may be useful in resolving some of the organisational problems.

Priorities:

▶ *Bioinformatics and Computational Biology:*

Improve content and utility of databases; develop better tools for data generation, capture, and annotation; develop and improve tools and databases for comprehensive functional studies; develop and improve tools for representing and analysing sequence similarity and variation; create mechanisms to support effective approaches for producing robust, exportable software that can be widely shared.

▶ *Training and Manpower:*

Nurture the training of scientists skilled in genomics and bioinformatics research; encourage the establishment of academic career paths for genomic and bioinformatics scientists. Technical people who are trained in molecular biology are available, as are those with computer and database skills, but it is the combination of skills that is rare and needed. Collaboration among industry and academic researchers can create opportunities for students to obtain the desired combination of skills. Interdisciplinary research centres focusing on cross training between experimental biologists, computational biologists, information technology experts, need to be established.

Further reading

Kell, D. Screensavers: trends in high-throughput analysis. Trends Biotechnol. 17, 89–91 (1999).

Archer, R. Towards the drug discovery factory. J. Assoc. Lab. Automat. 3, 4 (1998).

Frederickson, R. Macromolecular matchmaking: advances in two-hybrid and related technologies. Curr. Opin Biotechnol. 9, 90–96 (1998).

Young, K. *et al.* Identification of a calcium channel modulator using a high-throughput yeast two-hybrid screen. Nature Biotech. 16, 946–950 (1998).

Chapter 2
CROP BIOTECHNOLOGY

CROP BIOTECHNOLOGY

In the latter half of the 20th Century, major improvements in agricultural productivity have been largely based on selective breeding programmes for plants and animals, intensive use of chemical fertilisers, pesticides and herbicides, advanced equipment developments and widespread irrigation programmes. This has been a very successful model for raising productivity, yet, these improvements have brought corresponding problems of increasing uniformity in the genetic base of crop plants and domestic animals, pests resistant against chemical pesticides, adverse impacts on environmental quality, and capital-intensive production. The emerging biotechnology revolution is stimulating hope that it will provide the basis for more sustainable agriculture. In agriculture, biotechnology in the form of recombinant DNA (rDNA) technology is a powerful assistant to traditional plant and animal breeding. Traditional breeding programmes are time consuming, labour intensive and limited to transfers of genes between closely related species. In addition because the breeder has no control at the genome level, many undesirable traits can also be incorporated, such as lower yield and slower growth. Recombinant DNA technology permits the precise and predictable manipulation of genes. Single traits can be modified much more quickly than was possible using traditional selection and breeding methods alone. Because of the capability of moving genes between species, desirable traits from one organism can be transferred to another.

The initial phase of a revolution in crop agriculture has already occurred. Large areas of genetically modified (GM) crops of soybeans, maize, cotton, and canola have been successfully grown in the Western Hemisphere. In the United States in 1999, of the total of 72 million acres (29 million hectares) planted with soybeans, half were planted with GM herbicide-resistant seeds. When herbicide-resistant seeds were used, weeds were easily controlled, less tilling was needed, and soil erosion was minimised.

Molecular Markers

A valuable application of the power of genomics without genetic engineering is marker assisted selection which is a very usuful tool to help to accelerate the process of identifying and introgressing desired traits in cultivars. This has resulted in the identification of an increasing number of molecular markers using various approaches. Near-isogenic lines (NILs) resulting from backcrossing programs to introgress genetic traits have been used extensively. Another approach using Bulked segregant analysis (BSA) allows the rapid mapping of monogenic trait genes using segregating populations. Marker analyses have located many desirable genes to clusters in the genome, supporting data from classical segregation analyses of such genes. The mapping approach for single gene traits cannot be used for quantitative traits, however, because it is too difficult to distinguish changes in phenotype, so special QTL-mapping studies must be done, and a different set of mapping software used. In the near future, many additional markers associated with QTL's will be discovered and the capability to screen cheaply and rapidly for many DNA markers will be available to breeders.

This section will focus on the technology and its applications in crop plants, horticulture and forestry.

Plant Transformation

Progress in plant genetic engineering has been spectacular since the recovery of the first transformed tobacco plants in the early 1980s. The capacity to introduce and express diverse foreign genes has been extended to over 120 plant species in at least 35 families. Successes include most major economic crops, vegetables, ornamental, medicinal, fruit, tree, and pasture plants. Attention is increasingly being directed to achieving the desired patterns of expression of introduced genes and to solving economic constraints on practical plant molecular improvement.

Plant transformation is at a threshold. There has been over 20,000 field trials on 60 crops in 45 countries worldwide. These trials involve many plant species modified for various economic traits.

Figure 2: Plant biotechnology development is predicted to occur in three main waves...

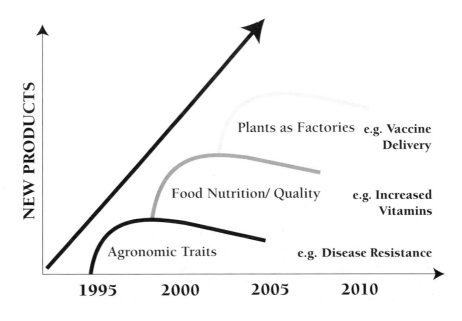

Agrobacterium-mediated transformation

Plant transformation mediated by *Agrobacterium tumefaciens* (or sometimes the related species, *A. rhizogenes*), a soil plant pathogenic bacterium, has become the most widely used method for the introduction of foreign genes into plant cells and the subsequent regeneration of transgenic plants. *A. tumefaciens* naturally infects the wound sites in dicotyledonous plants causing the formation of the crown gall tumours. It has the exceptional ability to transfer a particular DNA segment (T-DNA) of the tumour-inducing (Ti) plasmid into the nucleus of infected cells where it is then stably integrated into the host genome and transcribed, causing the crown gall disease. Early studies on the T-DNA transfer process to plant cells demonstrated three important facts for the practical use of this process in plant transformation. Firstly, tumour formation is a transformation process of plant cells resulting from transfer and integration of T-DNA and the subsequent expression of T-DNA genes. Secondly, the T-DNA genes are transcribed only in plant cells and do not play any role during the transfer process. Thirdly, any foreign DNA placed between the T-DNA borders can be transferred to plant cells, no matter what the source of the DNA. This knowledge led to the development of suitable expression cassettes, in which genes of interest, or marker genes, are equipped with appropriate expression signals (promoters etc.). These can be introduced into Ti-based, disarmed (with the oncogenes removed) in *A. tumefaciens*, and used to transform plant cells from which transgenic plants can be regenerated.

Great progress in understanding the *Agrobacterium*-mediated gene transfer to plant cells has been achieved. However, *Agrobacterium* species naturally infect only dicotyledonous plants and many economically important plants, including the cereals, remained inaccessible for genetic manipulation because of lack of effective transformation techniques until the early 90s. For these cases, alternative direct transformation methods have been developed, although more recently there has been progress in adapting *Agrobacterium*-based methods to cereal crops.

Direct DNA delivery methods

Several procedures have been developed for the direct delivery of DNA to plant cells, with various efficacy. These include:

- Polyethylene glycol (PEG)-mediated uptake of DNA into protoplasts
- Electoporation of protoplasts
- Electrophoresis
- Silicon carbide whisker-mediated uptake into cultured cells
- Microinjection

▶ Particle bombardment.

The last of these, particle bombardment, or "Biolistics" has become the most widely used of the procedures. The method known uses a "gene gun" to shoot metal particles coated with DNA into cells. Initially a gunpowder charge was used to accelerate the particles, but this has been replaced by high pressure pulses of helium gas in modern devices. There is a minimal disruption of tissue and the success rate has been extremely high for applications in several plant species. The technology rights are now owned by DuPont.

Genes and transformation constructs

To allow effective identification of those few cells that have been transformed, selectable marker genes (e.g. conferring antibiotic resistance) are generally used as they allow, under selective conditions, proliferation and plant regeneration and only of transformed cells. Reporter genes, which can be easily assayed, are also frequently used to rapidly evaluate transformation protocols, and monitor expression (e.g. to compare different promoters). Marker and/or reporter genes are usually included in the same constructs with genes encoding useful agronomic traits. A typical genetic construct will include a promoter, a coding sequence and a terminating signal.

Commonly used promoters for plant transformation include cauliflower mosaic virus (CaMV) 35S promoter, which is a constitutive promoter, suitable for driving the expression of foreign genes in dicots, and the maize ubiquitin promoter, also a constitutive promoter which drives strong expression of transgenes in monocots. Organ/ tissue specific promoters are also available to drive expression in particular parts of the plants. Some examples include:

▶ The vicilin and phytohemaglutinin promoters derived from the pea and bean respectively suitable for seed specific expression

▶ The high molecular weight glutenin promoter from wheat, also suitable for seed-specific expression

▶ The amylase promoter for expression in the aleurone of cereal grains

▶ The patatin promoter for tuber specific expression in potatoes

▶ The RuBisCo small sub-unit promoter for green tissue specificity.

The most common selectable markers are based on genes that code for proteins that detoxify metabolic toxins such as antibiotics or herbicides. Bacterial antibiotic resistance genes, *nptII* and *hpt*, which confer resistance to kanamycin and hygromycin respectively, are particularly widely used. Commonly used reporter genes include *uidA* (GUS), *luc* (firefly luciferase) and *gfp* (green fluorescent protein from jellyfish).

Transformation with multiple genes

The introduction and expression of foreign genes in plants by genetic transformation is now routine for many species. In most cases, one or a few genes are transferred to the plant genome along with a selectable marker that facilitates selection and recovery of transgenic tissues. Genetic transformation with a single target gene has been used for the production of transgenic crop plants expressing herbicide tolerance, as well as resistance to fungal, viral, and bacterial diseases and insect pests. In addition, improved agronomic characteristics have been achieved by manipulating metabolic pathways through over expression of a specific gene or the use of antisense sequences. As most agronomic characteristics are polygenic in nature, plant genetic engineering will require manipulation of complex metabolic or regulatory pathways involving multiple genes or gene complexes. Redirecting complex biosynthetic pathways and modifying polygenic agronomic traits requires the integration of multiple transgenes into the plant genome, while ensuring their stable expression in succeeding generations.

Integrating multiple genes by repetitive insertion of single coding sequences is impractical due to the time and effort required for the production and screening of transgenic tissues and the necessity of using a different selectable marker for each new transformation event. Transfer of multiple genes via *Agrobacterium*-mediated transformation, although possible, is technically demanding and becomes increasingly problematic as the number of genes and the size of the tDNA increases. However, researchers at the University of Illinois and the USDA-ARS lab in Urbana, developed a procedure using *Agrobacterium*. The key element in the approach is an all-in-one expression unit consisting of a single plant promoter linked to three individual genes arranged in tandem as a translational fusion. The genes are transcribed as a composite messenger RNA that is translated into a single long polypeptide. The individual coding sequences are separated by codons that specify the cleavage recognition sequences of a site-specific plant virus protease.

An alternative approach termed co-bombardment was developed by Dr. Roger Beachy's laboratory in Scripps, San Diego. Co-bombardment is a simple process in which genes carried on separate plasmids are mixed prior to transfer by particle bombardment. In this manner, numerous genes can be transferred simultaneously using a single selectable marker. They found that as many as 13 genes can be inserted into the rice genome by this method, and in many cases these are co-integrated at a single genetic locus.

Improved promoters

Despite all advances, expression of the introduced foreign gene in plant cells is still a challenging task. Especially in those projects aiming to develop plants as "biofactories" to produce novel enzymes, pharmaceuticals and industrial compounds, it is critical that introduced genes churn out the corresponding proteins in large amounts to make the venture economically feasible.

The level of gene expression is, in part, a function of the promoter to which the coding region of the gene is fused. Use of the most popular promoter in plant molecular biology research, the 35S promoter from cauliflower mosaic virus (CaMV), usually results in production of the foreign gene product at rates of less than one per cent of the total protein. Improvements to the CaMV 35S promoter such as the duplication of certain sequences and the addition of enhancers have boosted expression, but for some applications, the levels need to be still higher.

Now, a novel promoter developed at the laboratory of Stan Gelvin at Purdue University may come to the aid of plant scientists frustrated by low expression levels of introduced genes. In a "head-to-head" test, a new super-promoter, constructed by combining different regulatory elements from *Agrobacterium* genes, resulted in 156-fold more GUS (reporter gene) activity than did the -800 CaMV 35S promoter of pBI121. Although actual protein levels were not measured and other versions of the 35S promoter are somewhat stronger than the one used in the test, the results are nonetheless quite impressive. Gelvin's group were also successful in using this promoter to study very early transcription of introduced genes (within 18 hours) in tobacco and maize. The CaMV 35S promoter was too weak to show any activity at this time. Other researchers at various laboratories are now testing the new promoter to see if it helps boost levels of expression of their introduced genes in plants.

Another area of active research is into promoters which can be conveniently induced to express the transgene at the field level. Some transgenes are known to impact plant growth or yield, so it is prudent to turn them on only when needed. Examples include inducing male sterility for hybrid seed production without the need for a restorer line, turning on disease resistance genes only when the pathogen appears to counter pathogen adaptation, or delaying expression of transgenes when the new protein interferes with early plant growth. There are few available options for conditionally expressing genes under field conditions but a group led by Brian Tomsett and Mark Caddick of the University of Liverpool (UK), has developed a promising system employing the regulatory sequences of the alcA gene (encoding alcohol dehydrogenase I) from the filamentous fungus *Aspergillus nidulans*. This gene is turned on by ethanol and its promoter is widely used to overexpress proteins in fungi. They showed it could be used to drive alcohol-induced transgene expression, and Christiane Gatz of the University of Göttingen, an expert on chemically inducible promoters in plants, says that the alc system may develop into one of the most broadly applicable regulatory systems for plant gene expression.

T-DNA mediated site-specific recombination

In mammalian cells, the introduction of DNA at specific chromosomal sites via homologous recombination has successfully been applied to inactivate or modify specific genes. Such gene targeting can be done in plants as well, but has not been widely attempted due to the low efficiency with which transfected DNA recombines with homologous sequences in the plant genome. Use of site-specific recombination systems may have great potential for overcoming this limitation.

In a study carried out at the Institute of Molecular Plant Sciences at Leiden University in the Netherlands, the bacteriophage P1 Cre/lox system was used to insert *Agrobacterium tumefaciens* transferred DNA (T-DNA) into a specific chromosomal location in *Arabidopsis thaliana*. The Cre/lox system, consisting of a recombinase protein (Cre) and short 34 base pair recombination sites (lox), catalyses precise and stable insertional recombination between the respective DNA target sites. This approach may lead to development of more efficient systems, applicable to many plant species, that could target a transgene to a single pre-selected chromosomal site, thus eliminating variation in gene expression level.

Chloroplast transformation: biological containment and high expression of transgenes

In recent years the great biotechnological potential of the chloroplast genome (plastome) as a target for plastid transformation has been increasingly appreciated. It opens many exciting possibilities and it is no exaggeration to say that for a number of applications it is likely to eclipse nuclear transformation. Some of the special attractions of chloroplast transformation are as follows:

▶ **Biological containment.** Most crop plants exhibit strict maternal inheritance of the chloroplasts. This means that traits engineered into the plastome cannot spread to other varieties, or weedy relatives, through the pollen. This should go a long way to allaying the fears of those concerned that "gene escape" could lead to environmental risks, such as "superweeds".

▶ **High expression levels.** In contrast to the two copies of the nuclear genome present in the typical diploid cell, each chloroplast contains many copies of the plastome, and each plant cell contains a number of chloroplasts (or other plastid types). The plant can therefore be said to be "kiloploid" with respect to the plastome. This results in massive amplification of any transgene incorporated into the plastome, and can lead to levels of recombinant protein orders of magnitude higher than can be achieved by nuclear transformation.

▶ **Targeted integration.** As discussed in the previous section, targeted integration of foreign sequences into the nucleus is a goal difficult to achieve. Plastid transformation however, routinely proceeds through homologous recombination and is precisely targeted to any chosen site for which homologous flanking sequences have been included in the transformation construct. This ensures none of the potential problems associated with random integration into the nucleus (e.g. variable levels of expression, disruption of native genes) are encountered.

▶ **No gene silencing.** A common problem with nuclear transformants is that of "gene silencing" or "co-suppression" of the transgene when more than one copy of the same gene, or similar genes, are present in the same genome. This can lead to the loss of transgene expression, and hence the desired phenotype, even several generations after the initial transformation. The mechanism of gene silencing is poorly understood but seems to be absent from the plastome, which therefore exhibits stable, long term expression of the transgenes.

▶ **No antibiotic resistance genes.** Considerable concern has been expressed over the use, as selectable markers, of bacterial antibiotic resistant genes which lead to breakdown of the antibiotic. For chloroplast transformation, vectors have been developed based on mutations in the plastome itself which prevent the binding of the antibiotic to the chloroplast ribosomes. This type of "antibiotic insensitivity" marker does not pose the same risks as those perceived for the more conventional resistance genes.

The great potential of plastid transformation is supported by recent experimental results. For example, the laboratories of Pal Maliga at Rutgers University and Henry Daniell at Auburn University, in the United States have demonstrated the high expression levels that can be achieved (to several per cent of total protein), and also the potential use of the procedure for improving two important agronomic traits, insect resistance and herbicide resistance. In the former case, an extraordinarily high level of an insecticidal protein from *Bacillus thuringiensis* (Bt) can be produced in the chloroplast, conferring a high level of control against insect pests. In the latter case resistance to the herbicide glyphosate was achieved by over-expressing the target enzyme EPSPS (involved in aromatic amino acid biosynthesis) from *Petunia*, in tobacco chloroplasts. In Europe also there have been important developments. For example, a collaboration between laboratories in Ireland and Hungary has led to the development of the vectors which avoid bacterial antibiotic resistance genes (the American examples described above do include such genes), and demonstrated their effectiveness in selecting chloroplast transformants.

The main limitations of plastid transformation technology to date is that the procedures (employing biolistics, or PEG-mediated DNA uptake into protoplasts) are technically demanding. Almost all reports so far, relate to tobacco with recent successes extending the technology to closely related species, *Petunia* and potato. There is a single report on *Arabidopsis*, and researchers at Calgene have developed a procedure for oilseed rape. The main challenge is to extend the procedures to a wider range of crops, after which we can expect an explosion in the application of this technology. This has been recognised within the European Union, where research projects under the 4th and 5th Frameworks co-ordinated by Prof. PJ Dix, NUI Maynooth, Co. Kildare, have been supported to extend the technology to a broader range of crops of importance in the Community.

Clearly chloroplast transformation has great potential for the improvement of certain agronomic traits, such as herbicide and insect resistance. However, the real excitement generated by this field at present stems from the possibility of using the plastids as "factories" to produce large amounts of valuable recombinant protein, for example for use as oral vaccines, or for other medical and veterinary applications.

Alternatives to antibiotic selection

Plant geneticists routinely install an antibiotic resistance gene alongside the genes that confer the trait they want to introduce. This allows them to identify seedlings that have accepted the gene bundle, as they survive when exposed to the antibiotic, whereas others die. Once the plants have been screened, the resistance gene serves no further purpose. Fears that these genes could spread to dangerous bacteria, making them resistant to antibiotics, have made marker genes a subject to consider. Most researchers feel that these concerns are unjustified and the risks greatly exaggerated. However, the climate is such that many Biotech companies recognised the need to eliminate antibiotic resistance genes from their next generation of products. Several promising strategies are under investigation to achieve this:

▶ **Marker excision.** This involves elimination of the antibiotic resistance gene after it has carried out its function. Generally sequences are incorporated adjacent to the antibiotic resistance gene allowing it to be specifically cleaved out by a recombinase. The most studied system of this type is the cre:lox system.

▶ **Chloroplast transformation.** As discussed on page 28, a selection of chloroplast transformants can be based on structural alteration of the plastid ribosomes.

▶ **Alternative markers.** Herbicide resistance has already been extensively used, in the selection of herbicide resistant varieties, but of course poses its own questions concerning environmental impact. Several other alternative selectable markers have been developed including an ability to utilise exclusive carbon sources such as cellobiuronic acid on phospho-mannose isomerase and an intriguing new strategy based on triggering regeneration capacity in hormone-free medium. This method, developed by Nam-Hai Chua, at the Rockefeller University in New York, utilises a gene *ipt*, from *Agrobacterium tumefaciens*, which causes the production of the phytohormone cytokinin, associated with adventitious shoot initiation, under control of a steroid inducible promoter. When the steroid is included during *Agrobacterium*-mediated transformation, only transformed cells produce the cytokinin leading to shoot regeneration. The resulting transgenic plants can then be grown without the steroid so the hormone gene is not expressed (which would alter plant development), but other genes included on the construct can be. This system has proven effective in tobacco and lettuce, and shows promise for a wider range of species.

▶ **Double transformation.** Based on the observation that when two independent *Agrobacterium* strains are used for transformation, there is frequently simultaneous infection of competent plant cells with both. Thus a selectable marker (e.g gentamycin resistance) can be separated from the gene of interest onto different *Agrobacterium* strains. Antibiotic resistant shoots can then be screened (PCR) for the non-selected gene. Plants containing both genes can then be grown to maturity. If the unlinked genes have integrated at random, there is a good prospect, when screening the progeny, of identifying segregants carrying the gene of interest but not the marker gene. Kees van Dun and colleagues at Advanta seeds, The Netherlands have demonstrated the effectiveness of this strategy in the model system, tobacco, and it should be possible to extend it to other crop species.

▶ **Marker-free selection.** This report has already emphasised in Chapter 1, the development of high throughput screening methods. As procedures for carrying out DNA analysis on large numbers of small samples, with minimal preparation, it becomes feasible to screen thousands of regenerants obtained after

Agrobacterium or biolistic-mediated transformation, without any selection at all, to identify those carrying the transgene. One can predict an explosion in this approach, especially in the laboratories of Biotech Companies, where the investment in this more labour-intensive approach can be justified by the likely returns.

In addition to avoiding antibiotic resistance genes, the above approaches (except for "Alternative markers" have the added attraction of excluding all foreign DNA except the gene of interest and its regulatory elements. Exclusion of all extraneous sequences is desirable both from an aesthetic viewpoint, and for the improvement of consumer acceptance of the technology.

Transposon tagging

Transposable elements have been used as an effective mutagen and as a tool to clone tagged genes. Insertion of a transposable element into a gene can lead to loss or gain of function, changes in expression pattern, or can have no effect on gene function at all, depending on whether the insertion took place in coding or non-coding regions of the gene. Cloning transposable elements from different plant species has made them available as a tool for the isolation of tagged genes using homologous or heterologous tagging strategies. Large-scale insertion metagenesis and identification of insertion sites following a reverse genetics strategy appears to be the best method for unravelling the biological role of the thousands of genes with unknown functions identified by genome or expressed sequence tag (EST) sequencing projects.

Sequencing projects

Although many fundamental plant processes can be studied in the model species, *Arabidopsis thaliana*, for which the genome sequencing is well on its way to completion, some problems can only be studied in crop plants. Large scale sequencing projects for important crop plants such as maize or potato, using expressed sequence tags coupled with DNA chip technology, have the potential to dramatically enhance our knowledge of how complex agronomic traits such as yield or adaptation to stresses (e.g., salt and drought stress, temperature extremes) are controlled. The increased knowledge can provide powerful tools to redesign crop plants to be more productive under extreme environments.

Progress in the Production of Genetically Modified Crops

Between 1996 and 1999, eight countries, five industrial and three developing, have contributed to more than a fifteen-fold increase in the global area of transgenic crops. Adoption rates for transgenic crops are some of the highest for new technologies by agricultural industry standards. High adoption rates reflect grower satisfaction with the products that offer significant benefits ranging from more flexible crop management, higher productivity and a safer environment through decreased use of conventional pesticides, which collectively contribute to a more sustainable agriculture. 1998 was the first year for a commercialised transgenic crop to be grown in the countries of the European Union. Estimates suggest that introductory quantities of insect resistant maize were grown in Spain (20,000 hectares) and France (2,000 hectares). This is judged to be potentially a very significant development because it could have important implications for the further adoption of transgenics in countries of the European Union.

GM food products which have been approved by the regulatory processes (in the United States) are listed year by year in Appendix 1, and plant biotechnology products which have been marketed are listed in Appendix 2.

During this early phase of the plant revolution, the benefits of plant engineering have been largely confined to farmers. Apparently most of the agrochemical companies, including those in Europe, envisage a far more lucrative future when the plant revolution matures further. The next major phase will emphasise the engineering of desirable traits that are readily apparent to the consumer. Adoption of the next stage of biotech crops may proceed more slowly, as the market confronts issues of how to determine price, share the value, and adjust marketing and handling to accommodate specialised end-use characteristics. Furthermore, competition from existing alternative products will not evaporate. Pitfalls that have accompanied the first generation of biotech crops, such as the trade dispute with Europe over approval and labelling of genetically modified crops, will also affect the next generation of products. Some industry analysts believe the development of more end-use quality traits will largely decommodify the existing marketing system for field crops. In other words, there would be a movement away from bulk handling and blending of undifferentiated crops under very broad grades and standards categories and toward a system that can meet more specialised needs of buyers, even to the point of preserving the identity of a crop from the farm to the user.

While the application of biotechnology to reduce chemical inputs for disease and pest control is important, it is by no means the only application of biotechnology in agriculture. Other agronomic considerations that can benefit from the use of biotechnology include engineering natural fertilisers such as nitrogen fixing bacteria and their host plants, and developing crops that are more tolerant of abiotic stresses such as drought, non-optimal temperatures and marginal quality soils.

The technology can also be used to improve nutritional quality by engineering crops with a more balanced amino acid ratio, better vitamin and antioxidant quality, and to improve characteristics such as increased shelf-life, increased starch in potatoes to reduce fat uptake, increased solids in tomatoes for improved processing, improved cotton with high quality fibres and diverse colours without dying. We can harness biotechnology to produce completely novel products such as exotic oils in temperate crops thus reducing our dependence on imports, or engineer plants to produce natural, thermostable biodegradable plastics or even functional antibodies and other therapeutics. Specific examples of these applications will be covered in the following sections.

Biotic stress

Pest and disease resistance has been a primary objective of farmers and breeders throughout the history of agriculture. Genes identified in wild germplasm or recovered as spontaneous or induced mutations have been incorporated into cultivated varieties of many major crop species. This process is now being supplemented by the techniques of genetic engineering, and dozens of crop species are being engineered for improved pest and disease resistance.

Bt insecticidal crystal proteins

Bacillus thuringiensis (Bt) is a gram-positive soil bacterium noted for its abundant production during sporulation of insecticidal proteins in the form of a crystal or crystal- complex. The insecticidal crystal proteins are commonly designated as "Cry" proteins and the genes encoding them as *cry* genes. Cry proteins have been classified according to their insect specificity and nucleotide sequence (see Table 2).

The Cry proteins typically require both solubilisation and activation steps before they become biologically active toxins. For most, solubilisation occurs in the highly alkaline environment of insect midguts. Activation occurs *via* discrete proteolysis by insect gut enzymes and may occur concomitantly with the solubilisation step. The highly acidic nature of most mammalian guts is not a favourable environment for the Cry toxin. The low pH of most mammal guts would solubilise and denature the Cry proteins, making them susceptible to hydrolysis by native gut proteases into inactive small peptides and free amino acids. The Cry I type proteins are typically processed from a 130-kDa protoxin to the active 55 to 65 kDa form. It is generally accepted that the toxin recognises certain receptors on the surface of insect midgut epithelial cells. A pore-complex forms through the cell membrane, resulting in the loss of potassium ions which affects the insect's ability to regulate osmotic pressure. Eventually the animal dies due to massive water uptake.

It appears that several of the reported cases of insect resistance to specific Cry proteins are due to altered receptor binding specificities. Presently, our knowledge of the various Cry proteins is insufficient to predict how specific protein modifications may affect the efficacy or activity spectrum of a particular protein. However, as our knowledge base expands we can predict that protein chemists will be making alterations or fusions of the various Cry proteins or their domains, to increase both their potency and activity spectra.

Maxygen's DNA shuffling technique (Page 10) is another approach to increasing diversity in Cry proteins for insect resistance. Using this technology they have created and selected 53 new active recombinant Cry proteins.

Table 2.   Classification of cry proteins from *Bacillus thuringiensis* (based on Hofte and Whiteley, 1989; Microbiol. Rev. 53:242)

GENE	CRYSTAL SHAPE	PROTEIN SIZE (KDA)	INSECT ACTIVITY
cryI; A(a) A(b), A(c), B, C, D, E, F, G	Bipyramidal	130-138	Lepidopteran larvae
cryII; A, B, C	Cuboid	71, 71, 69	Lepidopteran and Dipteran larvae
cryIII; A, B, B(b)	Flat or Irregular	73, 74, 74	Coleopteran larvae
cryIV; A, B, C, D	Bipyramidal or Round	134, 128, 78, 72	Dipteran larvae
cryV – cryIX	Various	129, 73, 35, 38	Various

Engineering insect resistant plants: beyond Bt

A team of scientists from the University of Wisconsin-Madison, led by Richard french-Constant and David Bowen, has discovered new toxins from a bacterium that may represent the "next generation of microbial insecticide". The gram-negative bacterium *Photorhabdus luminescens* packs a considerable arsenal within its cell: toxins, antibiotics, antifungal compounds, lipases, proteases, and even light-producing genes. The bacteria thrive inside the gut of an insect-attacking nematode. When the nematode invades an insect host, it releases the bacteria into the insect's haemocoel. The bacteria then kill the insect and the nematodes then eat both the bacteria and insect carcass, with hundreds of nematodes eventually bursting out of a single insect victim.

One bacterial cell of *Photorhabdus* can kill an insect host in 24 to 48 hours. Even picomolar quantities of *Photorhabdus* toxin can be lethal to many pests such as caterpillars, mealworms, and even cockroaches and ants. It remains to be seen if these toxins are insecticidal when expressed in plants, particularly in light of their lack of toxicity when expressed in *E. coli*. The broad-spectrum activity of *Photorhabdus* could have numerous ecological effects from food web interactions to decreasing beneficial insect populations. The UW group is trying to boost the secretion of the *Pht* toxin and also testing its safety on humans and wildlife. The *Photorhabdus* technology has been licensed to the Indianapolis-based Dow AgroSciences

Monsanto Corporation scientists are also working on a new protein, cholesterol oxidase, produced by the soil microorganism *Streptomyces*. The discovery of the new protein provides another alternative to Bt and in some instances, it appears to be more effective against some types of insects such as boll weevils. Monsanto, which is seeking a patent for the protein in the highly competitive biocontrol market, reports that its scientist have isolated the cholesterol oxidase gene and inserted it into tobacco and tomato plants.

When attacked by insects, some plants produce insecticidal proteins as part of their natural defence response. Wounding caused by insect damage can induce plants to synthesise lectins, -amylase inhibitors, proteinase inhibitors, or other compounds intended to help ward off the attack. Proteinase inhibitors are a class of defence proteins that work by inhibiting enzymes in the predator's digestive system, so that feeding slows or stops and further development is delayed or arrested. Their utility as protective transgenes was first established in experiments with tobacco but has now also been demonstrated in rice.

Chitin, a substance found in the outer shell of crustaceans and insects and in the cell walls of many fungi, makes the shell or exoskeleton hard. Chitin also forms a protective membrane that lines the digestive tract of insects and protects them from internal penetration by bacteria or pathogens. Scientists working at the Horticultural Research Laboratory of the USDA's Agricultural Research Service (ARS) in Orlando, Florida, have found in some citrus plants large numbers of enzymatic proteins that break down chitin. The enzymes are called chitinases and chitosanases. The ARS scientists are now looking in citrus plants for the genes responsible for producing the enzymes and an appropriate promoter to link with it. Engineered into plants, the enzyme could defend against attacks by fungi, insects and nematodes that have chitin and chitosan in their cell walls, exoskeletons, and digestive tract lining, by breaking down the protective substance and exposing the organisms to pathogens.

Entomologists have long known that plants make use of a wide array of non-protein molecules to kill insects. Some of these compounds, such as the insecticide azadirachtin, isolated from the Neem tree, are widely used by people and are seen as safe biological pesticides. Unfortunately, these non-protein toxins are produced as a result of metabolic pathways that rely on several enzymes to produce the active molecule. Early research avoided work on these potent insecticidal molecules because it was thought that entire pathways would have to be engineered into a plant for production of the compound. However, since even the most complex molecules are derived secondarily from metabolic pathways common to many plants, there is the potential to identify insecticidal molecules that are a mere enzymatic step away from those existing pathways. Identification of the enzyme responsible for the terminal step and transfer of its gene to the crop plant may result in expression of the non-protein compound. Functionally, the engineered enzyme acts as a primary gene product.

A case in point is the non-protein compound limonene. This natural product occurs in many fruits and vegetables. Some experiments show that transformation of maize with the gene encoding limonene synthase results in enhanced accumulation of limonene (Meyer and Roth, 1994. International patent application No. PCT/US94/03011; International Publication WO 94/22304). This has led to control of some insect pests, and was accomplished without the need for complete reengineering of the plant. The ability to engineer plants to produce novel non-protein compounds will provide crop pest managers with an almost limitless number of options for controlling insect pests.

A viral insecticide

Employing viruses as biological pesticides has enormous potential for agriculture and the environment. However, the speed by which viruses kill their insect hosts must be increased if they are to be effective. Researchers at UC Davis (Bruce Hammock, Susumu Maeda) have engineered a virus that infects caterpillars, with the intent of making the virus a more effective destroyer of insect pests. Certain insect viruses, known as baculoviruses, effectively kill insect larvae. However, their action often is too slow, allowing significant crop damage before the larvae die. An enzyme known as juvenile hormone esterase is a key enzyme involved in larval development. It destroys juvenile hormone, causing the caterpillar to stop eating and pupate. If this enzyme is blocked, the result is caterpillars that can destroy a plant in one evening. Increasing the production of the enzyme might be expected to have an opposite, more favourable effect. Researchers transferred the esterase gene into a baculovirus, and infected larvae with the baculovirus. The infected larvae stop eating too early and die. Other approaches to enhancing the action of baculoviruses include using them to express the highly insect specific scorpion toxin and insect diuretic hormone which causes them to relieve themselves to death.

A trial was designed to test the genetically modified virus, which infects the alfalfa looper, in a field of cabbage under conditions where insect density was high and the larvae were large and capable of causing serious crop damage. Cabbage plants harbouring third instar larvae were sprayed with low, medium and high doses of genetically modified or wild type virus strains. Virus treatment significantly reduced insect damage compared to the untreated control plot, and plots treated with the modified virus had significantly less damage than those treated with the unmodified virus. This reduction was clearly a result of the earlier death of insects treated with the modified virus: larval died 10-15 per cent earlier than insects infected with the wild type virus.

Disease endogenous resistance (R) genes

The incorporation of resistance genes into important crop plants is the major disease control method utilised in worldwide production agriculture. However the strategy is frequently hampered by lack of availability, in certain plant species, of resistance genes against particular pathogens, and the emergence in some cases of new virulent pathogen races able to "overcome" a previously effective resistance gene.

If a large collection of disease resistance genes were molecularly cloned and deployed by transforming them into desired plant cultivars, substantial improvements in disease pest control could be quickly realised. Increased attention therefore needs to be given to strategies for efficiently cloning relatively large numbers of these genes from a variety of crop plants. There are several potential approaches to utilising cloned resistance genes if they are available:

▶ **Resistance genes introduced into plants by transformation would avoid negative characteristics from crossing and eliminate the time for extensive backcrossing**

▶ **The availability of several cloned resistance genes against a pest or pathogen should permit deployment of only those genes that are difficult for the pathogen to overcome**

▶ **New combinations of resistance genes could be released periodically to avoid problems with the emergence of virulent pathogen races**

▶ **Resistance genes effective against a certain pest or pathogen of a particular plant might be obtained from unrelated plant species**

▶ **The availability of cloned resistance genes might permit the construction of chimeric or synthetic resistance genes encoding novel recognition specificities.**

In 1994, applying information obtained from plant genetic mapping, scientists at Cornell and Purdue Universities first cloned and moved a disease-resistant gene from one crop variety to another. The researchers transferred the tomato Pto gene, encoding a protein kinase, which gives resistance to strains of the bacterium *Pseudomonas syringae pr. Tomato,* from resistant to susceptible cultivars of tomato, which in turn became resistant.

Another bacterial disease was beaten using R genes at UC Davis. In this case a gene conferring resistance to bacterial blight, caused by the bacteria *Xanthomonas oryzae* (a highly destructive disease of rice, often causing 50 per cent yield losses in some areas) was introduced.

Cloned R genes now provide novel tools for plant breeders to improve the efficiency of plant breeding strategies, via marker assisted breeding, and by using transformation for accelerating the introgression of useful R genes from related species. Hopefully, a combination of strategies will reduce the requirement for agrochemicals to control crop diseases and will accelerate effective retrieval and deployment of the natural variation in R genes of wild plant species.

Pathogen-derived resistance

Taking an alternative approach, rather than identifying resistance genes in the host organism or a related species, genes or gene fragments from the parasite itself are inserted into the host genome to confer resistance. This technique is claimed in a patent held by Stephen Johnston and John Sanford of Cornell Research Foundation, Inc. (CRF). The implications of this technique are broad and are already impacting on development of agricultural crops resistant to insects and many types of microorganisms.

The patent describes how a gene taken from a virus can be used as a defence against the virus by inserting it into the host organism, such as a bacterium. The viral gene is expressed in the bacterial host and disrupts normal function of the virus parasite by competing with, or interfering with, expression of the native viral gene. Although the patent describes the use of a virus replicase gene in a bacterium, the technology can be applied to any host, including other microorganisms such as industrial yeast or bacteria, plants, or even animals including mammals. The technology also applies to any parasite including fungi, bacteria, protozoans and insects, in addition to viruses.

It will be interesting to see how large seed or agricultural companies with products using parasite-derived resistance either on the market or in development, are affected by this patent. Seminis Vegetable Seeds has a patent for a virus resistant squash and melons which contain virus coat-protein genes. According to officials at Seminis, they are in the process of evaluating patent 5580716 and its implications, and are unable to comment until they know more about it. Marc Law, Research Director at

Novartis, believes the licensing strategy of CRF will dictate how widely parasite-derived resistance technology will be applied. According to Dr. Law, if CRF issues non-exclusive, low cost licenses, the technology could have broad implications. To date, most seed companies have shown limited interest in virus resistance compared to other pest problems. The commercial impact, therefore, may not be as great until fungal, bacterial and insect resistance has been demonstrated by this technique.

Virus resistance

Researchers at Washington University in St. Louis found that if a transformed plant expresses the coat protein of tobacco mosaic virus (TMV), the plant is protected against inoculated TMV. This was the first demonstration of genetically engineered resistance against a plant virus, and the technology subsequently has proved to be effective against a great variety of plant viruses when applied in several different crop species, including tomato and potato, each coat protein being more or less specific against the corresponding virus. The second genetically engineered crop to be commercialised in the US (Dec. 13 1994) was a virus resistant yellow crook neck squash developed by Asgrow Seed (now part of the Seminis Vegetable Seeds which in turn is part of the Mexican-based conglomerate ELM). The first on the market was marketed as "Freedom II" and has CP mediated resistance to zucchini yellow mosaic and watermellon mosaic viruses. It was field tested under 14 APHIS permits at 46 sites in 10 states. Seminis has since improved the genetic background of its virus resistant squash and now has squash and melons on the market carrying coat protein genes for resistance to CMV, PRSV, SqMV, WMV2, and ZYMV.

A particular success story in this area is the production, in Hawaii, of papaya plants rendered resistant to the devastating virus, Papaya ring spot virus (PRSV), through genetic transformation with PRSV coat protein gene. Because of the devastating nature of the epidemic facing the Hawaiian farmers the companies owning the technology, and the USDA co-operated in the rapid introduction of the new varieties. The transgenic papaya, named "Rainbow", has continued to withstand PRSV in the field and has been shown to yield at levels equal to or higher than the industry standard, with fruits viewed favourably in taste and appearance by consumers. The result is a model for how agricultural interests, biotechnology research, and the legal and regulatory processes can work together to solve a problem.

Potatoes present more than a few challenges to researchers working to limit the impact of yield-reducing virus diseases. Besides being susceptible to infection by a variety of unrelated viruses, most commercial potato cultivars have a tetraploid genome that makes breeding for resistance a slow process. The initial genetic engineering approach of coat protein mediated resistance, effective against individual virus diseases, has now been augmented by a strategy for broad-spectrum protection against virus infection. A group from the Max Planck Institute has reported that potato plants expressing a mutant version of the potato leaf roll virus (PLRV) movement protein were resistant not only to PLRV, but to potato virus Y and potato virus X. Protection against infection by any one of these three pathogens, which belong to taxonomically distinct groups, is not due to the expression of pathogenesis-related proteins that are part of an active defence mechanism referred to as 'induced resistance'. The transgene used in these experiments is a defective form of the PLRV movement protein, which is normally associated with the plasmodesmata of cells within phloem tissue and functions in cell-to-cell movement. The broad-spectrum resistance to unrelated viruses is thought to result from interference with systemic spread in the transgenic plants.

Another approach to genetically-engineered resistance against plant viruses is the use of antisense technology, in which RNA with virus RNA sequences but of the opposite "polarity" are expressed in the transformed plant. Researchers at the Agriculture Research Service's Florist and Nursery Crops Laboratory in Beltsville, Maryland inserted an antisense gene from bean yellow mosaic virus (BYMV) into the tobacco plant (*Nicotiana benthamiana*) and discovered that the gene reversal disarmed invading bean yellow mosaic viruses. The bean yellow mosaic virus antisense gene has the potential to be a defence against the virus in a whole range of ornamental flowers and crop plants susceptible to BYMV and other potyviruses. Plants with the reversed BYMV gene produce antisense RNA that binds to an invading virus' RNA. This binding apparently prevents the virus from reproducing itself in the plants. Other potential approaches include replicase and protease inhibition strategies and ribozyme catalysis on the RNA, a more potent variation of antisense technology.

Fungal resistance

Plants are able to defend themselves from pathogen invasion using a diverse array of mechanisms. Among others, these strategies may include the production of chemicals such as phytoalexins, pathogen wall-degrading enzymes, or ribosome-inactivating proteins. In many cases production of such defence compounds leads to localised cell death of plant tissue around the point of pathogen entry. Indeed, this local necrosis (called the hypersensitive response) is correlated with high levels of resistance to certain pathogenic fungi because the fungi rely on maintaining contact with living host cells, and are subject to starvation if cells around the point of hyphae invasion die. Another category of plant defence is the systemic acquired resistance (SAR), which is the plant-wide synthesis of a variety of defence-related proteins in response to an initial pathogen attack at one location.

Along with the diversity of defence mechanisms, a high degree of specificity has evolved in plant-pathogen interactions. For example, a given plant species may be resistant to one species of fungus, but susceptible to another. Alternatively, one species of fungus may thrive on certain plant species, but not on others. The power of biotechnology lies in the ability to transcend such species-specific limitations and it is now possible to transfer resistance mechanisms from one species to another or to modify the expression of a plant's own defence mechanisms.

There are several recent examples of how fungal resistance in plants has been increased by transferring or modifying plant defence capabilities:

▶ **Phytoalexin synthesis.** Tomatoes with stilbene synthase from grapevine have enhanced resistance to *Phytophthora infestans.*

▶ **Anti-fungal enzyme.** Cucumber with a chitinase gene from rice has enhanced resistance to grey mould (*Botrytis cinerea*).

▶ **Pathogen signal protein.** Tobacco with a fungal protein elicitor gene has enhanced resistance to *Phytophthora parasitica.*

▶ **Trypsin inhibitor.** Associated with inhibition of *Aspergillus flavus* infection in corn.

▶ **Fumonisin metabolising enzymes.** Pioneer Hi-Bred (now part of Dupont) have cloned genes encoding key enzymes were cloned, and their activity was confirmed in heterologous expression systems. Transgenic lines showed promising results in greenhouse ear mould assays and field tests.

▶ **Modifying hypersensitive response (HR).** HR is characterised by a rapid defence reaction in the area of pathogen ingress that culminates in programmed cell death (PCD) around the point of invasion, and appears as necrotic spots against a background of healthy tissue. HR is thought to curtail disease by restricting the development and spread of invading pathogens. Transformation of tomato plants with an inhibitor of PCD, by Dr. D. Gilchrist and co-workers at the University of California Davis showed that the baculovirus p35 gene, increased plant resistance to the fungus *Alternaria alternata* f.sp. lycopersici. By contrast, Maarten Stuiver of Zeneca-MOGEN has found success by engineering resistance to a broad range of fungi through inducing HR (and ultimately PCD), rather than inhibiting it. This strategy resulted in transgenic plants with enhanced resistance not only to fungi (*C. fulvum*, late blight, and powdery mildew), but also to tomato spotted wilt virus. The plants displayed necrotic lesions that were small in size relative to untransformed controls.

▶ **Calmodulin genes.** Two calmodulin genes shown to be involved with systemic acquired resistance (SAR) in soybean, rendered transgenic tobacco plants resistant to *Phytophthora parasitica var.*

nicotianae. A hypersensitive response was seen in transgenic plants, but not in wild type plants. The transgenic plants also had enhanced resistance to *Pseudomonas syringae* and TMV. Engineering constitutively expressed calmodulin genes may enhance plant defenses against microbial attack.

▶ **An SAR master switch.** Researchers at Duke University have cloned a "master-switch" gene (NPR1) in *Arabidopsis* that regulates many downstream pathogenesis related (PR) genes. Transgenic plants having only a modest increase in NPR1 protein showed dramatic resistance to the bacterial pathogen *Pseudomonas syringae* but also to the fungal pathogen *Pernospora parasitica*. Just three days after infection, the growth of bacteria was inhibited more than a thousand-fold in transgenic plants. These lines also showed an increased transcription of many PR genes, suggesting that the NPR1 gene activates a range of defence-related genes which may act synergistically to confer disease resistance. This study hints at a tantalising possibility that crop plants with durable and broad-spectrum resistance against many destructive diseases can be developed using just one gene. Several crops, including potato, maize, wheat, cabbage and canola, contain DNA sequences similar to the NPR1 gene.

Control of Nematodes

Nematodes are covered with an impermeable cuticle, which provides them with considerable protection. Chemicals with outstanding penetration characteristics are therefore required for nematode control. Many of the commonly used nematicides are known chemically as organophosphates, and behave as nerve toxins. As nervous system poisons, nematicides must be handled and applied with extreme care to avoid any direct contact with the compound or its dust. In recent years, continuing environmental and exposure problems associated with the use of nematicides have introduced a sense of urgency into the search for alternative methods of nematode management.

Genes that protect tomato plants against root-knot nematodes have become a prime target for breeders and molecular biologists alike. Efforts to clone these genes paid off recently as a research group at UC Davis, led by Valerie Williamson, working on the root knot nematode, *Meloidogyne incognita*, isolated the nematode-resistant *Mi* gene from a nematode-resistant wild tomato (*Lycopersicon peruvianum*). When introduced into susceptible plants, the gene confers resistance against attack by the nematode. Working with entomologist Diane Ullman, the group was surprised to find that these transgenic plants were also resistant against aphids.

The nematode/aphid resistance gene in tomato is similar in structure to other known plant genes that confer resistance to fungi and bacteria as well as nematodes. It has the characteristic nucleotide-binding sites and leucine-rich repeats. This report is the first to show that plant resistance mechanisms against a diverse class of pathogens and pests have a common underlying molecular theme. The results are still perplexing, though, because nematodes and aphids are so different and it is difficult to visualise a common mode of action employed by the plant in its fight against both pests. Williamson suggests that a mechanism involving cellular changes in the plant that interfere with nutrient uptake by the pests may work against such diverse organisms.

Tomato geneticist Charles Rick (UC Davis) believes the Mi gene cloning will accelerate tomato breeding for nematode resistance. While this gene provides remarkable resistance against many nematode species and a few strains of the potato aphid, he points out that it is ineffective under high temperatures typical in tropical agriculture, and thus calls for further search of additional genes in the wild tomato germplasm.

Despite these advances, many applied nematologists currently fear that more nematicides will be withdrawn from the market before there are suitable alternate methods of control.

Herbicide tolerance

Approaches to herbicide tolerance are included in the chart of approved crops (Appendix 1), and have been discussed in the section on Cholorplast Transformation (Page 28). Crops that are genetically modified to withstand applications of herbicides give farmers greater flexibility in their pest control strategy, allow them to use weed controls more selectively and to use environmentally gentler herbicides. Rather than applying herbicide before planting, farmers can wait into the growing season, after the herbicide tolerant crop emerges, to see where weed pressures develop before spraying. The herbicide tolerant trait allows farmers to spray herbicides over the top to control the weeds without harming the crops. The farmer uses safer controls, reducing overall environmental impact, and sprays less often, reducing the farmer's production costs. On both counts, farmer satisfaction increases, especially as superior weed control also increases productivity per acre. Soybean, cotton, corn and canola have herbicide-tolerant varieties. Wheat, rice and sugar beet are in development.

Abiotic stress

In their quest to feed the ever-increasing world population, agricultural scientists have to contend with the reality that arable land on this earth is very limited. Much of the *terra firma* is inhospitable to farming because of high salt, dry or frigid conditions. Even large tracts of land currently under agricultural cultivation around the world suffer from these maladies that limit crop productivity. If crops can be redesigned to better cope with stress, agricultural production can be increased dramatically. Genetic engineering has been used to make plants with additional stress response genes to counteract these environmental stresses.

Drought and salt tolerance

Although impressive strides have been made in engineering crops resistant to diseases and pests, making them hardier to drought and salt conditions has been more challenging. Many plants such as the cactus which brave the arid deserts do so because of a multitude of complex adaptive mechanisms which are yet intractable to gene manipulation. Nevertheless, molecular biologists are zeroing in on important secrets of organisms that tolerate salt or drought conditions, and using this knowledge to develop hardier crops.

One example is a recent report from Japan, where tolerance to salt and cold stress was engineered in plants by enabling them to accumulate glycinebetaine. Betaine, as it is also called, is found in organisms as diverse as bacteria, spinach and humans. Betaine is thought to insulate plant cells against the ravages of salt by preserving the osmotic balance, by stabilising the structure of proteins and by protecting the photosynthetic apparatus. The enzyme choline oxidase catalyses the production of betaine from choline. A group led by Norio Murata at the National Institute of Basic Biology in Okazaki has cloned a gene for choline oxidase (codA) from a soil bacterium. They then developed transgenic Arabidopsis plants with the codA gene fused to a transit peptide that directed the enzyme into chloroplasts. When seeds from transformed plants were tested under high salt conditions (200 to 300mM NaCl), most germinated well while regular seeds did not. Increased salt tolerance due to betaine accumulation was also observed in both seedlings and adult plants. Nonengineered adult plants died quickly when transferred to salt conditions (200mM NaCl), but transgenic plants continued to grow, albeit slowly. Engineered plants producing choline oxidase also showed increased resilience to damaging cold exposures. With increasing salt and cold conditions, transgenic plants maintained photosynthetic activity while control plants ceased such activity under stress. In another study with Arabidopsis, they have also demonstrated that betaine accumulation via choline oxidase can lead to significant improvements in tolerance to high temperatures. The Murata group has now extended this research to crop species and has developed rice plants with the stress-tolerant gene.

In addition to betaine, other compatible solutes such as mannitol and proline also promote drought tolerance in plants, and plants engineered to produce these compounds were also stress tolerant. The Japanese study further extends the horizons of the plant stress research, and collectively these studies foretell a scenario where biotechnology would arm our future crops with new tactics to survive in hostile environments.

Cold tolerance

Cold temperatures are a major environmental constraint in crop productivity in the temperate region. Classical plant breeding has had limited success in imparting cold hardiness to crop plants, in part because little is understood as to why some species withstand cold better than others. Use of biotechnology to isolate cold-tolerance genes thus may help in the development of crop plants that can survive frigid temperatures. This optimism is supported by a recent publication from Michael Thomashow's group at Michigan State University which provides some valuable insights into how plants respond to cold temperatures. The research shows for the first time that freezing tolerance in plants can be enhanced through insertion of a single gene involved in cold acclimation. Acclimation is the process whereby plants exposed to low, non-freezing temperatures somehow learn to put up with subsequent freezing temperatures. The underlying reasons for this phenomenon appear to be complex, but it is known that cold acclimation is controlled by many genes and that cell membranes are particularly vulnerable to cold damage. Thomashow and colleagues have isolated many genes that are turned on during cold acclimation in *Arabidopsis*. One such gene is COR15a, which is speculated to have a role in freezing tolerance.

The Michigan State group developed transgenic Arabidopsis plants expressing the COR15a gene in a constitutive manner. In normal plants this gene is turned on only through cold acclimation, while the transgenic plants showed COR15a gene product in both cold acclimated and non-acclimated plants. Chloroplasts in leaves of transgenic plants showed reduced damage to freezing temperatures compared to those from the control plants. Although the COR15a gene produces a chloroplast-targeted protein, the results indicate that the expression of the gene may also affect other cellular functions including improving the cryostability of the plasma membrane. The COR15a gene enhanced the freezing tolerance of chloroplasts in engineered plants by almost 2°C which was nearly one-third of the increase seen due to cold-acclimation. While this might not appear to be a large increase, a 2°C improvement in freeze tolerance could potentially benefit certain crop plants. There are many more COR genes, and if introduced together into a plant, even more dramatic cold tolerance, especially at the whole plant level, may be achieved.

Other promising strategies to improve cold tolerance include the expression in transgenic plants of fatty acid desaturase genes. These decrease the level of fatty acid saturation in membrane lipids, rendering them more tolerant of chilling stress. Again, *Arabidopsis*, has been the model for dissecting the influence of individual desaturases, but one can predict the extension of the results to amelioration of cold stress in crop plants.

Master switch to stress tolerance

No approach has so far produced commercial crop varieties with superior stress resistance. One possible reason for the lack of success might be that most investigators transferred individual stress genes, a tactic that results in selective improvement in the plant's response. In a study performed by Kasuga and colleagues, plants were modified with a stress-inducible transcription factor that turns on several stress response genes simultaneously. The resulting plants respond better to stress than those that have received single stress response genes.

A cis-acting element called the Dehydration Response Element (DRE) was found in the promoter region of rd29A, a regulatory element found in the promoters of many drought- and cold-induced stress genes. DRE-binding proteins specifically bind to and activate DRE-containing genes in *Arabidopsis*. To create *Arabidopsis* plants with a higher stress response, the authors first cloned a DRE-binding protein (DREB1A) on to the 35S CaMV promoter allowing constitutive expression of genes. This resulted in the continuous production of the DRE-binding protein and over expression of the stress genes controlled by DRE. Transformed plants were compared to wild type plants at days 35 and 53. Under normal growth conditions, the transformed plants showed growth retardation, which was severe in some cases, and greatly reduced seed numbers. However, under stress conditions, the transformed plants displayed increased tolerance to drought, salt, and cold.

To reduce the growth-limiting effects of continuous activation of stress genes, DREB1A was placed under control of a second stress-inducible promoter, rd29A. Plants transformed with this system showed only slight growth retardation under normal growth conditions. This correlated with slightly higher background levels of DREB1A expression in transformed plants compared to wild type plants. However, the seed counts for both sets of plants were similar. Although the rd29A promoter is not a constitutive promoter and the stress genes are not fully activated until the plant is stressed, multiple stress genes are rapidly and simultaneously expressed in response to stress. This resulted in a greater tolerance to stress while minimising growth retardation effects seen under normal conditions.

Yield

Enhancing crop productivity is a fundamental objective of agriculture, yet actually increasing plant growth is difficult because environmental conditions often put constraints on plant metabolism. Such environmental factors include sunlight, water, mineral nutrients, carbon dioxide and oxygen, and a lack of any of these may limit plant growth. Thus people have long tried to optimise plant utilisation of many of these resources, for example through enhanced water and nutrient availability and efficiency of use.

The majority of genetically engineered plants currently under development are the result of single-gene transfers. Such efforts, although important to raising actual yields, are unlikely to raise potential yields. To break yield barriers, the plants will have to be thoroughly re-engineered. Nordine Chiek director of Calgene research defines a number of parameters for yield increase including water use efficiency, thermostability, source capacity, starch synthesis, seed weight and nitrogen metabolism. He has taken two main approaches to increasing yield in maize. One is through increased starch biosynthesis, and the second is through improved nitrogen assimilation. For the former he has modified starch metabolism to increase sink strength and for this again he has taken two approaches both of which depend on a thorough understanding of carbon metabolism and starch biosynthesis.

One approach is to improve the activity of an existing enzymatic step, the second is to alter the metabolic pathway. There are many intermediary enzymatic steps in the metabolic pathway from sucrose to starch and Chiek has targeted the two ends of the pathway to increase the efficiency of going from source to product by increasing sucrose hydrolysis through altering the pathway and increasing sucrose biosynthesis by improving an existing enzymatic step. He achieved the former through the introduction of a new gene coding for sucrose phosphorylase which takes the pathway straight to Glucose-1-phosphate, thereby bypassing UDP-glucose. The second boost also was achieved by introducing a new gene but this time the gene has an endogenous counterpart. The idea of the new gene is that because it is from another source and under the control of a different promoter its activity was not subject to the same degree of inhibition by the plants native regulatory machinery. This new gene from *E. coli* codes for the enzyme ADP glucose pyrophosphoralyase and is under the control of a seed-specific promoter. Taking this approach, they found on average a 23 per cent increase in grain weight. Taking the same gene and this time placing it under the tuber-specific patatin promoter in potatoes, they increased starch content by over 30 per cent. This has an added bonus as the higher starch content results in a lower moisture content in essence giving not only more potato for your money but also far less fat absorption on frying as moisture lost during frying is replaced by oil uptake.

Increased yields by improved nitrogen assimilation may be the next breakthrough. Benefits of improved nitrogen assimilation in crops include optimisation of crop response to fertiliser, increased yield potential at low and high levels of nitrogen, positive environmental impact, reduction of nitrate in ground water, improved crop quality and seed composition, and higher protein in leaf and seed.

Nitrogen is fixed, or combined, in nature as nitric oxide by lightning and ultraviolet rays, but more significant amounts of nitrogen are fixed as ammonia, nitrites, and nitrates by soil microorganisms. More than 90 per cent of all nitrogen fixation is effected by them. The major sources of nitrogen-fixation for plants are soil and symbiotic bacteria such as Rhizobium, associated with leguminous plants. Nitrates and ammonia resulting from nitrogen fixation are assimilated into the specific tissue compounds of algae and higher plants. Asparagine and glutamine are the main forms of transported nitrogen in cereals. Higher plants are more versatile than animals; they can make all of the amino acids required for protein synthesis, with either ammonia (NH_3) or nitrate (NO_3) as the nitrogen source. Chiek has improved the assimilation process by taking advantage of the fact that ammonia is incorporated into the intermediates of metabolic pathways mainly *via* the glutamate dehydrogenase (GDH) reaction. He has introduced a GDH from an algal origin, bypassing two intermediate steps in the metabolic pathway for the production of glutamine and has thereby increased kernel protein by 6-12 per cent.

A recent article in Nature Biotechnology by Leif Bülow and co-workers suggests oxygen supply can also be productively manipulated. They have generated tobacco plants that synthesise a bacterial hemoglobin molecule (VHb) and demonstrated that these transgenic plants have increased productivity compared to their non-transformed counterparts. Analysis of two lines of transformants showed that transgenic plants had higher growth rates and altered activity of metabolic pathways. The VHb-containing plants germinated 3 to 4 days earlier than non-transformed control plants and developed faster, accumulating 80 to 100 per cent more fresh weight after 35 days. In addition, the transgenic plants contained greater chlorophyll and nicotine content than non- transformed controls. The increases in chlorophyll and nicotine were attributed to a greater availability of O_2 as a substrate in their biosynthetic pathways, thus leading to a shift toward metabolism requiring oxygen. The mechanism by which the VHb hemoglobin functions in the tobacco system is not clear. The authors suggest that it acts through a combination of increasing availability of O_2 as a substrate for cellular metabolism and by increased O_2 leading to higher levels of ATP available for powering cellular metabolism. It is also possible that the hemoglobin scavenges free O_2 and its radicals, thus protecting the cell from these harmful molecules.

It remains to be seen whether the enhanced productivity reported here can be repeated in other crops, or how any increase in growth will translate into additional yields under field conditions. However, this research is significant because it points out the importance of a previously neglected area of study and demonstrates that there is still more room for improving plant productivity. This is all the more promising because the effect was produced by the insertion of just a single gene.

Another approach would be to alter the plants leaf architecture by altering the stomata, the porelike openings that stipple a plant's epidermis and control the in- and outtake of oxygen, carbon dioxide, and water. To allow dry-land crops to use water more efficiently, stomata might be bioengineered to close more readily under drought stress, while in water-rich areas, they might be modified to stay open even longer. That would give you better ventilation in the leaf, decreasing the canopy temperature and giving better transport of CO_2, both of which could boost the rate of photosynthesis, and hence yield. Researchers have their eyes on two molecular targets that play a role in regulating the stomata: the plant hormone abscisic acid, which triggers closing, and an enzymatic process called farnesylation, which seems to impede ABA By altering farnesylation, researchers may, in theory, be able to adjust plants' sensitivity to ABA and thus the tendency of the stomata to close.

Other researchers are exploring ways of using *Arabidopsis* genes to prevent flowering in an effort to increase productivity. For annual crops such as lettuce and potato plants, flowering is a prelude to death. It sends a signal to the leaves telling them to shut down photosynthesis. Blocking that signal might mean farmers could grow the crops for longer and perhaps get bigger yields because the plants would no longer need to invest resources in making flowers. Nobody has engineered crops this way yet, but the discovery of an *Arabidopsis* gene called *Frigida* could encourage researchers to try. The gene seems to function to prevent flowering, or at least to delay it until winter is over. Caroline Dean, at the John Innes Centre in Norwich is attempting this by inserting *Frigida* into sugar beet to see what happens.

That task is daunting enough, but other researchers would like to go even further and tinker with the mechanisms of photosynthesis itself. Controlling such basic multigene traits is a complex, unpredictable task. Photosynthesis is a process that evolution hasn't changed fundamentally in a couple billion years. To improve crops' ability to turn atmospheric carbon dioxide into food, genetic engineers have focused on RuBisCo, the principal catalyst for photosynthesis and a notoriously inefficient enzyme. Laboratories across the world are trying to improve the RuBisCo in food crops by either replacing the existing enzyme with a more efficient form identified in red algae, or bolting on what could be thought of as molecular superchargers.

Some critics, however, question whether this approach will benefit agriculture. Since at least 1970, research has shown little correlation between crops' photosynthesis rates and their yields, suggesting that improvements in RuBisCo won't automatically translate into better harvests. So, even if the work is a technical success, the payoff may be minor, as traditional plant breeding has already pushed up crops' harvest index and ability to capture sunlight about as high as they can go. Still, altering photosynthesis remains a hope for the future of agriculture. Once all the relatively obvious steps have been taken photosynthesis is what is left.

Postharvest qualities

Biotechnology is also being used to develop crops that have better processing qualities, or are tastier, more appealing, more nutritious and have a longer shelf life without the addition of preservatives.

Processing characteristics

Bread rises because large protein molecules in wheat flour help form a network that gives dough a combination of strength, elasticity, and extensibility that enables the dough to trap CO_2. Wheat is unique among cereals in having this property, much of which can be traced to the presence of a complex mixture of proteins called gluten. The most important of these proteins for determining dough elasticity are the glutenins, which comprise a group of high molecular weight proteins that interact with each other during mixing and kneading to form large (greater than one million kDa) polymers. Because the baking industry is very interested in these proteins and their influence on dough quality, considerable effort has been put into selecting and breeding wheat varieties with high glutenin content.

Unfortunately, it is not a simple matter to develop wheat lines that consistently express high levels of glutenin. The glutenin proteins are encoded by six genes and the total glutenin content of the grain is proportional to the expression of these genes. However, specific gene silencing often results in one or more of these genes not being expressed, with the result that varieties may not reach optimal glutenin content. Increasing expression of glutenin genes is therefore a realistic target for crop engineering.

Shelf life

The first genetically engineered crop product approved for sale was a tomato in which ripening had been modified through the use of antisense genes. Calgene, Inc., of Davis, California, commercialised the FLAVR SAVR tomato which is transgenic for antisense RNA that reduces production of the enzyme polygalacturonase. Polygalacturonase degrades the "glue" that holds plant cell walls together and for this reason is the central enzyme in softening (and increased susceptibility to disease) of ripe tomatoes. A tomato with reduced production of this enzyme can be picked red and more flavourful, rather than green, and still survive transport to market.

The genetic information that codes for the polygalacturonase enzyme is transcribed into another nucleic acid called messenger RNA (mRNA). This is then translated into the enzyme. When Calgene placed the gene coding for the polygalacturonase enzyme back into the tomato genome in the opposite orientation, the two mRNAs annealed and effectively blocked translation of the enzyme. Efforts also have been directed at using antisense technology to switch off one of the genes involved in the production of ethylene, the key hormone in fruit ripening. The pathway for the biosynthesis of ethylene is well understood.

The enzyme ACCsynthase converts SAM (S-adenosylmethionine) to ACC (1 aminocyclopropane-1-carboxylic acid), which is in turn converted to ethylene by ACC oxidase. Florigene has isolated carnation genes for both ACC synthase and ACC oxidase. By using antisense technology to suppress expression of these genes ethylene production is blocked, leading to flowers which have a long life after cutting. The same result has also been achieved by co-suppression. Introducing additional copies of the genes for ethylene synthesis leads to suppression of both the transgene and the native genes. This research is being extended to other crops including broccoli, raspberries and bananas.

Another strategy for increasing shelf-life will be more widely applicable to leafy crops, and involves regulating the level of cytokinin, the hormone responsible for delaying leaf senescence. The *Agrobacterium gene ipt* has already been discussed in a different context (Page 24). It encodes an enzyme isopentenyl transferase which catalyses a key step in cytokinin biosynthesis. The laboratory of Richard Amasino in the United States, placed the *ipt* gene under control of the promoter from a senescence associated gene from *Arabidopsis*. They were able to demonstrate that in transgenic tobacco the leaf cytokinin level is auto-regulated, i.e. as the leaf ages the promoter is activated, triggering just enough cytokinin production to reverse the senescence process, without disturbing other aspects of plant development. A spectacular delay in the ageing (yellowing) of the leaves was the result.

This observation clearly has exciting implications for shelf-life of vegetable crops. Normally leaves yellow rapidly after harvest as the supply of cytokinin from the roots is severed. A European Consortium, co-ordinated from Ireland, has now demonstrated similarly spectacular results to Amasino's, in lettuce, cauliflower, and tomato. In fruit crops like tomato, the benefits could lie in extending photosynthetic life of the plant, which might effect yield, and reducing fungal infection (fungi favour senescent leaves).

Seedless crops

The commercial success of seedless oranges and grapes shows consumers' eagerness for easy-to-eat produce, but currently few fruits come in seedless varieties, and when available they may be more expensive. The higher cost reflects the difficulties of making a marketable seedless fruit, which requires either mutant lines, infertile hybrids, or costly and labour-intensive treatment of flowers with phyto-hormones. However, an Italian researcher Angelo Spena and colleagues in Italy and Germany have developed a new and elegant method for tricking plants into making fruits with no seeds.

In normal plant reproduction, a fruit is formed only after successful fertilisation of the ovule in the flower ovary. Levels of auxin, a plant hormone, rise in response to fertilisation, and stimulate seed growth and formation of fruit tissue surrounding the seed. Spena and co-workers produced transgenic eggplant and tobacco plants that set seedless fruit by engineering them to produce auxin in the unfertilised ovary. To do this they took the coding region of the iaaM gene from the plant pathogenic bacterium *Pseudomonas syringae pv. savastanoi*, which leads to the production of auxin in plant tissue and placed it under control of an ovule-specific promoter from snapdragon. Transgenic tobacco plants that expressed the new gene construct grew normally, but in the absence of fertilisation produced smaller-than-normal capsules that contained only aborted seeds. However, if flowers of these plants were self-pollinated, they set normal capsules and fertile seeds. Similarly, transgenic eggplants showed vegetative development identical to that of untransformed control plants, but when emasculated to prevent fertilisation, they set fruit that was equal in size and shape to fruit of fertilised flowers, yet contained no seeds. Similar approaches, using plant hormone genes from *Agrobacterium* have since led to the production of seedless tomatoes. This could be of great benefit to tomato processing (paste, Ketchup etc.) industry. Not only would the removal of seeds be unnecessary, but the solid content of the fruit is likely to be enhanced.

As well as the attractions offered by seedless fruit, another tangible benefit is the reduction on the dependence on pollination, which can be adversely effected by weather conditions during flowering, for fruit formation. However, at present seedless fruits are only obtained when flowers are not pollinated. Incorporation of a male sterility gene will be required in most crops before seedless fruit can be produced under large-scale field conditions.

Secondary plant metabolites - nutraceuticals

The relentless search for new compounds to treat human disease has led to the formation of specialised biotechnology firms searching for plant compounds that demonstrate some therapeutic value. Recently, a number of articles have sprung up in biotechnology publications describing this emerging sector called the "nutraceutical"industry, another burgeoning industry in which biotechnology combines with agriculture to produce products with possible health benefits. Nutraceuticals are foods or parts of foods that are believed to have medicinal value. One example is sulforaphane, found in broccoli, that has been shown to prevent breast cancer in mice.

Modifying the nutritional composition of plant foods is an urgent worldwide health issue as basic nutritional needs for much of the world's population are still unmet. Even in industrialised nations, where both food abundance and variety are excellent and daily caloric intake is often excessive, micronutrient deficiencies are surprisingly common owing to poor eating habits. In addition to essential vitamins and minerals, plants also synthesise 80,000 of the 100,000 characterised secondary metabolites on the planet. Many phytochemicals also have significant consequences for human health and are thought to be a major reason that plant-rich diets are associated with lower morbidity and mortality in adult life.

One way to ensure an adequate dietary intake of nutritionally beneficial compounds is to manipulate their levels in plant foods. Until recently such work had been hindered by the difficulty in isolating the relevant genes (e.g. for vitamin biosynthesis). However, the advent of genomics during the past five years has provided new routes for such work. One aspect of genomics is the complete sequencing of an organism's entire genome. This means that genes for vitamin synthesis from simple organisms like bacteria and fungi can be used to rapidly identify vitamin biosynthetic genes in more complex organisms like plants. In the past year, University of Nevada researchers in Dean Della Penna's laboratory have developed and applied this approach called Nutritional Genomics, to dissect and manipulate the synthesis of Vitamin E in plants. Vitamin E is the most important fat-soluble antioxidant in our diet; cannot be synthesised by humans and must be obtained from plant sources in our diet. Unfortunately, obtaining the required amount from the average diet is extremely difficult. The reason for this is that the major vitamin E sources in our diets, plant oils, contain vitamin E precursors that are 10 to 50 times less active than the most active form of the vitamin, alpha-tocopherol. Indeed, soy and maize oils contain 90 per cent and 60 per cent, respectively, of their potential vitamin E as these low activity precursors.

Using Nutritional Genomics Della Penna isolated a gene that can convert the lower activity precursors to the highest activity Vitamin E compound, alpha-tocopherol. With this technology they have increased the vitamin E content of *Arabidopsis* seed oil nearly 10-fold and are now working with industry to move the technology to agricultural crops such as soybean, maize and canola.

Vitamin A is a highly essential micronutrient and widespread dietary deficiency of this vitamin in rice-eating Asian countries has tragic undertones: five million children in South East Asia develop an eye disease called xerophthalmia every year, and 250,000 of them eventually become blind. Improved vitamin A nutrition would alleviate this serious health problem and, according to UNICEF, could also prevent up to two million infant deaths because vitamin A deficiency predisposes them to diarrhoea diseases and measles. Flowers and fruits owe their dazzling colours to carotenoid pigments. Beta-carotene, the best-known carotenoid, which gives carrots and sweet potatoes their orange colour, is a precursor to vitamin A. Rice is a staple that feeds nearly half the world's population, but milled rice does not contain any beta-carotene or its carotenoid precursors. A research team led by Peter Burkhardt and Ingo Potrykus of the Swiss Federal Institute of Technology in Zurich, in collaboration with scientists from the University of Freiburg in Germany, discovered, however, that rice contains geranyl geranyl diphosphate (GGPP), a 20-carbon isoprenoid molecule. Condensation of two such molecules produces a 40-carbon molecule called phytoene, the first carotenoid precursor in the biosynthetic pathway leading to the production of beta-carotene.

Burkhardt and colleagues used microprojectile bombardment to engineer rice with a gene from daffodil (*Narcissus*) that codes for phytoene synthase (psy), the enzyme that synthesises phytoene from GGPP. Rice plants transformed with the daffodil gene produced phytoene in the immature endosperm; non-transgenic control plants did not have this carotenoid. The team have now developed transgenic rice plants carrying bacterial phytoene desaturase and daffodil lycopene cyclase genes, thus providing all enzymes necessary to produce the beta-carotene in rice. These plants are now being subjected to biochemical tests, and Burkhardt feels confident that the enzymes will be active in the rice endosperm. The success of this work could have significant implications for alleviating vitamin A deficiency in the developing world.

Iron is the most commonly deficient micronutrient in the human diet and iron deficiency affects an estimated 1-2 billion people. Anemia characterised by low hemoglobin is the most widely recognised symptom of iron deficiency, but there are other serious problems such as impaired learning ability in children, increased susceptibility to infection and reduced work capacity. Women of child-bearing age are especially prone to iron deficiency and suffer from tragic consequences such as premature child birth, babies with low birth weight and even greater risk of death.

Increasing the iron content in rice is an appealing strategy to supply the mineral inexpensively and effortlessly to a large sector of the world's disadvantaged population. Rice feeds half of the world, and is eaten every day in those parts of the world where iron deficiency is most prevalent. A research group led by Toshihiro Yoshihara and Fumiyuki Goto at the Central Research Institute of Electric Power Industry in Japan employed the gene for ferritin, an iron-rich soybean storage protein, under the control of an endosperm-specific promoter. Grains from transgenic rice plants contained three times more iron than normal rice. Potrykus' team in Zurich, has developed similar transgenic rice with the ferritin gene from beans, and the plants are now being evaluated.

Seeds store the phosphorus needed for germination in the form of phytate, a sugar alcohol molecule having six phosphate groups attached. In terms of food and feed, though, phytate is an anti-nutrient because it strongly chelates iron, calcium, zinc and other divalent mineral ions, making them unavailable for uptake. Potrykus and his group have developed a series of transgenic rice lines designed to deal with this problem. One approach has been to reduce the phytate in rice endosperm by introducing a gene from the fungus *Aspergillus niger* that encodes phytase, an enzyme that breaks down phytate. To counter phytate from other sources in the diet, the Swiss group is using another gene that encodes for a heat-stable phytase from *Aspergillus fumigatus*. This enzyme can survive boiling and has two pH optima - acidic for the stomach and alkaline for the intestine. To further promote the reabsorption of iron, a gene for a metallothionein-like protein has also been engineered. Potrykus commented that all these transgenics will soon be tested and eventually the traits will be combined into a multiply-engineered line.

Phytate also has implications for animal nutrition. A team of scientists at the University of Wisconsin and the USDA-ARS Dairy Forage Research Center (Madison, Wisconsin) has genetically engineered alfalfa to produce phytase. The resulting transgenic alfalfa lines performed well when grown in the field, with no yield reduction. In a poultry feeding trial, better results were obtained using transgenic plant material than with the commercially produced phytase supplement. Poultry grew well on the engineered alfalfa diet without any inorganic phosphorus supplement, which shows that plants can be tailored to increase the bioavailability of this essential mineral. Thus phosphorus supplements can be eliminated from poultry feed, which could reduce costs and mitigate the problem of phosphorus pollution.

Interest in isoflavonoids as nutraceuticals has been strengthened by reports that the soybean isoflavones genistein and daidzein, in addition to exhibiting estrogenic and anticancer activity, help prevent artherogenic oxidation of low density lipoproteins, and have positive effects on improving bone mass. Of the enzymes necessary for engineering isoflavone nutraceuticals into plants, only two, the 2-hydroxylase and dehydratase of the isoflavone synthase complex, have yet to be characterised at the molecular level. The dimeric lignans similarly have potent anticancer and antioxidant activity, and genes encoding all the enzymes for the conversion of coniferyl alcohol to secoisolariciresinol, a major dietary phytoestrogen, have been cloned. These include the remarkable dirigent protein that co-acts with oxidases to confer stereochemical free radical coupling, and the (+)-pinoresinol/(+)-lariciresinol reductase that shares extensive sequence similarity to legume isoflavone reductases.

Utilising chalcone synthase and dihydroflavonol reductase constructs, it has been possible to alter the content and composition of condensed tannins in birdsfoot trefoil clover (*Lotus corniculatus*). These studies are important because condensed tannins are believed to help prevent bloat in ruminants feeding on highly digestible forages. More global upregulation of phenylpropanoid biosynthesis by over-expression of L-phenylalanine ammonia-lyase results in increased local and systemic resistance of tobacco to microbial pathogens, but compromised systemic resistance to herbivorous insect larvae. This underlines the potential for unexpected metabolic cross-talk during genetic manipulation of natural product pathways.

Research to improve the nutritional quality of plants has historically been limited by a lack of basic knowledge of plant metabolism and the often daunting task of dissecting whole branches of plant secondary metabolism. The advent of genomics provides new integrative approaches to plant biochemistry that allow crossing of species, family, and phyla barriers. As a result, the increase in our basic knowledge of plant secondary metabolism during the coming decade will be truly unparalleled and will place plant researchers in the position of being able to modify the nutritional content of major crops to improve aspects of human and animal health. For essential minerals and vitamins that are limiting in world diets, the need and way forward is clear, and improvement strategies should be pursued, as long as attention is paid to the upper safe limit of intake for each nutrient. However, for many other health-promoting phytochemicals, decisions will need to be made regarding the precise compound or compounds to target and which crops to modify such that the greatest nutritional impact and health benefit is achieved. Because these decisions will require an understanding of plant biochemistry, human physiology, and food chemistry, strong interdisciplinary collaborations will be needed among plant scientists, human nutritionists, and food scientists in order to ensure a safe and healthful food supply for the coming century.

Carbohydrate

Plants make both polymeric carbohydrates like starch and fructans, and individual sugars like sucrose. The biosynthesis of these compounds is sufficiently understood to allow the bioengineering of their properties, or to engineer crops to produce polysaccharides not normally present.

Genes responsible for the synthesis of fructans can be used to modify plants of higher agromomic value to produce this polymeric carbohydrate. Fructans are an important ingredient in functional foods as they promote a healthy colon and help reduce the incidence of colon cancer. The crop of predominant interest for elevated fructan production is the sugar beet, because the major storage compound of this species is sucrose, the direct precursor for fructan biosynthesis. Andries J. Koops, of CPRO-DLO, Wageningen, The Netherlands, has reported high level fructan accumulation in a transgenic sugar beet, achieved by expression of a Jerusalem artichoke gene encoding 1-sucrose:sucrose fructosyl transferase (which mediates the first steps in fructan synthesis). Despite the storage carbohydrate having been altered, there was no visible effect on phenotype and it did not affect the growth rate of the taproot as observed under greenhouse conditions. Their work has implications both for the commercial manufacture of fructans and also for the use of genetic engineering in obtaining new products from existing crops.

Engineering starch content in potatoes is also of interest, (see p48 for details). Monsanto have introduced a gene to modify the starch metabolic pathway in potatoes by introducing a new gene which has an endogenous counterpart. The idea of the new gene is that because it is from another source and under the control of a different promoter its activity is not subject to the same degree of inhibition by the plants native regulatory machinery (other applications covered under Yield). This new gene from *E. coli* codes for the enzyme ADP glucose pyrophosphoralyase, and when introduced into potatoes under the control of the tuber-specific patatin promoter, led to a 30 per cent increase in starch content. This has an added bonus as the higher starch content results in a lower moisture content leading to far less fat absorption on frying, as moisture lost during frying is replaced by oil uptake.

Starch is used in a wide range of industrial applications such as coatings for paper and textiles, as a gelling agent in the food industry. It is now possible to make some high value starches, for example starches that are free of the amylose fraction making the generic product more valuable. In the past two years, large amounts of genetically modified potatoes producing an amylose-free starch have been produced. This will be the first example of genetically engineered starch with superior quality over traditional starches entering the markets. It is likely that starches with other alterations will follow in the next few years. Examples will be starches with an altered amylopectin chain length distribution or a modified phosphate content, as it is possible now to specifically engineer these traits. It can also be envisioned that a broad range of novel starches will be produced through combining the downregulation or overexpression of several genes.

Novel oils

Agriculture's traditional role in providing food, feed, and fibre is being expanded by biotechnology into entirely new forms of production. Some farms in the future will be living factories churning out industrial oils and chemicals from genetically engineered crops. Through genetic engineering, "designer" oils may be created by altering the chain length and saturation of the fatty acids. In addition, genes from various plant species may be introduced to produce unusual fatty acids in oilseed crops.

Confections, coffee creamers, whipped toppings and other products now can benefit from a new high-laurate canola oil from Calgene. Laurical is the first commercial genetically engineered food oil. Genes from the California bay laurel were cloned and transferred to canola (low-erucic acid rapeseed) oil crops. An enzyme from bay laurel selectively modifies canola oil to contain C12 fatty acids. In high-laurate canola oil, the C12 (lauric acid) molecules are esterified at the one and three positions of the triglyceride. The non-saturated C18 fatty acids predominate at the two position. The interaction between the fatty acid composition and the esterification gives Laurical its unique features and benefits. In addition to functional benefits, genetically engineered oils have many other advantages as the supply is more stable. Calgene's canola crops are grown in North America. These crops are less affected by the weather and political influence than imported oils. The degree of hydrogenation of Laurical products can be varied to suit specific applications. Laurical contains a minimum 38 per cent lauric acid and is a liquid oil at ambient temperatures. Melting points between 75-120 degrees F can be obtained with appropriate hydrogenation. The Food and Drug Administration has approved Laurical for use in food products.

There also are research projects bringing a high-stearic canola, medium-chain fatty acid canola, a high-myristic-palmitic canola and a high-carotenoid canola to market. These will be commercialised in the next decade.

Erucic acid (22:1) for the manufacture of industrial lubricants is currently obtained from high-erucic (HEAR) varieties of rapeseed. These triglycerides (TAGs) lack erucoyl residues in the sn-2 position, and there has been considerable interest in raising the erucate levels further by overcoming this compositional limitation. Such an oil would not only serve as a higher-yielding source of erucoyl residues, but would also provide trierucin for certain clinical applications. Calgene have approached this objective by cloning a gene responsible for the initial reaction of the cytoplasmic fatty acyl elongation system, i.e. ketoacyl-CoA synthase (KCS), from the jojoba plant, *Simmondsia chinensis*. In its native species this enzyme is part of the elongase system that produces the C20, C22, and C24 acyl groups that predominate in the stored wax esters. The introduction of this gene into canola resulted in the production of TAGs containing up to 58 per cent of their acyl groups as these very long-chain fatty acids (VLCFAs). The KCS gene will now be used to isolate the homologous gene from HEAR, in order to over-express it and so to obtain an erucate content higher than the typical HEAR value of 40 per cent to 50 per cent.

Within a few years we can expect the rapeseed grower to be planting a whole series of new rapeseed cultivars that will have sufficiently different applications to represent entirely new crops. These lines will be engineered for the production of diverse oils having well-defined uses in the food, detergent, and lubricants industries. Speciality oils may also be developed with pharmaceutical and chemical feedstock applications in mind. The genetic engineering of oilseed plants promises to be one of the most impactive and impressive sources of new crops for both new and existing applications.

Industrial applications for modified oils are also of interest. Research projects involving scientists from Sweden, Australia, and England have developed plants producing unusual oils used in the production of polymers, plasticisers, lubricants, and other industrial products, thus providing a renewable alternative to petrochemical oil. Acetylenic and epoxy fatty acids are critical raw materials used in the production of polymers such as plastics and certain chemicals. These fatty acids, which are modified forms of those present in edible oils, are currently derived from either non-renewable petroleum or chemically processed vegetable oils. Many wild plants, such as various species of the genus *Crepis*, a member of the Compositae or sunflower family, are known to produce these unusual fatty acids. An epoxygenase gene cloned from *C. palaestina* encodes an enzyme responsible for making epoxy fatty acids, which are major components in the production of polymers used in manufacturing adhesives. The acetylenase gene, cloned from *C. alpina* by the Swedish team, produces acetylenic fatty acids which have potential applications in the synthesis of high quality surface coatings and ester-type lubricants.

Seeds from transgenic Arabidopsis plants expressing these genes contained up to 15 per cent by weight epoxidated vernolic fatty acid or up to 25 per cent acetylenic (crepenynic) acid. The control plants did not contain even a trace of these fatty acids. Allan Green of the Commonwealth Scientific and Industrial Research Organisation (CSIRO) says that "the possibilities are immense - components of detergents, nylon, glue, paints, lubricants, and plastics could all be produced from plants, rather than fossil materials. Plants could provide a renewable, biodegradable source of these high-value specialty products". He anticipates that it may be another five to eight years before crop "mini-factories" are producing high value industrial compounds down on our farms.

Biopolymers: plastics from plants

Biodegradable plastics are part of the solution to the problem of plastic waste management. These materials can be degraded by the action of enzymes secreted by microorganisms, reducing the volume of solid waste in landfills and lessening the deleterious impact of plastics on the environment.

While there are a number of inherently biodegradable plastics available, growing interest is focused on the group of polyhydroxyalkanoates (PHAs). These polymers are produced by bacterial fermentation, but their production is an expensive process, making them substantially more expensive than synthetic plastics made from fossil fuels. The demonstration of PHA synthesis in transgenic plants raises the possibility that biodegradable plastics could be produced on a large scale at a cost comparable to nondegradable synthetics.

Chris Somerville and co-workers at Carnegie Institution of Washington in Stanford, CA, introduced biosynthetic genes for polyhydroxybutarate (PHB) from the bacterium *Alcaligenes. eutrophus* into *Arabidopsis thaliana*, including targeting elements so that the enzymes they encoded would be targeted to the plastid. This modification successfully localised PHB synthesis to the chloroplast, where inclusions were found exclusively. PHB content in leaves increased over the life span of the plants, reaching as much as 10 mg/g fresh weight. No major deleterious effects on growth or seed yield were detected.

Although these studies have been done in a model plant system having no agricultural significance, their importance and promise stems from the fact that *Arabidopsis* is closely related to the major oil-producing crop oilseed rape. Both Zeneca Seeds in the UK and Monsanto in the US are working to develop oilseed rape for PHA production; Monsanto is also working on soybean.

In another development, researchers at Monsanto have achieved the technically difficult feat of producing a genetically engineered plant that makes the organic polymer PHBV in its seeds. This polymer can be processed into a biodegradable thermoplastic. Polymers such as PHBV are produced naturally by some species of bacteria, which accumulate them as nutritional stores. It turns out that PHVB can be heat-formed into a flexible plastic suitable for many applications where biodegradable plastics are desirable, such as packaging. PHVB has been produced on a commercial scale using the bacterium *Ralstonia eutropha*, but is uneconomic compared with petroleum-based plastics. The bacteria have to be supplied with the raw materials, which must first be extracted from plant material.

To get oilseed rape (*Brassica napus*) to produce PHVB the researchers had to introduce no fewer than four different bacterial genes that modify two separate metabolic pathways. Three are from *R. eutropha*, and accomplish the three final steps in the polymer pathway. The crucial fourth gene kick-starts the biochemical pathway that leads eventually to valeric acid, and comes from the bacterium *Escherichia coli*. There is still a long way to go, however, before grow-your-own plastic becomes a reality. The Monsanto team estimate that polymer concentrations need to be around 15 per cent dry weight to make its extraction and processing economic, while in their plants concentrations are less than 3 per cent. Much more research will be needed, and there will be no quick returns: Monsanto has, in fact, recently abandoned its plant plastics research programme.

A novel perspective was brought by the expression of the PHB biosynthetic pathway in the cytoplasm of cotton fibre cells. In this system, the polymer is produced in plants to change the physical properties of the fibre and not as a source of extractable biopolymer for industrial uses. Accumulation of PHB to only 0.3 per cent dwt of the fibre was sufficient to significantly decrease the rate of heat uptake and cooling of the fibre, resulting in a higher heat capacity and improving the fibre's insulating properties.

Further development of crop plants that produce biodegradable plastics will require a thorough knowledge of enzymes and genes contributing to PHA synthesis in bacteria, coupled with more complete elucidation of plant biosynthetic pathways. Improvements in the physical properties and cost-effectiveness of biopolymers will make them increasingly competitive with petroleum-derived plastics. Although only a small fraction of fossil resources are used for the production of organic chemicals including solvents and plastics, the environmental advantages of using biodegradable plastics in consumer products are sufficient to drive the technology forward.

Therapeutics - vaccines

For centuries, plants have been a valuable source of natural pharmaceuticals. In the past decade, intensive research has been focused on expanding the use of plants as pharmaceutical production systems by genetic engineering. It is now clear that plants can be manipulated to produce a wide variety of such compounds, from vaccine antigens and monoclonal antibodies to pharmaceutically valuable secondary metabolites. Producing vaccines against animal and human diseases in plants is one of the most intriguing applications of plant biotechnology.

Definite proof that plant-based vaccines indeed protect animals against infection was demonstrated by scientists in Europe when they showed that a vaccine produced in cowpea plants protects mink against an infectious virus that causes diarrhoea and anorexia. The mink enteritis virus (MEV) belongs to a group of viruses that also causes disease in cats and dogs. The current vaccine against this disease consists of inactivated viruses cultured in animal cells. The European group fused a small segment coding for the epitope of MEV into the coat protein gene of cowpea mosaic virus. The engineered plant virus with the mink virus epitope on the coat protein multiplied in infected cowpea plants. Scientists were able to recover abundant amounts of chimeric virus from the plants and injected small amounts into minks. All the immunised mink resisted a subsequent challenge inoculation of MEV while most of those not immunised quickly succumbed to the disease.

Research in the Plants and Human Health group at the Boyce Thompson Institute for Plant Research at Cornell University, led by Drs. Charles Arntzen and Hugh Mason, is focused on developing both production and delivery systems for sub-unit protein vaccines. They have reported that transgenic plants can express a variety of antigenic proteins, such as hepatitis B virus surface antigen, Norwalk virus capsid protein, and the B sub-unit of the *Escherichia coli* heat labile enterotoxin (LT-B). In 1995, this group showed that not only could transgenic potato plants express the *E. coli* LT-B protein, but also that tubers expressing this protein could induce a specific immune response against LT-B when fed to mice as part of their normal diet. These results suggested that transgenic plant tissues expressing vaccine antigens could be used for immunisation against a myriad of diseases, and raised hopes that this technology might solve many of the problems associated with delivery of safe, effective vaccines to people in developing countries. Production of recombinant sub-unit vaccines could be as cheap as agriculture, distribution as convenient as marketing fresh produce, and administration as simple and as safe as feeding a baby a banana. The report describing the results of the first human clinical trial of a plant-derived vaccine provides further important proof that transgenic plants could be used as "edible vaccines". This trial used *E. coli* LT-B-expressing potatoes produced by the Boyce Thompson Institute group.

Enterotoxigenic *E. coli* (ETEC) and *Vibrio cholerae* are the primary pathogens responsible for acute watery diarrhoea. Both bacteria initiate disease by colonising the intestinal epithelia and both produce multi-sub-unit enterotoxins, which cause the diarrhoeal symptoms. The heat labile enterotoxin (LT) of ETEC is closely related to cholera toxin (CT). There is currently no reliable and effective vaccine against either ETEC or cholera. In the clinical trial, two groups of volunteers consumed either 50 g or 100 g of raw potato tubers expressing LT-B (equivalent to 0.5 mg or 1 mg LT-B per dose, respectively) and were compared with a third group that ate untransformed potato tubers. The first two groups developed specific anti-LT-B mucosal and systemic immune responses while the control group did not. These responses are comparable to those observed when humans are challenged with 109 ETEC bacteria. The human clinical trials demonstrate that edible plant vaccines are immunogenic in humans, as was previously shown in mice; proving that they can protect humans against a challenge is the next logical step.

In 1995, Julian Ma of Guy's Hospital in London, UK, and colleagues showed that transgenic tobacco plants could express and assemble recombinant secretory antibodies. This was in itself a significant advance since these molecules are fairly complex, consisting of four separate polypeptide chains. Ma's group expressed a hybrid secretory monoclonal antibody (SIgA/G) directed against the cell surface adhesion protein of *S. mutans*. When the antibody is present in the oral cavity it prevents bacterial colonisation and subsequent development of dental caries. The authors expressed each of the four proteins in separate tobacco lines, and created a line which expressed all four by sexually crossing the four lines. They were able to show that the four polypeptides - a hybrid IgG-IgA heavy chain, IgG light chain, a joining chain, and a secretory component - assembled into a functional secretory immunoglobulin molecule. For the human trial, the oral cavity of adult human volunteers was effectively sterilised with a bacteriocidal mouthwash, and the antibody solution applied to the teeth. Overall, the results of this trial were spectacular. The plant-derived SIgA/G survived for longer periods of time than the IgG (3 days compared with 1 day) in the human mouth, probably because SIgA molecules have markedly enhanced stability in comparison with IgG. The recombinant antibody prevented recolonisation of the teeth by *S. mutans*, but not other bacteria, for at least four months, while volunteers who received control treatment all had significant *S. mutans* recolonisation within two months.

In neither human clinical trial studies, were any major side-effects observed. These reports therefore represent significant advances in plant biotechnology, and have shown that transgenic plants may indeed be cost-effective, efficient and effective production systems for protein pharmaceuticals.

A plant-based transient expression system has been employed to produce a vaccine against cancer in a mouse model system, according to a recent report. The study shows that a therapeutic vaccine produced in tobacco plants helps prevent tumours in mice by stopping the growth of non-Hodgkin's lymphoma cells. The NIH-funded study, jointly conducted by Biosource Technologies (now called Large Scale Biology, Vacaville, CA) and Stanford University, reported in 1999 that cancer-specific antibodies were transiently expressed in *Nicotiana benthamiana* plants using the tobacco mosaic virus. The virus-infected plants produced the vaccine protein "quickly, abundantly and in the correct conformation". Eighty per cent of the mice that received the plant-derived vaccine survived the lymphoma, while all untreated mice died within three weeks after contracting the disease. The researchers are now testing other surface markers to validate the method's application to a broad population. They envision the use of a similar approach in humans, provided these vaccines pass the necessary safety tests. Biosource hopes to begin clinical trials within a year.

This approach has also been applied to diabetes. A recent scientific report describes the development of a potato-based insulin vaccine that is almost 100 times more powerful than the existing vaccine in preventing insulin-dependent diabetes mellitus (IDDM) in a mouse mode. IDDM, which affects nearly a million Americans, is the leading cause of non-congenital blindness and accounts for 25 per cent of cardiac surgery and 40 per cent of kidney failures, and thus has a staggering socioeconomic impact. It is an autoimmune disease in which the insulin-producing cells of the pancreas are destroyed by the cytotoxic T lymphocytes. Plants such as potatoes can be engineered to supply the needed antigenic proteins easily and inexpensively. To increase the efficiency of oral tolerance, however, it is critical that these autoantigens be directed to the site of their action, and in the case of diabetes, it is the gut-associated lymphoid tissues (GALT) that are involved in the inflammatory response. The enterotoxin in *Vibrio cholerae*, the causative agent of cholera, includes a nontoxic sub-unit B (CTB) that helps the toxin bind to gut cells. CTB is also immunogenic as it stimulates an antibody response in humans and animals. A team led by William Langridge at Loma Linda University in California addressed this problem by attaching the insulin protein directly to the GALT cells using CTB.

Thus, the conjugated cholera sub-unit-proinsulin protein was effectively delivered directly to the intestinal immune system tissues. The blood levels of IgG antibody that suppressed the immune response to insulin was 100-fold higher in animals eating the CTB-insulin potato compared to those that were fed potatoes producing insulin or CBT protein alone. People eat only cooked potatoes, so the effect of boiling on the properties of CTB expressed in transgenic potatoes was examined. After boiling for five minutes, over half of the vaccine protein survived in its biologically active form, providing evidence that cooking does not always inactivate edible vaccines. Thus, the spectrum of plant species for producing edible vaccine may be expanded beyond raw-food plants such as fruits.

Forestry

Forest trees are one of the world's most important natural resources. As crop plants, they are in the earliest stages of domestication, and much of our wood is still harvested from natural forests. Until now, the types of genetic changes that made possible the domestication of agricultural crops have not been possible for trees because of their long life cycle. Biotechnology provides the opportunity to make such changes through genetic engineering in a matter of years, rather than centuries. Potential targets for tree improvement identified 15 years ago are still relevant: apical dominance, nutrient use, wood quality, disease, pest and herbicide resistance and lignocellulose degradation. Success has already been achieved for tree species in the generation of somaclonal and protoclonal variation, the formation of haploids, triploids and polyploids, somatic hybrids and cybrids and the introduction of foreign DNA through transformation.

Despite considerable research, most forest planting stock still derives from genetically undefined seed origins, with the possible exception of poplars (*Populus spp.*), Eucalyptus and willows (*Salix spp.*). This has arisen chiefly because of the long juvenile period and the length of time required to investigate fully the performance of promising selections derived from crosses. Breeding could become more rapid if, as has been achieved for bamboos, micropropagation can be used to speed up the onset of flowering in trees. Early selection of superior seedlings could be facilitated if markers can be found in juvenile trees that predict aspects of the adult phenotype. In apple, for instance, the percentage of rootbark and the number of stomata can be used to predict the likely effects that apple seedlings would have on scion dwarfing, if they were subsequently used as rootstocks. Similarly, the isoenzyme GOT.1 (glutamate oxaloacetate transferase) can be used as an indicator of certain incompatibility alleles in apple seedlings.

Genetic transformation.

Rapid advances in the practice and application of plant transformation will depend largely on useful tree regeneration procedures. As with other areas of biotechnology, the routine generation of transgenic trees will not become a reality until procedures for plant regeneration are better understood. It is encouraging, however, to find that many tree species are susceptible to infection by *Agrobacterium*, and that foreign DNA can be incorporated into tree genomes and expressed. In some woody species, for which regeneration techniques have been developed, transgenic plants have been recovered from transformed tissues. Transgenic poplar trees more tolerant of herbicides have been developed, a trait which would facilitate the chemical control of weeds in the early management of clonal plantations. Transgenic plants have also been obtained for pine, walnut, apple, Allocasuarina, plum, and peach.

With further improvements in regeneration techniques for woody plants, and in the understanding of factors that affect virulence of *Agrobacterium* to trees, examples of successful genetic transformation of trees are likely to become more common. Genes that confer resistance to insects, such as those that code for cowpea trypsin inhibitor or Bt toxin, if transferred to trees, could provide an important contribution to the management of orchards and forest plantations. Furthermore, expression of viral coat proteins could assist in preventing yield reductions caused by systemic viruses. A common criticism of the use of such genes in isolation, however, is that the resulting qualitative resistance could be overcome rapidly by the pest. It is possible that resistance to browsing insects, the primary consumers, will disturb the food chain and thus serve to destabilise the woodland ecosystem and potentially reduce overall productivity. For these reasons, combined with public concern over the release of genetically manipulated organisms and the longevity of the crop, it is questionable whether single gene resistance, introduced in this way, will be of long-term value in trees. Quantitative resistance to pests is probably silviculturally and environmentally more acceptable. Traditionally, quantitative traits have been introduced into crops through techniques of plant breeding. Thus, as with other plant species, if transformation is to be useful for the generation of pest resistant trees, it will be necessary to transfer a larger number of genes than has so far been achieved.

In the meantime, transformation techniques could provide a useful means to transfer more qualitative features, such as branching habit and herbicide resistance, the latter facilitating the establishment of clonal plantations. It is likely that transformation will provide a valuable tool in the utilisation of molecular approaches, such as the use of antisense sequences and overexpression of genes, to investigate the genetic control of juvenility, which has important implications for growth rates and ease of rooting of conventional cuttings, and to reduce lignin production that would improve the pulping qualities of timber.

Control of flowering in trees

New work on flowering trees may have a payoff in speeding up productivity. Three years ago, for instance, Detlef Weigel of the Salk Institute in La Jolla and Ove Nilsson at the Swedish University of Agricultural Sciences in Umeå identified two genes in *Arabidopsis* that act as master switches for triggering flower formation at the ends of shoots. When the researchers engineered *Arabidopsis* so that the genes would be active all over the plant, every shoot produced a flower. And when they inserted one of the two genes, leafy, into aspen, a tree that normally takes up to two decades to flower was fertile after two months. A spectacular result given that slow sexual development is the bugbear of tree breeding.

Trees for phytoremediation

One of the most exciting examples of tree biotechnology is research done by a team of scientists led by Richard Meagher at the University of Georgia who have developed novel yellow poplar trees that extract toxic mercury from the soil and release it into the air as vapor, thus providing a new technique for cleaning heavy-metal contaminated soil and water. Pollution with toxic substances such as lead, cadmium, arsenic, and mercury are significant health and environmental threats with cleanup costs estimated at $200 billion in the U.S. alone. Mercury, a highly noxious metal, is an especially worrisome water contaminant that eventually accumulates in the food chain worldwide. Mercury has been extensively used for bleaching by paper and textile industries, and as a catalyst in paint pigments and agricultural fungicides. Very little work has been done to clean up toxic mercury because of the prohibitive costs.

Phytoremediation, a new technique in which plants are used to absorb and detoxify the hazardous chemicals in polluted soils, is now gaining increased attention. With their extensive root systems and rapid growth, trees are a logical choice for hazardous chemical removal and disposal, and are an improvement over small plants such as Indian mustard currently used for phytoremediation. Dr. Meagher chose the yellow poplar (*Liriodendron tulipifera*), an elegantly beautiful landscape tree found in the Southeastern U.S. that is both fast growing and pest resilient, as a suitable candidate for mercury phytoremediation. In previous work using *Arabidopsis thaliana*, Meagher's group showed that transgenic plants expressing a mercury-resistant bacterial *merA* gene converted toxic ionic mercury in the soil, Hg(II), to a less-toxic elemental form, Hg(0). Three versions of modified *merA* gene were introduced into yellow poplar tissue culture cells using microprojectile bombardment. One particular line of regenerated plantlets that grew vigorously in normally toxic levels of mercuric ion was capable of absorbing and releasing up to ten times more mercury as vapor than control plants. The mercury vapourisation rate of the transgenic poplar plants was three times greater than that observed previously in *Arabidopsis*.

The mercury scavenging poplars now need to be field tested to determine if they can successfully detoxify ionic mercury in polluted soils and release the nonionic form harmlessly into the atmosphere. According to PhytoWorks, a company that has licensed the mercury treatment technology from the University of Georgia, mercury vapor released into the air by transgenic plants is minute and "at levels below what people with mercury amalgam fillings inhale with every breath".

Lignin modification

Qualitative traits in trees are if anything more important as a focus area. Vincent Chiang has demonstrated that antisense construct for a gene in the lignin pathway can greatly reduce lignin, increase cellulose, and dramatically stimulate growth in transgenic aspen. Such changes could be important in tree domestication and could ultimately lead to trees that are profoundly different from their current undomesticated progenitors.

Fast-growing, low-lignin trees could provide significant practical benefits. Removal of lignin from the wood cell walls is the most energy intensive and environmentally damaging step in wood processing for pulp and paper, so reducing the lignin content in trees could provide both economic and environmental benefits. Although aspen is not one of the most commercially valued trees, if the results achieved by Chiang and colleagues are extended to more widely planted trees, such as eucalyptus or pines, they will have a very large economic impact globally. Even more importantly, any increase in efficiency that allows production of more wood and wood products from less land helps conserve natural forests and reduces the environmental impact of processing wood into pulp and paper.

Most intriguing is the enhanced growth of the transgenic trees. Previous studies suggested that even large changes in lignin composition can occur without impairing growth. In the present study, the lignin content, not composition, was altered. The absence of an explanation for the effect of reduced lignin on growth does not detract from its potential impact as a possible way for controlling growth and development in trees. These results further support the view that the potential for modifying wood properties through genetic engineering may be far greater than first anticipated. The next step will be to follow these trees through to maturation and see how they perform in the field through successive generations, particularly for wood properties and resistance to pests and pathogens.

Future forestry

Forest tree breeding has hardly begun to show its potential - unlike some crops, no plateau in yield potential has yet been observed for tree breeding. Major improvements could therefore be achieved through the application of existing technology and knowledge, and it is estimated that most yield improvements in forestry between 1998 and 2028 will be attributable to conventional tree breeding, fertiliser use, and site selection. Improvements in *Pinus patula* alone have led to a 50 per cent yield increase. With such improvements achievable through freely available, existing know-how, the forestry industry is skeptical about the value of investing in molecular technologies.

Nevertheless, establishing a competitive advantage through conventional breeding will be difficult as the theory and practice of it are available to all. Increased market demand for superior germplasm, as the industry looks for added value, could provide the incentive to integrate biotechnology into tree breeding: what is on sale in forestry, unlike agriculture, is the commodity product itself, not seed. Whereas biotechnology business tends to be topic-based, with company strategies flexible and able to adapt quickly, and small groups creating business from proprietary information, forestry is still highly traditional, with geographical constraints and long-term business plans, where large groups exploit knowledge in the public domain. Nevertheless, forestry will need to continue to take the long-term view, picking and choosing now from the portfolio of technologies and information available through molecular biology to remain competitive two decades hence.

Plant architecture

Evolutionary adaptations sometimes run counter to agricultural productivity. When forced to compete for light, for example, plants respond by growing taller. Resources are directed into stem elongation at the expense of assimilate storage, leaf expansion, or flower, fruit and seed development. Under the standard agricultural practice of high density monoculture cropping, the ecologically advantageous response can limit yield.

A genetic engineering strategy to overcome this shade-avoidance response by disrupting the photosensory system now has been validated in field studies. Harry Smith's lab at the University of Leicester, has led a decades long effort to understand how environmental factors shape plant architecture and influence the allocation of photoassimilate into plant tissues and organs. Plants' perception of light and shade is mediated by the phytochrome photoreceptor system. The phytochrome molecule exists in two interconvertible forms, red light absorbing (Pr) and far red light absorbing (Pfr); the ratio of the two forms is a function of the ratio of red to far red photons reaching the plant. Chlorophyll strongly absorbs red photons, thus light reflected from or filtered through leaves of neighbouring vegetation is enriched in far red photons. A plant senses this aspect of light quality, a signal of competition, as the ratio of Pr to Pfr forms of phytochrome. This apparently simple mechanism is actually quite subtle and complex. Phytochromes constitute a small family of photoreceptors having discrete functions, differing light labilities, and various and in some cases antagonistic effects on stem growth.

The UK group engineered tobacco plants to express high levels of one member of the phytochrome family, phyA. When grown in the field under normal daylight, the plants did not exhibit shade avoidance. At high field densities, the plants were severely dwarfed and showed an enhanced allocation of assimilates to leaves. Encouraging results with the model system suggest that the architecture of crop plants could be similarly modified so that a greater proportion of resources are directed into harvestable components. The authors note that even if that promise should not be borne out, proximity-conditional dwarfing would nonetheless be useful for minimising lodging and nutrient wastage, and the approach may have applications in ornamental and forest tree species.

Another approach is also being taken to alter plant architecture. Plants transformed with the rolABC genes of *Agrobacterium rhizogenes* exhibited altered shoot morphologies in comparison to untransformed plants. Altered growth and development characteristics included retarded growth, suppressed apical dominance, shortened internodes, smaller highly lanceolated leaves and smaller, sterile flowers. Pronounced leaf wrinkling was a common feature of the transgenic plants. Differences in root formation abilities between transformed lines in response to the different treatments were found. This strongly suggests that the rol genes participate in the metabolism of growth regulators and/or in their activity. However, the precise way in which the rol genes participate in the biochemical pathways resulting in changes in the level of growth regulators and consequently of plant development is poorly understood. It has been demonstrated that *rolC* product releases active cytokinins from inactive conjugates, but a similar role for *rolB* on auxin has not been confirmed.

Abhaya Dandekar at UC Davis has used this system to transform walnut trees with rolABC and has found a major impact on the architecture of the trees. The effect of the genes has been to produce compact cylindrical trees, the notion being to make them more amenable to harvesting and reduce water usage.

Ornamentals

Cut flowers are an internationally traded, high value commodity. World-wide, retail trade is worth over US$25 billion per annum. The largest markets are Germany, Japan and the USA. The retail value of each of these markets is US$3-5 billion per annum. Other important markets are the individual countries of Western Europe, which have the highest per capita consumption of cut flowers in the world.

Twenty to thirty types of cut flowers account for the vast majority of international sales. Within each of these flower types there are many varieties, and each year new ones are released. In addition to agronomic characters, novelty is an extremely important factor in the successful marketing of new varieties as the cut flower industry is essentially a fashion industry. 'Classical' flower breeding by continuous crossing and selection has its limitations; for example, no one has succeeded in breeding a blue rose or an orange petunia. However, the ability to introduce individual genes into plants (molecular breeding) has made the development of flowers with novel aesthetic properties possible.

Biotechnology of flowers involving tissue culture, cell and molecular biology offer opportunities of developing new germplasms that may better cope with changing demands. Genetic engineering strategies are highly desirable for species like rose as they facilitate the modification (or introduction) of single gene traits without disruption of the pre-existing, commercially valuable phenotype characteristics of the target variety. A range of transgenes are of potential value, including those for pest and disease resistance, flower colour, morphology and vase life, together with plant architecture and fragrance.

The principle company involved in this research is in Australia. Research at Florigene has been directed to adding value to both growers and consumers of two of the worlds most popular flower crops - rose and carnation. The company has developed proprietary methods to introduce genes into these crops and now has 50 patents issued or pending in jurisdictions including the USA, Europe, Japan and Australia protecting genes which can impact economically important traits in cut-flowers.

Colour modification

New and novel colours add considerable value in the marketing of flowers. As many of the most popular flowers do not have the necessary gene(s) they can never produce the pigment responsible for mauve/blue colour. Florigene has developed technology to produce this pigment in the top selling flowers, rose, carnation and chrysanthemum.

Flower colour is due to two types of pigments; flavonoids and carotenoids. Carotenoids are found in many yellow or orange flowers, while the flavonoids contribute to the red, pink and blue hues. The class of flavonoids most responsible for these colours are the anthocyanins, which are derivatives of a biochemical pathway which only operates in plants. The cyanidin and pelargonidin pigments are generally found in pink and red flowers, while delphinidin is commonly found in blue flowers. Delphinidin pigments have never been found in rose or carnation. Because they lack flavonoid 3',5'-hydroxylase (F3'5'H) activity they are, therefore, unable to generate purple or blue flowers. Petunia, on the other hand, contains two loci, termed hf1 and hf2, that encode a Cyt P450 with F3'5'H activity. To introduce true blue and purple colours, Florigene have isolated the F3'5'h transgenes for delphinidin production from petunia and have introduced them into rose and carnation. From this the company have produced a variety of coloured carnations. In June 1999, it launched the violet carnation, which it has named Moonshadow, at a major horticultural show in Kansas City and in November, the plant will be launched in Europe at a global flower convention in Aalsmeer, the Netherlands. Next year, it will launch a black carnation.

While the colour worked effectively in carnation it was found that there is a tight linkage between the genes for pH and anthocyanin formation. For rose the low vaculor pH affected the formation of the colour so further work is being done to introduce genes to raise pH and allow colour development in the rose.

Longlife and availability

As discussed in page 35, Florigene scientists have developed a range of carnations that no longer produce a naturally produced plant hormone, ethylene. As the production of this compound induces the flower to deteriorate, the genetically modified flowers, which produce no ethylene, last longer. This is a significant advantage to the grower, who no longer has to use preservative chemicals and as the new varieties require less chemical input they are environmentally cleaner. This is of great interest to the Dutch industry where the government is legislating to reduce the amount of chemical used in horticultural production. The ability to guarantee a good vase life is also central to quality assurance programmes which are now being introduced by the better growers.

At the University of Leicester, Garry Whitelam and his colleagues have engineered asters so that they flower in the middle of winter, not just in summer. Growing conventional cut flowers in greenhouses in winter is expensive because of the extra lighting needed to make them flower. In a bid to cut costs, the researchers manipulated an aster gene so that it would produce higher than normal levels of a phytochrome protein that enables plants to sense changes in daylength. The GM asters required only 6 hours of daylight to flower compared with the usual 14.

Floral architecture

Knowledge of the genetic sequences that specify the physical arrangement of a flower's sepals, petals, stamens and carpels is so advanced that it is already possible to design "fantasy flowers" that have any of these organs in any position in the flower. The initial steps of flower development involve two classes of consecutively acting regulatory genes. Meristem-identity genes, which act early to control the initiation of flowers, are expressed throughout the incipient floral primordium. Homeotic genes mentioned above termed ABC, which act later to specify the identity of individual floral organs, are expressed in distinct domains within the flower.

Homeotic mutations lead to the conversion of a particular body part or organ into another. Homeotic mutants have been described in both animals and plants. In *Arabidopsis thaliana*, homeotic mutations in flower development have been intensively studied. Flowers of *Arabidopsis* are composed of four concentric whorls of organs with, from the outer to the innermost whorl, four sepals, four petals, six stamens and two fused carpels. The `ABC' model describes how three genetic functions called A, B and C, each represented by one or several genes, specify each four whorl identity by overlapping and combinatorial actions. The class A genes function in whorls 1 and 2, the class B in whorls 2 and 3, the class C in whorls 3 and 4. Nearly all *Arabidopsis* homeotic genes belong to the family of MADS-domain transcription factors.

A detailed understanding of these processes has allowed both the abundance of flowers (See page 67 for applications in Forestry), and individual flower morphology to be modified. With these tools the morphological and subsequently aesthetically appealing variations on a floral theme can be finely tuned.

Fragrance

Plant volatiles play an important role in the interaction of plants with their environment. A major group of volatiles are called monoterpenes. Monoterpenes represent a large group of anti-microbial and fragrantly active compounds. Most are synthesised in the epidermal layer of petals and leaves. Many herbs have specific epidermal hairs, modified for oil secretion. Citrus fruits such as lemons and oranges secrete their essential oils into specialised secretary cavities in the outer rind.

Terpenes are all derived from simple five-carbon isoprene precursor molecules. Two isoprene units are joined together to form the precursor monoterpene, geranyl pyrophosphate. From this a large variety of monterpenes can be formed by the activity of further enzymes. The exact type of monoterpene depends on the nature and combination of enzymes present within the plant cell. Since the precursor geranyl pyrophosphate is common to most plants, it should be possible to engineer the production of a given monoterpene fragrance in a non-fragrant plant by transferring a specific cyclase gene to a plant lacking that enzyme.

One of NovaFlora's projects involves inserting a gene into roses that would enable their petals to produce the lemon fragrance monoterpene, limonene. The gene encodes the enzyme limonene synthase, from citrus plants. The researchers have already transferred the gene to petunias and are waiting for their first crop of what they hope will be a lemon scented transgenic flower. An important aspect of this work is the use of an epidermal promoter isolated from pea, which allows for the specific expression of foreign genes in the epidermis and associated glandular hairs of a broad range of crop plants. The promoter is active in both vegetative and floral organs and NovaFlora believes that its epidermal promoter technology will be useful for the expression of numerous value-added traits, including pesticidal compounds, oils, pigments and fragrances to the plant's surface.

In addition to limonene, there are hundreds of different monoterpenes synthesised by different enzymes as well as other types of plant fragrance molecule. In future genetic engineers will be able to create finely-tuned fragrances to order in almost any plant. Among the many possibilities would be lemon scented golf courses and GM camomile lawns that are much easier to maintain than the traditional kind.

The Industrial Scene

To complement merger and acquisition activities designed to acquire new technologies, the major corporate players in the pharmaceutical and agrochemical sector are continuing to seek out partnerships with innovative biotechnology firms, particularly in such areas as agrigenomics (the study of the make-up of, and interaction between, genes in crops), genomics and combinatorial chemistry (see Appendix 2.3). Zeneca, who are now merging with Novartis to form Syngenta, have announced a major collaboration in agrigenomics with Incyte Pharmaceuticals which expanded an earlier pharmaceutical-related agreement between the two companies. Under the agreement, Incyte will apply its high-throughput gene sequencing and bioinformatics capabilities towards generating information for crop plants designated by Zeneca for inclusion into Incyte's proprietary sequence database. In turn, Zeneca will gain access to Incyte's microarray technology in order to study gene pathways and monitor gene expression in plants. Terms of the agreement were not announced.

Bayer bolstered its crop protection discovery programme by establishing an agreement with Paradigm Genetics. In the US$40 million deal that includes up-front money, research funding, milestone payments, and additional fees for marketed products, Paradigm will lend its expertise in identifying gene function, bioinformatics and assay development. The objective is to identify new crop protection products from high-throughput screening of new target genes.

Not to be left out of the flurry of agbiotech corporate activity, Novartis announced in 1998 the planned investment of US$600 million over the next ten years to fund one of the largest initiatives in plant genomics. The first step was the creation of the Novartis Agricultural Discovery Institute (NADI), which will be one of the largest single research endeavours dedicated to agricultural genomics research and development. Located in San Diego, California, the main campus of NADI will have a team of about 180 researchers in 50 laboratories. NADI researchers will apply genomics technologies to the development of improved plant traits, new methods for crop protection, and new animal health products. NADI will focus on matching genes with traits, primarily through the production and exploitation of gene and protein databases, supported by tools for protein function and structure analyses, and engineering. Initially, NADI will explore plants, fungi, bacteria, viruses, nematodes, and insects, including some model systems

NADI will be a cornerstone of Novartis' biotechnology research, designed to allow cooperation between other Novartis groups including Crop Protection and Seeds. It will work in tandem with the Novartis Agribusiness Biotech Research facility at Research Triangle Park, North Carolina, and with numerous Novartis research stations worldwide. The placement of NADI near the recently announced Novartis pharmaceuticals genomics institute (Novartis Institute for Functional Genomics), which is being built in La Jolla, has the goal of optimising cross-business synergies in genomics research in both agribusiness and in pharmaceuticals. The planned investment begins with an initial phase involving US$250 million, to be used in part for the establishment and operation of the NADI, a wholly-owned entity of the Novartis Research Foundation. Approximately US$50 million will go towards the building of NADI, with another US$55 million anticipated for annual operating budget.

Novartis, also strengthened its discovery portfolio by signing a collaborative agreement with Pharmacopeia, a company that focuses on the integration of bioinformatics, combinatorial chemistry, and high-throughput screening. By agreement, Novartis Crop Protection will screen collections of small molecule libraries provided by Pharmacopeia, who will receive payments from Novartis for each library provided. Pharmacopeia will also be entitled to milestone and royalty payments as compounds progress through development and commercialisation.

Not only are the large agrochemical companies likely to benefit from these relationships, but corporate partnerships also have become a major source of capital and stability for smaller biotechnology firms in all sectors of the industry. Smaller firms have been lagging, economically, due to the public stock market's current disdain for biotechnology, and the subsequent inability of companies to raise public money.

Issues and Concerns

From its earliest years, biotechnology attracted interest outside scientific circles. The scientific community has acknowledged the legitimacy of that interest: In mid-1974, at the suggestion of leading scientists, the scientific community accepted a temporary moratorium on certain experiments, and at a related international conference held in February 1975 in Asilomar, California, USA, invited press coverage. Scientists have participated vigorously in the subsequent widespread public and political debates. Initially the main focus of public interest was on the safety of recombinant DNA technology, and of the possible risks of creating uncontrollable and harmful novel organisms. Debate on the deliberate release of genetically modified organisms, and on consumer products containing or comprising them, followed some years later.

Consumer perception

The success of agricultural biotechnology is heavily dependent on its acceptance by the public, and the regulatory framework in which the industry operates (see Chapter 7) is also influenced by public opinion. Therefore, it is worth looking at the climate of acceptance in North America and Europe.

North America

Over the past decade, consumer awareness and acceptance of biotechnology in the US and Canada has been remarkably stable. Regardless of how public perceptions are measured, between two-thirds and three-quarters of North American respondents to surveys are positive about biotechnology. For three years - 1992, 1994, and 1998 - US consumers were asked whether they supported or opposed agricultural biotechnology. The results have been identical throughout; just over 70per cent expressed support. In 2000, this level has dropped to 65% which reflects the negative coverage of this subject in recent times. Research also shows that most North American consumers recognise the benefits of biotechnology and are willing to buy food developed through biotechnology. North American consumers are quite supportive of the use of biotechnology to develop new varieties of crop plants. In the context of food risks generally, biotechnology is seen by US consumers as much less risky than microbial contamination, pesticides, or even food additives.

There are several reasons for North America's lack of concern about biotechnology. In the US and Canada, there is strong public support for and appreciation of science and technology. Furthermore, US consumers tend to be more pragmatic about food. They are largely interested in taste, nutrition, convenience, and price. How the seeds or product ingredients are developed is irrelevant for most people. Perhaps, though, the main reason for sustained US popular support for biotechnology has been the long-term efforts to educate opinion leaders and consumers. Government, industry, universities, and third-party groups began working to understand and address public perceptions well before the first biotechnology products were released. Providing factual information increases acceptance among US consumers. In the US, people have the most trust in independent health and scientific experts. In particular, acceptance increases significantly when US consumers learn that groups such as the American Medical Association (Chicago, IL), other independent scientific experts, and regulatory bodies such as the US Food and Drug Administration (Rockville, MD, USA) agree that foods from biotechnology are safe. Unlike the experience in Europe, groups with reservations about biotechnology have had very little impact on the perceptions of opinion leaders or consumers in North America.

Europe

In Europe, too, the importance of public opinion in shaping the prospects for biotechnology was recognised early. In 1982, the European Commission's "futures group" or FAST (Forecasting and Assessment in Science and Technology), emphasised the key role that public perception would play in the acceptance or rejection of the products of the biological revolution.

Subsequently, the EC's programmes of research and technological development included initiatives to promote public understanding and dialogue with consumers. Over the past ten years, several workshops were organised, bringing together representatives of consumer bodies such as the BEUC (European Bureau of Consumer Associations; Brussels) or the ECAS (Euro-Citizen Action Service; Brussels), and scientists and industrialists. These workshops resulted in publications for the lay public.

But neither these activities nor comparable national initiatives has apparently persuaded much of the public in the European Union to look as favourably on biotechnology as the North American public does. The EC's "EuroBarometer" system of public opinion measurement has been used three times—in 1991, 1993, and 1996—to gauge public response to a carefully chosen range of questions on biotechnology. These could be summarised as: "What do you know?" " What is your opinion?" " What should be done by government?" And: "Who do you trust to tell you the truth about such matters?" The answers to this last question provide, perhaps, the most telling insight. In Europe, the public's faith is in consumer and environmental organisations rather than in governments, industry, or academia.

The EuroBarometer has also consistently revealed wide and persistent differences of opinion between different member countries. These underlie the differences in national (governmental) positions regarding biotechnology-based innovations. Those differences in position generate friction and controversy within the European decision-making bodies that authorise the marketing of products.

The European institutions—Commission, Parliament, and Council—endeavoured through the 1980s and 1990s to develop and implement a "Community strategy for Biotechnology in Europe", complementing the similar initiatives under way in member countries. However, from the 1986 Gene Technology Act (in Denmark) onward, it was clear that in some countries, and in some political groups, especially the "Greens", there were growing reservations about genetic engineering and its products. Whether these reservations reflected political opportunism or real popular concerns, it was becoming clear that consumer acceptance of the products of biotechnology could not be taken for granted.

Thus, it was in Europe that technology-specific biotechnology oversight came into being. It was initially a political necessity: National divergences obliged the EC to propose technology-specific directives, and these were adopted in 1990. Beyond safety concerns, demands for product separation, identification, and explicit labelling have followed. The directives have subsequently been, and currently still are, the object of amendments.

Bio-conflicts

The result of these developments is that by the end of the 1990s, the world community had become deeply divided in its view of the products of biotechnology. Since the European Union and the US do not see eye-to-eye, transatlantic trade disputes loom. The multinational companies of the developed world (which have developed much of the technology) cannot reach agreement with those in developing countries (who, arguably, have the most to gain). Above all, there is a rift between the general consensus of the scientific community (at least in some European countries), and the opinion of the general public or average consumer.

The North American experience shows that consumer acceptance of biotechnology may depend on a recognition of its benefits, and on feeling assured that the applications of biotechnology are ethically acceptable and safe. To this end, it will be important to build trust among the public that governments and scientists are serving the public interest.

With widespread commercialisation of GMOs in the US since 1996 and the broadbased adoption by producers it was thought that the battle for public acceptance was won. However, the outcry in Europe about GMOs is starting to spill over into American markets and now it is not just confined to fringe groups but in strategic choices being made by American producers. The giant commodity buyer Archer Daniels Midland, faced with the combined resistance of fervid European consumer activists and protectionist European governments, has signaled it will switch, not fight: It has asked farmers to segregate modified and non-modified products so that the latter can be sold to Europe. Down the production chain, such companies as Gerber have pledged to look for non-genetically engineered sources of maize and soybeans so they can market their food as free of such elements. In Gerber's case, this is a real concern as they are owned by one of the market leaders in agricultural biotechnology namely Novartis. This issue was quite clearly a bid to retain market share in the short term in the cut-throat business of baby food but none the less it sends out very conflicting messages to the general public.

All this properly disturbs U.S. farmers, who complain they are being asked to absorb heavy costs and left hanging after investing in the new modified crops. Their plight is part of the double-edged sword of globalisation. Big producers here will alter course to satisfy a large overseas market even when, as now, that market is acting irrationally. International free-trade pressure may, and should, eventually force European governments to lift official barriers to GMOs. But that doesn't reach the parts of the issue fuelled by emotion and culture or by Europe's unhappy history with food safety regulation.

The strategy of opposition

As Douglas Powell, University of Guelph points out, the activist groups follow a standard script. First, they will attack the science, playing up any obscure scientific study that suggests an unacceptable level of risk, even if the overwhelming majority of scientific evidence declares the products in question safe. A typical example of this strategy was the credence given to Pustzai's research at the Rowett Research Institute in Aberdeen, Scotland. He reported to television cameras on Aug.10, 1998, that, after feeding genetically engineered potatoes to five rats for 110 days, some suffered harmful effects, and that was due to the act of genetic modification alone, and not to the specific gene (encoding a lectin) which was introduced. No matter that an independent review by the Royal Society soundly refuted his results. Another example was the infamous BT Monarch butterfly research that has been mis-represented to the public.

Perhaps, beyond the shrill sound bites there is a way to extract whatever benefits genetic engineering can bring to food production and minimise the unknowns that come along with any new technology, while at the same time establishing trust. After all, most food purchasing decisions are overwhelmingly based on trust.

Environmental impact

Insect resistance genes

One of the obstacles to approval for commercial growth of GM insect resistant crops in Europe is the potential for insects to become resistant to the Bt toxin. This issue is also of concern in the U.S. and is being addressed by a number of organisations including the Environmental Protection Agency (EPA) and the National Maize Growers Association (NCGA). U.S. producers of Bt crops strongly encourage farmers to grow non-engineered plants in plots alongside Bt-expressing varieties, hoping that creation of this Bt-free refuge community will postpone the evolution of Bt resistant insects. Seed companies, embroiled in a no-holds-barred marketing battle, have agreed on the importance of planting Bt-free refuges, which shows the importance they place on this issue (rightly so, as evolving insect resistance could make or break Bt technology).

A general consensus has been reached on the need to maintain non-Bt refuges to thwart the emergence of insect resistance; however, some aspects of this insect resistance management (IRM) approach continue to be challenged. The rationale behind leaving Bt-free refuge communities is to provide a source of susceptible mates for any resistant insects that survive exposure to the Bt toxin. The strategy, though, is based on the assumption that resistance is a recessive trait, therefore the offspring of such a mating will be susceptible. This assumption has been questioned in some quarters but as yet there is little evidence that resistance is dominant.

A second unresolved issue is how to handle IRM when insects have access to more than one Bt crop. A prime example is maize earworm (*Helicoverpa zea*) which feeds on maize in the spring and early summer, then migrates to cotton where it is called cotton budworm. Also currently in contention is the size of the refuge area required to discourage evolution of resistant pests. The NCGA is currently recommending a 20 per cent refuge in primary maize-growing regions and 50 per cent in primary cotton-growing areas. These allotments may have to be increased if farmers find they need to use additional chemical pesticides to protect crops in times of unusually heavy insect predation, since sprays increase the risk of developing Bt resistance. There is also some concern that if farmers determine they need to spray a large percentage of their acreage, they may elect to spray the entire crop. Eventually they may find it more economical to spray than to employ Bt technology.

After considering some of the difficulties inherent in maintaining a Bt-free refuge, it becomes clear that continued advancements in Bt technology would be welcomed. One recommended strategy is to genetically alter crops to express multiple protein toxins, including non-Bt toxins. The availability of such "stacked" products could eventually permit a reduction in refuge size. Other suggestions include increasing the level of Bt expression, and targeting expression to tissues particularly sensitive to damage.

Recombinant viruses

The U.S. Department of Agriculture's Animal and Plant Health Inspection Service and the American Institute of Biological Sciences convened a workshop in 1995 to address risk issues associated with the possible generation of new plant viruses in transgenic plants expressing viral genes that confer virus resistance. The following are some of the conclusions from the workshop:

▶ There is no evidence to support the notion that frequent recombination events occur between viral taxa (e.g., between tobamoviruses and potyviruses) from growing season to growing season

▶ Comparing rates of recombination between two viruses in an infected plant with rates of recombination between a virus and a viral gene being expressed in a transgenic plant must be made with caution

▶ Genomic viral RNA transcapsidated with coat protein produced by a transgenic plant should not have long-term effects, since the genome of the infecting virus is not modified

▶ Any new virus problem that might result from the use of transgenic plants would be detected by farmers, seed producers, and scientists, as would any new plant virus or virus disease.

The potential benefits of transgenic virus resistance include increased yield, reduced pesticide use to control vectors, improved crop quality, and increased potential for multiple virus resistance traits. Most workshop participants believed that current data obtained from laboratory and field research indicate the risk associated with the generation of new plant viruses through recombination is minimal and should not be a limiting factor to large-scale field tests or commercialisation of transgenic plants expressing viral transgenes.

Gene flow

Among the ecological issues associated with transgenic crops is the possibility that some newly introduced traits, such as pest or pathogen resistance, could confer added fitness to the crop. As a result, the crop may gain weedy characteristics if its ability to survive and spread outside of cultivation is enhanced. A second issue arises if such crops are grown in the vicinity of compatible wild or weedy related species; transfer of the trait by natural hybridisation may produce hybrid progeny that are more aggressive or more difficult to control. These issues are not hypothetical, as at least seven groups of crops being engineered for pest resistance are known to have sexually compatible wild or weedy relatives

Assessing the risks

Assessing the potential for transgenic herbicide or pest resistant crops to become problem weeds, or to enhance the weediness of nearby sexually compatible relatives, is a complex task. Information is required from many disciplines - weed science, agronomy, population biology and genetics, entomology, plant breeding, ecology, plant pathology, molecular biology, and more. Scientific evidence in support of informed risk assessment and decision-making thus lies in the collective knowledge of experts from these fields. It is also self-evident that a crop-by-crop approach is needed.

With this in mind a working group recently considered this issue with respect to a number of crops. To illustrate the kind of considerations involved it is worth looking at the conclusions for one crop, oilseed rape (*Brassica napus*) for which concerns are most commonly expressed. Available information indicates that cultivated transgenic B. *napus* will hybridise with a number of weedy species and that introgression of transgenes is probable. Ecological studies show that in many environments insects are the principal factor limiting plant population growth, suggesting that acquired pest resistance genes could increase the fitness and hence the population range of weedy *Brassica* species. However, too little information is available to definitively state that this risk would outweigh the benefits of having crops with enhanced pest resistance. A number of areas of research were identified that would contribute to our knowledge of pest resistance gene impact on *Brassica* species:

▶ The creation of a database of sexually compatible species and varieties

▶ The development of a geographic information system of pest influence. This would combine species ranges with environmental information required to predict the impact of pests on a given host

▶ Long-term studies on weed populations to examine changes in pest resistance gene frequencies and the effect of such changes on pest populations

▶ Pest exclusion studies to measure the influence of pest pressure on plant reproductive rates

▶ Hybridisation and introgression experiments using resistance-conferring transgenes to measure the performance and persistence of transgenes in the environment

▶ Observational studies of basic reproductive biology of lesser-studied related species

▶ Modelling projects to synthesise available knowledge and direct future research.

The group also came to few general conclusions (not always unanimous):

▶ Conventional agricultural activity entails certain environmental and ecological risks. Given that, the group concluded that the genetically engineered pest resistance traits currently being field tested or commercially released present no fundamental differences from similar traits bred into crops using traditional techniques

▶ Crops engineered with multiple pest resistance or other fitness traits present more complex ecological questions

▶ Organisation of working groups around crop types is a very effective approach for synthesising what is known and what needs to be known about ecological effects of introduced pest resistant genes

▶ It is a feasible task to generate essential biological and ecological information on the more widespread outcrossing crop species, which would increase our ability to make educated determinations of risk posed by release of genetically engineered varieties.

Controlling fertility

Many biotechnologists increasingly believe that the ultimate answer to containment is to engineer plant infertility. By destroying, or severely curbing, a plant's ability to produce flowers or viable pollen or seed, they believe they can make it all but impossible for a transgene to escape. A wide range of genetic tricks for neutering crops are already in the pipeline. A male sterile oilseed rape has already been commercialised. The plant contains the barnase gene from *Bacillus amyloliquefaciens* under the control of a tapetum-specific promoter so it is only turned on in the tapetum tissue of the anthers, thus selectively cutting off pollen production. Fertility can be restored by crossing with a fertility restorer lines expressing the barstar gene from *Bacillus amyloliquefaciens*. This male sterility allows production of higher yielding hybrid seeds, whereby male-sterile plants are fertilised with pollen from specially selected sources. Genetically engineered systems for controlling male fertility are used to produce hybrid seed of important crops such as oilseed rape, maize, and rice. The technology also is applicable to tomato, lettuce, and a wide range of other crop plants. These advances eliminate the need for costly, labour-intensive hand or mechanical removal of anthers in making hybrid crosses and will have a major impact on the billion-dollar hybrid seed industry. In addition, the knowledge gained by studying anther development and fertilisation at the molecular and genetic levels will reveal other approaches that can be used to produce novel varieties of hybrid crop plants.

In the past few years, patents have been issued for techniques linking "suicide" genes to DNA "switches" that can be tripped inside pollen cells, wrecking their development, and also for techniques based on genes that kill off hybrid seeds as they attempt to germinate. Some companies even aim to turn crop fertility into a trait that can be switched on or off with sprays. Despite Monsanto's short-term decision not to pursue the terminator technology the probability is in the long term we are going to see a greater impact of this technology. The impetus behind terminator technology was not concern for the environment. Companies see the control of plant fertility as the key to preventing growers from pirating their technology. As long as crops remain fertile, there is a risk that growers will secretly use transgenic seed which they have saved from the last season.

This puts a paradox at the door of the opponents of GM crops. On the one hand they regard the terminator technology as an attack on the age-old rights of farmers to save and store harvested seed. Yet on the other hand they also complain about the risks of "genetic pollution".

Containment using chloroplasts

The many attractions of chloroplast transformation as a means of producing large amounts of recombinant protein are discussed on page 28. These include the fact that in most plants the plastids are inherited maternally, thereby greatly reducing the risk of pollen spread. This is supported by a study recently carried out by Scott and Wilkinson. They studied a 34 km region near the Thames River, U.K. where oilseed rape is cultivated in the vicinity of a native weed, wild rapeseed. Oilseed rape, the cultivated form of *Brassica napus*, and the wild rapeseed (*B. rapa*) are capable of exchanging pollen to produce viable hybrids. The study was designed to determine whether oilseed chloroplasts could be transferred to wild rapeseed, and how long the hybrids and maternal oilseed plants would survive in the wild. To identify chloroplasts, the authors created primers specific to chloroplast DNA non-coding regions which yielded PCR products diagnostic for the two species. In all cases, the chloroplasts from hybrid plants contained the PCR product of the maternal line demonstrating that they are not transferred in pollen.

Another possible route of transgene release is accidental distribution of seed. This occurs during transportation, seeding, and harvesting. Oilseed that is spread outside cultivated fields can cross with weeds allowing the transgene to enter the feral population. The authors studied the frequency of hybrid formation and viability of oilseed and hybrids in non-cultivated areas over a three-year period. Their studies show that oilseed has a very low survival rate outside cultivated fields. On average, only 12-19 per cent of oilseed survived each growing season. At the same time, a very low level of natural hybridisation was observed (0.4 1.5%). Taken together, the results indicate that there is a very low, but real, possibility of transgene movement into feral populations of maternal lineage. However, the persistence of the maternal line in the wild will be of limited duration.

Food safety

There are numerous checks and balances built into the tight regulatory procedures for novel and GM foods, both in Europe and the United States (discussed in Chapter 7).

Demanding proof that genetically modified foods are safe is all very well, but without a rational system for testing conventional foods, we may never get it. The antibiotech lobby rejoiced when Arpad Pusztai, a biochemist who used to work at the Rowett Research Institute in Scotland, said he had shown that GM potatoes were harmful to rats because of their genetic modification alone (see page 76), disregarding both flawed experimental design, and the nature of the gene (encoding a lectin) which had been introduced. In response to the resulting cry for a moratorium and a ban on all GM crops, Monsanto's business manager in Ireland, Dr. Patrick O'Reilly, said no company would use such lectin proteins and they were "not present in any of the crops coming to commercialisation". He rejected suggestions that the research reflected an absence of long-term mammalian testing of genetically modified products. John Hammond, head of development at AgrEvo UK, a company which is also developing GM crops, was quoted as saying, "The Rowett work is a bit unusual - they have taken a gene that generates a potentially quite potent insecticide and found it doesn't meet the safety criterion".

Politicians, taken aback by huge public mistrust of "Frankenfoods", are also realising that safety testing of these foods is not straightforward. In Britain, a Cabinet Office memo, leaked by Friends of the Earth, asks: "Why don't we require a pharmaceutical-type analysis of the safety of these foods, with proper trials?" However, as the following illustration shows, such a proposition is a non-starter. Harry Kuiper of the State Institute for Quality Control of Agricultural Products in Wageningen, Netherlands, tested a GM tomato by freeze-drying it and feeding so much to rats that each got the equivalent of 13 of fresh tomatoes a day. Any more, and they would have been poisoned by the basic nutrients, such as potassium, in the tomato powder.

"But toxicologists still said we hadn't fed them enough to get a meaningful result", says Kuiper. The usual approach for testing a new food additive, for instance, is to feed it to a rat until a toxic effect is observed. That way, you get an idea of the nature and threshold of any toxicity. But with tomatoes, the researchers never managed to reach that threshold. In standard toxicological terms, says Kuiper, they have not been adequately tested. Others would argue that if such large amounts are harmless, the food cannot reasonably be called toxic.

The production of a novel protein is only one of the potentially harmful changes that occur in when a foreign gene is inserted into a plant. Because the positioning of the novel gene within the plant's DNA is essentially random, it may alter the plant's expression of its own genes with unpredictable effects. It is this kind of change that stymies conventional toxicology. Food is a complex mixture of substances that occur in different quantities in different varieties of crops and in the same variety grown under even slightly different conditions. When is a change in one or several of those substances a problem? Unfortunately, says Peter Kearns of the OECD in Paris, no one has ever tested conventional food for toxicity, so no one quite knows where to start. One exception is potatoes. Conventional plant breeders in the US and the Netherlands test new potato varieties for elevated levels of known toxins such as solenines.

Economics and psychology of food labelling

Special interest groups have called for stringent labelling requirements, but these may not be in the best interest of consumers. Labelling can add significantly to production costs of foods, particularly those that are produced from pooled fresh fruits and vegetables. To maintain the accuracy of such labels, recombinant DNA-modified fruits and vegetables would have to be segregated through all phases of production (planting, harvesting, processing, and distribution), which would add costs and compromise economies of scale. These added production costs constitute, in effect, a special tax levied on producers who use a new technology. They reduce profits to plant breeders, farmers, food processors, grocers, etc. in the distribution pathway, while also decreasing competition and increasing prices.

Furthermore, over-regulation in the form of compulsory labelling could change the course of future research and development. In the United States and other countries, under current regulatory regimes for field testing that focus exclusively on organisms manipulated with recombinant DNA techniques, R&D has become limited primarily to a small number of commodity crops that are grown on a vast scale, at the expense of opportunities to improve important small-acreage crops. In 1998, the top four recombinant crops (soybean, maize, cotton, and oilseed rape) accounted for more than 99 per cent of the global acreage. Innovation seldom targets the genetic improvement of environmentally threatened species such as trees, or of subsistence crops such as millet, cassava, and yams.

The language of the FDA's principal enabling statute, the federal Food, Drug, and Cosmetic Act, firmly supports (indeed, to a large extent, dictates) the FDA's policies toward biotech foods. These policies were upheld indirectly by the U.S. Court of Appeals for the Second Circuit, which found in a pivotal 1996 decision regarding another product of biotechnology that food labelling cannot be compelled just because some consumers wish to have the information. In overturning a Vermont law that required labelling of dairy products from cows treated with recombinant bovine somatotropin, the court found that such regulation merely to satisfy the public's "right to know" is a constitutional violation of commercial free speech. "Were consumer interest alone sufficient, there is no end to the information that states could require manufacturers to disclose about their production methods", the court wrote.

The FDA's policy toward labelling biotech food is in contrast to that in Europe and Asia, where regulators have permitted politics, public misapprehensions, and the blandishments of anti-technology activists to dictate policy. Perhaps the scientifically defensible and risk-based approach of the FDA in the United States can illustrate that sound public policy can safeguard public health and stimulate new technology.

To add to this, the subtly altered products on our plates have been put through more thorough testing than any conventional food has ever been subjected to. Many of our daily staples would be banned outright if subjected to the same rigorous standards. Potatoes and tomatoes are members of the deadly nightshade families and contain toxic glycoalkaloids, which have been linked to spina bifida, kidney beans contain phytohaemagglutinin and are poisonous if undercooked. Dozens of people die each year from cynaogenic glycosides from peach seeds and grayanotoxin in honey produced from the nectar of rhododendrons. Yet none of those are labelled on our supermarket shelves. At this stage literally millions of people have eaten the products of genetic engineering and no adverse effects have been demonstrated. The proper balance of safety testing between companies and the government is a legitimate area for further debate, as are environmental safeguards. The purpose of such debate however, should be to improve biotech research and enhance its benefits to society, not stop it in its tracks.

Priorities for Ireland

With the present controversy surrounding crops that have been modified for improved agronomic characteristics one of the purported reasons for the less than wholehearted acceptance by consumers is that the benefits are non-obvious to this constituency. The great hope for biotechnology in crop agriculture is the potential to use this technology to create crop products with obvious benefits to the consumer. Some of the potential target traits are as follows:

▶ Improved shelf-life

▶ Nutrients (Nutraceuticals)

- Macro: Protein, Carbohydrates, Oils/Fats

- Micro: Vitamins, Minerals, Antioxidants, Isoflavonoids, Phytoestrogens, Condensed tannins

- Anti-nutrients: Phytase, Toxin and allergen removal

▶ Taste

▶ Novel Crop Products (e.g. oils, pharmaceuticals, vaccines)

Other priorities should be in research aimed at addressing consumer fears, and technical advancements in precision of transgene integration, and efficiency and stability of gene expression. Some important areas for research are:

▶ Marker excision, and marker-free selection methods

▶ Improvements in gene targeting and transgene reulation

▶ Chloroplast transformation for biological containment and high level protein production (cell factory applications)

▶ Environmental impact assessment of transgenic plants.

In addition, traditional agonomic traits (e.g. pest and disease resistance, resistance to herbicides and abiotic stresses) which can be addressed through biotechnology, remain important targets for future improvement.

Further reading

Thomzik, J.E. *et al.* (1997). Synthesis of a grapevine phytoalexin in transgenic tomatoes (*Lycopersicon esculentum* Mill.) conditions resistance against *Phytophthora infestans*. Physiol. Mol. Plant Pathol. 51:265-278.

Tabei, Y. *et al.* (1998). Transgenic cucumber plants harbouring a rice chitinase gene exhibit enhanced resistance to grey mould (*Botrytis cinerea*). Plant Cell Rep. 17:159-164.

Kohno T *et al.* (1990). Refolding of recombinant proteins. Methods in Enzymology 185:187-195.

Arakawa,T. (1998) Efficacy of a food plant-based oral cholera toxin B sub-unit vaccine. Nature Biotech. 16: 292-297.

Ma, J.K-C. *et al.* (1998). Characterisation of a recombinant plant monoclonal secretory antibody and preventative immunotherapy in humans. Nature Medicine 4: 601-606.

Haq, T., H.S. Mason, J.D. Clements, and C.J. Arntzen. (1995). Oral immunisation with a recombinant bacterial antigen produced in transgenic plants. Science 268: 714-716.

Arntzen, C. J. (1997) High-tech herbal medicine: Plant-based vaccines. Nature Biotech. 15: 221-222.

Dalsgaard, K. et al. (1997) Plant-derived vaccine protects target animals against a viral disease. Nature Biotech. 15: 248-252.

Dixon, R. A. & C. J. Arntzen (1997) Transgenic Plant Technology is Entering the Era of Metabolic Engineering. Trends in Biotech. 15: 441-444.

Johnson, E. (1996) Edible Plant Vaccines. Nature Biotech. 14: 1533.

Hayashi, H. et al. (1997). Transformation of Arabidopsis thaliana with the codA gene for choline oxidase; accumulation of glycinebetaine and enhanced tolerance to salt and cold stress. The Plant Journal 12:133-142.

Holmberg, N., G. Lilius, J. E. Bailey, and L. Bülow. (1997). Transgenic tobacco expressing Vitreoscilla hemoglobin exhibits enhanced growth and altered metabolite production. Nature Biotech. 15:244- 247.

Whitham SA, Yamamoto ML, and Carrington JC. (1999). Selectable viruses and altered susceptibility mutants in Arabidopsis thaliana Proc Natl. Acad. Sci. USA. 96:772-777.

Bowen, D. et al. (1998). Insecticidal toxins from the bacterium Photorhabdus luminescens. Science 280:2129-2132.

Strauss, E. (1998). Possible new weapon for insect control. Science 280:2050.

Huang F. et al. (1999). Inheritance of resistance to Bacillus thuringiensis toxin (Dipel ES) in the European maize borer. Science 284: 965-967.

Rossi, M. et al. (1998). The nematode gene Mi of tomato confers resistance against the potato aphid. Proc. Natl. Acad. Sci. USA 95:9750-9754.

Cook, J. (1998). The molecular mechanisms responsible for resistance in plant-pathogen interactions of the gene-for-gene type function more broadly than previously thought. Proc. Natl. Acad. Sci. USA 95:9711-9712.

Alia,.Hayashi H, Sakamoto A, and Murata, N. (1998). Enhancement of the tolerance of Arabidopsis to high temperatures by genetic engineering of the synthesis of glycinebetaine. Plant Journal 16:155-161.

Barro, F., et al. (1997). Transformation of wheat with high molecular weight sub-unit genes results in improved functional properties. Nature Biotech. 15:1295.

Rugh, C.L. et al. (1998). Development of transgenic yellow poplar for mercury phytoremediation. Nature Biotech. 16:925-928.

Salt, D. E. 1998. Arboreal alchemy. Nature Biotech. 16:905.

Kota M et al. (1999). Overexpression of the Bacillus thuringiensis (Bt) CryA2Aa2 protein in chloroplasts confers resistance to plants against susceptible and Bt-resistant insects. Proc. Natl. Acad. Sci. USA 96:1840-1845.

Chapter 3

ANIMAL BIOTECHNOLOGY

ANIMAL BIOTECHNOLOGY

The Technology

Animals in many capacities have been important components of human enterprise since prehistory, as food, shelter, transport, work, companionship and, in more recent times, to determine safety and efficacy of therapeutics and as models to study disease. The development of the capacity to modify animals at the molecular level has expanded their roles especially in the latter areas and has added a new dimension to this compendium, "molecular pharming", the production of valuable products in milk.

For most of our long intertwined history the most consistent contribution from animals has been within the agricultural arena. With increased social awareness their role in this capacity has been subject to question and debate and with the advent of genetic engineering this took on a new level of complexity. This section will attempt to provide a reasonable overview of the development and use of transgenic animals and will touch on the ethical and societal implications but will leave a more expanded analysis of these issues to more qualified reviewers.

Transgenic animals have tremendous potential to act as valuable research tools in the agricultural and biological sciences. They can be modified specifically to address scientific questions that were previously difficult if not impossible to determine.

The first scientific contribution to reproductive physiology in animals was the successful attempt to culture and transfer embryos in 1891. The development of artificial insemination helped with the costs and control of breeding but the first technological shift came with Gurdon's 1970 transfer of a nucleus of a somatic adult frog cell into an enucleated frog ovum and the birth of viable tadpoles. This experiment was of limited success as none of the tadpoles developed into adult frogs. In 1977 Gurdon expanded the field further through the transfer of mRNA and DNA into toad (Xenopus) embryos where he observed that the transferred nucleic acids were expressed. Also in the 1970s, Ralph Brinster developed a now-common technique used to inject stem cells into embryos. When these embryos became adults, they produced offspring carrying the genes of the original cells. In 1982, Brinster with his colleagues gained further renown by transferring genes for rat growth hormone into mice under the control of a mouse liver-specific promoter and producing mice that grew into "supermice" - twice their normal size.

During the two years 1980 and 1981, there were several reported successes at gene transfer and the development of transgenic mice. Gordon and Ruddle first coined the term "transgenic" to describe animals carrying exogenous genes integrated into their genome. Since that time this definition has been extended to include animals that result from the molecular manipulation of endogenous genomic DNA, including all techniques from DNA microinjection to embryonic stem (ES) cell transfer and "knockout" mouse production.

Notwithstanding the advent of successful nuclear transfer technology with the dawn of 'Dolly' the sheep, the most widely used technique for the production of transgenic animals including mice is by microinjection of DNA into the pronucleus of a recently fertilised egg. Using various transgenic tools such as antisense technology (putting a reverse copy to switch off expression), it is now possible to add a new gene to the genome, increase the level of expression or change the tissue specificity of expression of a gene, or decrease the level of synthesis of a specific protein. An additional factor added by the new nuclear transfer technology is the capability of removing or altering an existing gene via homologous recombination. There are now a number of different mechanisms for creating transgenic animals:

▶ Integration of retroviral vectors into an early embryo

▶ Retroviral infection of germinal vesicles oocytes

▶ Injection of DNA into the pronucleus of a newly fertilised egg

▶ The incorporation of genetically manipulated embryonic stem cells into an early embryo

▶ The incorporation of genetically manipulated primordial germ cells into an early embryo

▶ Sperm delivery

▶ Nuclear transplantation

▶ Microprojectile injection.

The new retroviral transformation system

Retroviruses are a type of highly evolved transposable element, which have the ability to infect other cells and insert their genes into the host cells. It has been estimated that about ten per cent of the genomes of higher organisms are related to transposable elements. It is clear that these transposable elements have co-evolved with higher animals, and that this co-evolution appears to have been mutually beneficial. Replication competent retroviruses were first used to produce transgenic mice two decades ago and have since been used to produce transgenic birds, fish, and livestock. Great strides in our understanding of retroviral biology have resulted from efforts in AIDS research and the engineering of retroviral vectors for gene therapy.

In 1998, scientists at Gala Design, and the Universities of Wisconsin and California reported a novel, highly efficient method of producing transgenic livestock. By inserting genes into the unfertilised oocytes of cattle, using a non-replicating gene-transfer vector, large numbers of transgenic embryos were produced. A group of embryos transferred to surrogate mother cows resulted in the birth of several transgenic founder cattle.

The novel approach - called transgametic technology - has clear advantages over other methods of producing transgenic livestock, including microinjection and cloning. The system based on the genetic engineering of replication incompetent retroviral vectors is complex. Gala claim that using pseudotyped, replication defective, retrovectors in bovine oocytes undergoing meiosis it is possible to produce transgenic cattle with efficiencies approaching 100 per cent and that this increase in efficiency of gene transfer achieved by the transgametic (TM) technology will greatly reduce the high costs of production of transgenic livestock. Dairy livestock carrying the genes for specific proteins can provide a cost-effective source of complex drug molecules. Protein pharmaceuticals include antibodies, enzymes, hormones, and many others now only available through costly bioreactor production. The transgametic (TM) method complements a second technology Gala Design has developed for rapid protein expression, using gene therapy to insert genes directly into the cow's udder. The second transomatic (TM) method enables protein production in milk within a few weeks.

Sperm delivery

For mice, microinjection into fertilised eggs is very wasteful. Hundreds of eggs must be injected, and fewer than one in ten of the embryos that survive to full term take up a working copy of the injected genes. The rest are killed, and this waste of life is causing increasing alarm. A new technique should reduce this wastage. Tony Perry and his team at the University of Hawaii in Honolulu working with colleagues at Osaka University and the Obihiro University of Agriculture in Japan, fertilised mouse eggs by intracytoplasmic sperm injection (ICSI) - the same technique that allows men with low sperm counts to father. children. Before mixing the sperm with foreign DNA and injecting them into eggs, the researchers disrupted the cell membranes of the sperm by rapid freezing and thawing. When Perry mixed his treated sperm heads with the gene for jellyfish green fluorescent protein, more than two-thirds of the eggs he injected began to develop and glowed green. He then implanted all the embryos into female mice and found that one in five of the pups that were born glowed. The green protein is mildly toxic and may have killed some embryos, so the true efficiency could be higher. Perry also expects the success rate to rise as they refine the technique.

Animal welfare campaigners are pleased. As well as avoiding the destruction of dozens of failed transgenic mice, there would be no need for large stocks of stud males to fertilise eggs the old-fashioned way, according to Richard McGowan, a spokesman for the Fund for the Replacement of Animals in Medical Experiments in Nottingham. Sperm could simply be kept on ice.

Transient expression

The generation of transgenic animals is a powerful technology that has allowed the study of gene action in vivo and production of valuable pharmaceutical proteins. However, for some studies, such as the evaluation of gene regulatory elements or delivery of recombinant proteins to specific tissues, the time and expense of creating a transgenic animal is not necessary. Instead, only a method to transiently transfect DNA into animal tissues is needed. A number of methods such as needle and syringe injection, microparticle bombardment or a jet-injection based gene gun have been successfully used to directly transfect a variety of animal tissues. Transgene expression is usually transient and persists for only days to weeks, but this length of time is often sufficient to complete the promoter analysis.

One of the most promising applications of direct transfection technology is its use as a method to produce foreign proteins in specific tissues in order to induce an immune response in the animal. This method has been termed "genetic immunisation". Intramuscular injection of transgenes expressing bovine herpesvirus 1 glycoprotein in cattle or influenza virus hemagglutinin glycoprotein in chickens resulted in the induction of an immune response to the viral protein. In the latter case, the chickens were further found to be protected against a lethal influenza challenge. Direct transfection technology represents a novel vaccination strategy that has clear advantages over standard immunisation techniques, which rely on attenuated or killed virus.

Progress To Date

Table 3, taken from a report by Pinkert and Murray (1999) lists the vertebrate species that have been genetically engineered to date.

Table 3:   Genetically engineered vertebrate species

MAMMALS	BIRDS	FISH
Mice	Chickens	Salmon
Rats	Japanese Quail	Trout
Rabbits		Talapia
Cattle		Carp
Pigs		Channel
Sheep		Medaka
Goats		Zebrafish
		Loach
		Goldfish
		Catfish

The applications for transgenic animal research fall broadly into two distinct areas, namely medical and agricultural. The recent focus on developing animals as bioreactors to produce valuable proteins in their milk can be catalogued under both areas. Underlying each of these, of course, is a more fundamental application, that is the use of these techniques as tools to ascertain the molecular and physiological bases of gene expression and animal development. This understanding can then lead to the creation of techniques to modify development pathways.

As noted by Pinkert and Murray, there are still fundamental limitations to the wide spread use of transgenic technology in all animals except the mouse. Limitations include:

▶ Lack of knowledge concerning the genetic basis of factors limiting production traits.

▶ Identification of tissue and developmentally - specific regulatory sequences for use in developing gene constructs, expression vectors, and in gene targeting.

▶ Establishment of novel methods to increase efficiency of transgenic animal production.

In medicine no doubt the most versatile animal model has been the mouse and this especially applies since the technology has been perfected to customise the engineering of mice. Up until recently the principle advantage that the mouse held over all other species was the ability to isolate, with relative ease, embryonic stem (ES) cells. ES cells are derived from the inner cell mass of the blastocyst formed during early embryogenisis. Distinguished from all other stem cells, they are pluripotent, able to develop into virtually any and all cells and tissues in the body; and, consistent with their expression of telomerase, self-renewing, a potentially limitless source of cells. One of the areas in which the mouse has been supreme is the ability, using these embryonic stem cells, to target with great specificity regions within chromosomes via what is termed homologous recombination. Using this method, researchers can:

▶ Incorporate a novel foreign gene into a mouse genome.

▶ Modify an endogenous gene.

▶ Delete a portion of a specific endogenous gene creating a "loss-of-function" mutant termed a "knock-out" mouse to study phenotypic effects of inactivating genes.

Nuclear transfer

The other great advance in the field of reproductive biology and methods for genetic engineering was Ian Wilmut's landmark work using nuclear transfer technology to generate the lambs Morag and Megan reported in 1996 (from an embryonic cell nuclei) and the truly ground-breaking work of creating Dolly from an adult somatic cell nucleus, reported in February, 1997. Wilmut and his colleagues at the Roslin Institute demonstrated for the first time with the birth of Dolly the sheep that the nucleus of an adult somatic cell can be transferred to an enucleated egg to create cloned offspring. The procedure that produced Dolly demonstrated that egg cytoplasm is capable of reprogramming an adult differentiated cell (which is only expressing genes related to the function of that cell type). One of the key procedures was putting the cell culture through a quiscent step where the DNA programming was effectively set to time zero. This reprogramming enables the differentiated cell nucleus to once again express all the genes required for the full embryonic development of the adult animal. Since Dolly was cloned, similar techniques have been used to clone mice and cattle from donor cells obtained from adult animals. These spectacular examples of cloning normal animals from fully differentiated adult cells demonstrate the universality of nuclear reprogramming and should play a significant role in the development of new procedures for genetic engineering in a number of mammalian species. Following on the heels of Dolly; Polly and Molly became the first genetically engineered transgenic sheep produced through nuclear transfer technology. Polly and Molly were engineered to produce human factor IX (for hemophiliacs) by transfer of nuclei from transfected fetal fibroblasts. Until then germline competent transgenics had only been produced in mammalian species, other than mice, using DNA microinjection.

Researchers at the University of Massachusetts and Advanced Cell Technology (Worcester, MA) have teamed up to produce genetically altered calves utilising a strategy similar to that used to produce transgenic sheep. Foetal fibroblasts were grown in culture and genetically modified with a marker construct containing a fusion gene (beta galactosidase-neomycin resistance). Clonal lines of genetically modified cells were isolated and used as nuclear donors. Three calves surviving the process were phenotypically and genetically identical. Analyses by PCR and Southern blot demonstrated that the genomic organisation of the foreign DNA was identical among the three calves. By the researchers' estimation, the somatic cell nuclear transfer process is more efficient than the classical microinjection method. The ability to select for genetically modified cells in culture prior to nuclear transfer opens up the possibility of applying the powerful gene targeting techniques that have been developed for mice. One of the limitations of using primary cells, however, is their limited lifespan in culture. Primary cell cultures such as the foetal fibroblasts used in this study can only undergo about 30 population doublings before they senesce. This limited lifespan would preclude the ability to perform multiple rounds of selection.

To overcome this problem of cell senescence, these researchers showed that fibroblast lifespan could be prolonged by nuclear transfer. A foetus, which was developed by nuclear transfer from genetically modified cells, could in turn be used to establish a second generation of foetal fibroblasts. These foetal cells would then be capable of undergoing another 30 population doublings, which would provide sufficient time for selection of a second genetic modification.

The list of animals cloned now includes mice, pigs, cattle and goats. They were generated by a protocol similar to that used to produce cloned sheep.

For a pharmaceutical study the goat foetuses were used for establishing foetal cell lines which were generated by mating nontransgenic females to a transgenic male containing a human antithrombin (AT) III transgene. This AT transgene directs high level expression of human AT into milk of lactating transgenic females. As expected, all three offspring derived from female foetal cells were females. One of these cloned goats was hormonally induced to lactate and secreted 3.7-5.8 grams per litre of AT in her milk. This level of AT expression was comparable to that detected in milk of transgenic goats from the same line obtained by natural breeding.

The successful secretion of AT in milk was a key result because it showed that a cloned animal could still synthesise and secrete a foreign protein at the expected level. It will be interesting to see if all three cloned goats secrete human AT at the identical level. If so, then the goal of creating a herd or flock of genetically identical transgenic animals, which secrete identical levels of an important pharmaceutical, would become a reality. No longer would variable production levels exist in subsequent generations due to genetically similar but not identical animals. This homogeneity would greatly aid in the production and processing of a uniform product. As nuclear transfer technology continues to be refined and applied to other species, it may eventually replace microinjection as the method of choice for generating transgenic livestock. It has several advantages:

▶ Nuclear transfer is more efficient than microinjection at producing a transgenic animal

▶ The fate of the integrated foreign DNA can be examined prior to production of the transgenic animal

▶ The sex of the transgenic animal can be predetermined

▶ The problem of mosaicism in first generation transgenic animals can be eliminated.

Gene targeting

Homologous recombination (HR) was first demonstrated in mammalian cells in the mid 1980's. During the last 10 years, the combination of mouse embryonic stem (ES) cell technology, with the optimisation of HR and enrichment strategies, has produced more than 800 mouse lines, with precise germline genetic modifications; including gene knock-outs, knock-ins, and subtle mutations. The knockout mice have provided valuable animal models for studying human disease, immunology, cancer, and developmental biology, as well as providing key information on gene structure/function relationships. Targeting genes by homologous recombination is now possible in somatic livestock cells. For example, an alpha-1-antitrypsin (AAT) transgene, under control of the mammary-specific ovine beta-lactoglobulin (BLG) promoter was inserted, in combination with the marker gene, at a precise target locus and a cloned sheep has been born from AAT-targeted cells. There is also promising progress in producing gene knockout pigs by homologous recombination.The gene for a-1,3 galactosyl transferase has been successfully knocked out in somatic pig cells. These cells can be used in combination with porcine nuclear transfer to produce knockout pigs, whose cells and organs are devoid of gal-a-1,3-gal sugar residues, a key step in overcoming hyperacute rejection associated with the transplantation of xenogeneic tissues. The extension of this technology to knockout of genes in cow cells will open the door for large-scale production of a variety of novel pharmaceutical and nutritional products.

Transgenic animals in medicine

The development of transgenic animals has tremendous potential in medical research and therapeutic applications including the creation of models to study disease, early development, aging, and specific gene function and the production of valuable proteins in milk. For example pigs have been engineered as large animal models for studying cone photoreceptor survival and degeneration in retinitis pigmentosa.

Xenotransplantation: transgenic animals as organ donors

A novel use is the creation of engineered animals where the surface antigens of the organs, such as the heart, have been altered so that they can be used for transplantation without rejection by the recipient as the latter's immune system will not see the transplants as foreign.

Advances in medical science have made many organ transplants, such as heart, kidney, and liver, almost routine procedures. However, the chronic shortage of suitable organs for transplantation limits the number of these life-saving operations. Of the estimated 60,000 people annually that need an organ transplant, only half actually receive a transplant. In the U.S. alone, approximately 3,000 people die each year waiting for a transplant.

Increasing public awareness about the importance of organ donation has not effectively increased the supply of organs to meet the demand. As an alternative approach, xenotransplantation or the transfer of organs between species has been proposed as a possible solution to alleviating the shortage of transplantable organs. As with any organ transplant, whether it be human-human or animal-human, the major medical obstacle that must be overcome is hyperacute rejection of the transplant by the host immune system. To prevent rejection of animal organs in humans, researchers are developing transgenic animals that express human shield proteins on the surface of their organs. Imutran (Cambridge, U.K.), a Novartis subsidiary, and DNX (Princeton, NJ) are two of the leading companies developing transgenic animals as organ donors. Pigs are the favoured model for these transgenic studies because the size, anatomy and physiology of pig organs are compatible with humans. Also, there are very few swine diseases that can be transmitted to humans. Imutran has successfully produced transgenic pigs that express the human shield protein, decay accelerating factor (DAF). Transfer of DAF-expressing pig hearts into monkeys under severe immunosuppression showed an increase in survival time of the transplant. DNX has also produced transgenic pigs expressing shield proteins and likewise has demonstrated a delay in the onset of hyperacute rejection of the genetically modified organ. Although these results show promise in mitigating hyperacute rejection by the complement system, further technical obstacles need to be overcome. For example, the xenograft must still survive later attack from other components of the immune system.

Transgenic animals in agriculture

Mammals

To date, for agricultural species, the types of transgenes used fall into two main types, those encoding growth factors and those encoding proteins for expression in the mammary gland.

The work with growth factors was carried out in an attempt to alter the efficiency of meat production and alter the partitioning of nutrient resources towards increased lean production. Gene constructs designed to express directly or indirectly various growth factors, and thus to alter body composition, constitute the largest class of transgenes transferred into livestock species. The majority of these transgenes expressed growth hormone (GH), although other constructs based on growth hormone releasing hormone and insulin-like growth factor-I (IGF-1) have also been used. In general, pigs and sheep expressing these constructs were leaner and more feed-efficient, but they also suffered from a number of complications as a consequence of the high, unregulated levels of circulating growth hormone, indicating the need for tight control of hormone secretion. Recently, two groups reported preliminary data on the development of GH and IGF-1 transgenic pigs with enhanced growth performance traits. In both experiments, preliminary data indicated desirable effects on growth and body composition traits without apparent abnormalities, suggesting that useful animals could become available to swine breeders in the future. In addition, to the work with livestock transgenic for growth factor, considerable effort has been directed towards increasing the efficiency of wool growth in Australian sheep by insertion of the two bacterial or yeast genes required for sheep to synthesise *de novo* the sulphur amino acid cysteine.

Milk is one of the principle targets for engineering productivity traits. This includes altering the properties or proportions of caseins, lactose, or butterfat in milk of transgenic cattle and goats. Another focus is engineering for enhanced resistance to viral and bacterial diseases including development of "constitutive immunity" or germline transmission of specific, modified antibody genes. Castilla reported in the April 1998 issue of Nature Biotechnology the generation of transgenic mice that secrete virus neutralising antibodies in their milk. These antibodies were directed against transmissible gastroenteritis coronavirus (TGEV). TGEV infection is an important disease in swine that causes a mortality close to 100 per cent in three week old piglets and severe diarrhoea in young pigs. Therefore, the development of transgenic sows which synthesise virus neutralising antibodies in their milk could reduce the serious effects resulting from TGEV infection in newborn swine. A number of pharmaceutically important proteins have also been expressed in the mammary gland (See table 4).

Poultry

Since DNA microinjection into pronuclei of embryonic cells in poultry is not feasible, transfection using retroviruses has prevailed. Methods have included transfection of genes into cells of embryonic blastoderm; insertion of genes using replication-competent retroviruses; the use of replication-defective retroviruses; and sperm-mediated gene transfer. The development of avian transgenesis has been slowed by the lack of an efficient, non-viral mediated gene transfer system but researchers at the Roslin Institute, UK, have now reported in a highly efficient method of transferring DNA into chickens using the mariner transposable element from *Drosophila*. The mariner element is capable of transposition, that is, excision from one DNA fragment and insertion into another, in a wide variety of organisms including protozoa, mosquitoes, and fish. The transposition event is mediated by a mariner-encoded transposase enzyme, which performs the essential DNA cut-and-paste function.

To determine if mariner is active in avian species, a plasmid containing an active mariner element was microinjected into the cytoplasm of the germinal disc of newly fertilised chicken eggs. Twenty seven per cent (12/44) of the surviving 12-day embryos contained the mariner element present at a level equivalent to one copy per genome. This gene transfer frequency was much greater than that observed following microinjection of DNA without a mariner element (0.4%) and was similar to the frequency observed for transposition of mariner into its natural host, *Drosophila*. The successful use of the mariner element for efficient, stable, germline gene transfer represents a significant advance in the development of methods for avian transgenesis.

As with mammalian system, advances in stem cell research is greatly enhancing the development of transgenic chickens as economically viable. Pluripotential cells with an embryonic stem cell (ES) phenotype can be derived from stage X chicken blastoderms and from primordial germ cells isolated from embryos. Foreign DNA can be introduced into chicken ES cells by conventional protocols such as lipofection or electroporation and the foreign DNA is expressed. When genes that confer antibiotic resistance are introduced into chicken ES cells, they can be selected in media containing the antibiotic. Perhaps the most important attribute of chicken ES cells is their ability to integrate into somatic tissues and the germline when injected into recipient embryos. The contribution to somatic tissues and the germline in chimeras can be recognised using ectodermal markers such a feather pigmentation, using mesodermal markers such as the MHC loci that are expressed on red blood cells and using parentage to establish rates of germline transmission.

Applications of transgenesis in chickens include the production of pharmaceutically important proteins in eggs and the production of human antibodies in chickens lacking the ability to secrete endogenous immunoglobulins. Agricultural applications include the production of transgenic chickens with enhanced resistance to specific diseases and the production of birds with increased metabolic capability to facilitate the use of feedstuffs that are indigestible in unimproved stocks.

Aquatic organisms

Oceanic organisms constitute a major portion of the Earth's biological resources, yet most of these organisms (primarily microorganisms) have yet to be identified. Recent advances in molecular biology, biosensor technology, aquaculture, and bioprocess engineering now promise fundamentally new approaches and opportunities for identifying, using, and managing biological resources from the seas.

Gene transfer techniques have been applied to a large number of aquatic organisms, both vertebrates and invertebrates. Gene transfer experiments have targeted a wide variety of applications, including the study of gene structure and function, aquaculture production, and use in fisheries management programmes. This section briefly reviews the status of development of transgenic aquatic organisms.

Because fish have high fecundity, large eggs, and do not require reimplantation of embryos, transgenic fish prove attractive model systems in which to study gene expression. Transgenic zebrafish have found utility in studies of embryogenisis, with expression of transgenes marking cell lineages or providing the basis for study of promoter or structural gene function. Although not as widely used as zebrafish, transgenic medaka and goldfish have been used for studies of promoter function. This body of research indicates that transgenic fish provide useful models of gene expression, reliably modelling that in "higher" vertebrates.

Perhaps the largest number of gene transfer experiments address the goal of genetic improvement for aquaculture production purposes. The principal area of research has focused on growth performance, and initial transgenic growth hormone (GH) fish models have demonstrated accelerated and beneficial phenotypes. DNA microinjection methods have propelled the many studies reported and have been most effective due to the relative ease of working with fish embryos. Bob Devlin's group in Vancouver has demonstrated extraordinary growth rate in coho salmon which were transformed with a growth hormone from sockeye salmon. The transgenics achieve up eleven times the size of their littermates within six months, reaching maturity in about half the time. Interestingly this dramatic effect is only observed in feeding pens where the transgenics' ferocious appetites demands constant feeding. If the fish are left to their own devices and must forage for themselves, they appear to be out-competed by their smarter siblings.

However most studies, such as those involving transgenic Atlantic salmon and channel catfish, report growth rate enhancement on the order of 30-60 per cent. In addition to the species mentioned, GH genes also have been transferred into striped bass, tilapia, rainbow trout, gilthead sea bream, common carp, bluntnose bream, roach, and other species.

Shellfish also are subject to gene transfer toward the goal of intensifying aquaculture production. Growth of abalone expressing an introduced GH gene is being evaluated; accelerated growth would prove a boon for culture of this slow-growing mollusc. A marker gene was introduced successfully into giant prawn, demonstrating feasibility of gene transfer in crustaceans, and opening the possibility of work involving genes affecting economically important traits. In the ornamental fish sector of aquaculture, ongoing work addresses the development of fish with unique colouring or patterning. A number of companies have been founded to pursue commercialisation of transgenics for aquaculture. As most aquaculture species mature at 2-3 years of age, most transgenic lines are still in development and have yet to be tested for performance under culture conditions.

Broad application of transgenic aquatic organisms in aquaculture and fisheries management will depend on showing that particular GMOs can be used in the environment both effectively and safely. Although our base of knowledge for assessing ecological and genetic safety of aquatic GMOs is limited, some early studies supported by the USDA biotechnology risk assessment programme have yielded results. Data from outdoor pond-based studies on transgenic catfish reported by Rex Dunham of Auburn University show that transgenic and non-transgenic individuals interbreed freely, that survival and growth of transgenics in unfed ponds was equal to or less than that of non-transgenics, and that predator avoidance is not affected by expression of the transgene. Laboratory studies of transgenic medaka by Bill Muir and colleagues at Purdue University indicated that large males gain a higher frequency of matings, but that transgenic offspring exhibit decreased viability.

Given the desire, in the United States, to pursue research and development with genetically modified aquatic organisms in the face of incomplete knowledge regarding environmental risks, a decision support tool for assessing and managing risks was developed. The Performance Standards for Safely Conducting Research with Genetically Modified Fish and Shellfish serves as a guide for a researcher to assess potential risks associated with a proposed experiment with an aquatic GMO, and to adopt appropriate environmental and biological confinement, should any risk be identified e.g. using triploid females that are infertile. Documented completion of the performance standards should help the researcher gain approval for the experiment from an institutional biosafety committee.

Domestic animals as bioreactors

Another general area of interest has been the development of lines of transgenic domestic animals for use as bioreactors. One of the main targets of these so-called "gene pharming" efforts has involved attempts to direct expression of transgenes encoding biologically active human proteins. The goal is to recover large quantities of functional proteins that have therapeutic value, from serum, urine or from the milk of lactating females. A summary of the progress to date is given in Table 4, while Table 5 illustrates the requirement for some of these products, and the herd size of transgenic animals required to meet these needs.

The use of transgenic animals offers a viable and economic approach for large-scale production of recombinant proteins in addition to therpeutics. Nexia is using transgenics to manufacture a family of recombinant spider silks named Biosteel. Orb-web spinning spiders produce and spin as many as seven different types of silks each one with very specialised mechanical properties distinguishing them from other natural or synthetic fibres. For example, dragline silk is one of the toughest materials known: it can exhibit up to 35 per cent elongation, with tensile strengths approaching those of high performance synthetic fibres such as Kevlar while the energy absorbed before snapping exceeds that of steel. With such extreme properties Biosteel has several potential uses (medical devices, ballistic protection, aircraft and automotive composites etc.), and applications similar to those of Kevlar.

Nexia's transgenic programme uses a patented mammary epithelial cells (MAC-Ts) and BELE (Breed Early Lactate Early) goat system in combination with pronuclear microinjection and nuclear transfer technologies for the production of Biosteel in milk.

Table 4: Human proteins produced in animals.

PROTEIN	USE	SPECIES
å -1 anti-protease inhibitor	å -1 antitrypsin deficiency	Goat
å -1 - antitrypsin	Anti-inflammatory	Goat, Sheep
Anti-thrombin III	Sepsis and disseminated intravascular coagulation	Goat
Collagen	Burns, bone fracture, incontinence	Cow
Factor IX & VIII	Hemophilia	Sheep, Pig
Fibrinogen	"Fibrin glue," burns, surgery,	Pig, Sheep
Localised chemotherapeutic	Drug delivery	
Human fertility hormones	Infertility, contraceptive vaccines	Goat, Cow
Human hemoglobin	Blood replacement for transfusion	Pig
Human serum albumin	Burns, shock, trauma, surgery	Goat, Cow
Lactoferrin	Bacterial gastro-intestinal infection	Cow
LAtPA	Venous stasis ulcers	Goat
Monoclonal antibodies	Anti-colon cancer	Goat
Tissue plasminogen activator	Heart attacks, Deep vein thrombosis, pulmonary embolism	Goat

Table modified from GEN

Table 5: Transgenic animals and protein yields

Estimated herd size for selected proteins produced in the milk of transgenic animals.

PROTEIN	ESTIMATED ANNUAL NEED, KG	ESTIMATED HERD SIZE	SPECIES
Protein C	100	33 1,100	cows pigs
tPA	75	600	goats sheep
a 1-anti-trypsin	5,000	33,000 42,000	sheep goats
Factor IX	2	13 22	sheep pigs
Human serum albumin	1,000	300 8,300	cows goats

The number of lactating animals may be calculated as: (expression in g/L) x (annual milk production in L) x (purification efficiency)

The Future of Animal Biotechnology

Early on the transgenic animal community identified integration rate, embryo survival and transgene behaviour as the three major areas impeding efficient production of transgenic animals. Over the past decade and a half at least seven new gene delivery approaches have been developed to try to address one or more of the inadequacies of pronuclear microinjection. Two of the more recent technological developments, nuclear transfer with transfected somatic cell nuclei and retroviral infection of germinal vesicles oocytes, stand out as methods with unique potentials. Most of the new gene transfer approaches offer solutions for low integration rate and/or poor embryo survival. Less optimistic however, are any proposed solutions to the problem of unpredictable transgene behaviour. Many reports on successful application of transgenic technology for both agricultural and biomedical uses are a clear sign that even though many are still trying to fix the system, transgenic animal technology's promise to create new types of beneficial animals and their products is real.

Agriculture

Ongoing research in the laboratory of Gary Anderson and Jim Murray at U.C. Davis, California is exploring the potential uses of transgenic technology in the dairy industry. A reasonable expectation is that genetically engineered dairy cows could become available to the industry within the next two decades. Such genetically engineered animals would be of two types: those with added or altered proteins to increase the yield of cheese and the range of products that can be made from milk, and those that have had the milk altered to yield a more healthy milk for human consumption. The addition of naturally occurring human milk proteins with antimicrobial properties, and the addition of genes to alter the fatty acid composition of milk towards a more heart-healthy mix, are currently underway in mice. Thus, it is reasonable to assume that dairy cows carrying these types of transgenes could become available to the industry by 2025. The use of such transgenic cows could result in the gradual separation of the genetic backgrounds of herds being used for fluid milk production from those used for producing milk for manufacturing of cheese. For example, the antimicrobial nature of lysozyme-containing milk for fluid consumption may interfere with the microbes used in cheese and yogurt production.

Livestock production, particularly intensive systems like dairy, swine, poultry, and aquaculture, needs to reduce the amount of nitrogen, phosphate, and other minerals that contribute to elevated levels of these minerals in surface and ground water. If an enzyme can be added to increase the efficiency of utilisation of a feed additive, the amount of that additive in the feed can be reduced. For example, if a more effective phytase can be expressed in the digestive tract of an animal, then the amount of phosphate provided in the diet can be reduced, reducing the amount of non-utilised phosphate excreted by the animal. The potential exists for these genetically modified animals to become available to various animal industries within the next 10 to 15 years.

Choosing sex of domestic animal offspring

Scientists at the U.S. Department of Agriculture's Germplasm and Gamete Physiology Lab have developed technology to separate Y chromosome-bearing sperm cells from those with the X chromosome. X-bearing sperm cells marked with a dye fluoresce more intensively, allowing the two populations (X-bearing and Y- bearing) to be separated. Using this methodology, offspring of predetermined sex have been produced in pigs, rabbits, sheep, and cattle. This will have particular impact on the cattle industry, in that dairy producers can shift the offspring ratio toward heifer calves and other producers can, as needed, shift toward bull calves.

Enhancing reproductive potential of valuable female animals

In contrast to sperm production in the male, which begins at puberty, egg production in the female begins at the foetal stage and ends shortly before or after birth. Thus the full reproductive potential of the female is established early in life. In cattle there are approximately 150,000 eggs present in the ovaries of a young calf. Under normal circumstances less than one per cent of these eggs will proceed to develop to be viable eggs - all others will degenerate throughout the reproductive life of the animal. If the immature eggs can be recovered from the ovaries, they may be caused to mature, fertilised under laboratory conditions, and become viable embryos. One of the projects being studied by Jerry Yang (University of Connecticut) is how oocytes gradually acquire their embryogenic competence during puberty development. Dozens of offspring have been produced in Yang's programme using eggs from prepubertal calves. However, the efficiency of embryo development of calf oocytes is still low and further investigation is needed to improve the efficiency.

Upon a heifer reaching puberty at 11-12 months of age, her oocytes may be retrieved weekly or even twice weekly for embryo production and embryo transfer via ultrasound-guided transvaginal oocyte pickup (OPU) and *in vitro* fertilisation followed by embryo transfer. One of the recent breakthroughs in the practical world of animal reproduction is the combined application of the existing IVF technology and the state-of-the-art OPU technique in cattle. Although, a cow may ovulate only about 200 oocytes in her lifetime, there are tens of thousands of oocytes in her ovaries as indicated earlier. Yang's long-range goal is, through the application of various assisted reproductive technologies, to improve the reproductive efficiency of the genetically elite females, particularly cattle.

Cloning and transgenics in medicine

The creation of Dolly, the sheep, the first cloned animal from an adult animal was something of a scientific revolution. While Dolly was cloned from the mammary cell of a pregnant sheep, Japanese and New Zealand Scientists subsequently cloned cows using cow ovary (cumulus) and oviduct cells. All these clones, however, were created using female reproductive system cells, raising the question whether non-reproductive cells are competent for cloning. Recent success in cloning several calves using ear skin cells from an aged cow provided direct evidence that cloning may not be limited to the female reproductive system cells and that animal age may not compromise its cloning competence.

This recent discovery confirms that cloning may have numerous applications. High-merit farm animals may be cloned to increase agricultural production at low cost. The effort in preserving endangered species may be accelerated as skin tissue can easily be sampled and banked. Valuable genetically engineered animals may be created and duplicated by cloning. In future, cloning may become a valuable means to create homogeneous populations of cells, tissues and even organs for therapeutic transfer to cure terminal organ failure patients. Finally, cloning offers a unique tool to study gene function, genome activation, cancer, aging and many unsolved mysteries in life sciences.

There is no question that the use of transgenic animals in medical research has already made contributions in undertanding physiological processes. It shows much promise for the future in providing tools to elucidate the mechanisms of development, disease and aging, to develop effective therapeutics including gene therapy and effective approaches to disease prevention and health maintenance, to generating animals for the production of valuable proteins and modified organs for xenotransplantation. The recent acquisition of Roslin Bio-Med by Geron juxtaposes three of the major advances in this field in the last two years namely, nuclear transfer technology, pluripotent stem cells and telomerase which allows cells to remain viable. The combined technologies are expected to enhance and accelerate the development of new transplantation therapies for numerous degenerative diseases such as diabetes, Parkinson's disease, cancer and heart disease.

Issues and concerns

The potential application of cloning and genetic engineering technology to livestock improvement raises a number of issues and concerns. While transgenic animal technology continues to open new and unexplored frontiers, a number of major regulatory and public perception hurdles exist that may affect the commercialisation of transgenic animals. These include safety issues related to food produced from genetically engineered animals, consumer perception, and ethical considerations such as animal welfare.

Livestock transgenics: Implications of large offspring syndrome

Pronuclear injection, somatic cell nuclear transfer and gene targeting in livestock have provided many new opportunities for transgenic applications in livestock species. However, a wide range of congenital abnormalities has been associated with many of these embryo technologies, currently termed "Large Offspring Syndrome" (LOS). These abnormalities include extreme foetal overgrowth, organ overgrowth and placental defects.

Development of a diagnostic marker or series of markers indicative of LOS induction in the pre-transfer embryo would be beneficial in avoiding the syndrome and may provide the basis for improving embryonic and foetal survival. Imprinted genes, expressed from only one parental allele, provide the most likely candidates to date. These genes, particularly those related to insulin-like growth factor II (Igf2) induce similar overgrowth phenotypes in mice and humans when their expression is disrupted. Furthermore, imprinted genes undergo significant changes in their DNA methylation status during early embryogenisis, when LOS is known to be induced. Since most of the genome is demethylated and thus less vulnerable to epigenetic alteration during this period, imprinted genes may provide the basis for a reliable diagnostic system for Large Offspring Syndrome.

Dolly's real age

In the May 27, 1999 issue of Nature it was reported that Dolly and two other sheep cloned by nuclear transfer exhibit shorter telomeres than age-matched control sheep. These findings, while based on a small sample, may have important implications for the use of nuclear transfer and telomerase in transplantation medicine.

Telomere shortening occurs as organisms age and cells divide. Telomere shortening eventually results in cellular senescence. One characteristic of senescent cells is that they no longer divide. In cloning, especially in genetic engineering of cloned cells or animals, cellular senescence limits the efficiency and potential of the technology. In addition to the fact that senescent cells stop dividing, they also become destructive to surrounding tissue *in vivo* and contribute to various age-related conditions. Preventing or reversing telomere shortening and cellular senescence *in vivo* could extend the healthspan of cells, tissues and organisms and thereby postpone or treat these age-related conditions.

Ethical concerns

Considering the long and winding path that genetically modified crops are taking on the road to acceptance, it is expected that for animals the path will be even more convoluted and fraught with obstacles. Animal welfare groups feel that transgenic technology could lead to increased animal suffering. Are we devaluing animal life by reducing it to a commercial commodity? However, we already eat animals, wear them and put leashes on them. Historically, genetic material has been exchanged by classical hybridisation. The new technologies take less time, and allow for specific genes to be transmitted. Farm groups are afraid that the family farm could be hurt. This will surely boost the cost of production as a result of payment of royalties, and a concentration in production of animals.

Environmental activists are concerned that the laws of nature might be upset. Are we violating species integrity? However, there already exists much fluidity and variability within a species naturally. At presently, relatively small numbers of genes are being manipulated (fewer than 20, in an animal that may contain from 50,000-100,000 genes). Identity as a species is unlikely to be disrupted by this amount of change. Most of the domestic animals that are now the subjects of transgenic research are themselves the products of generations of human manipulation.

Religious leaders feel that Divine Law is being violated. But who interprets "Divine" Law? Many ethicists are concerned about how this issue affects our view of humanity. With genes and even blood and organs from other mammals, will our human spirit ("karma") be impaired? However, there are great potential benefits for humanity in this technology. Clearly, we need to consider the risks and benefits. Also, it is unlikely that any genes originating in animals will ever be inserted into humans, as the ability to synthesise genes becomes available. In the final analysis our DNA sequences have been shown to differ little from those of our close mammalian relatives. Diabetics have been treated for decades with insulin from pigs and cows. Religions which prohibit pig meat in their diets are concerned about the use of porcine produced pharmaceuticals. But in Judaism, at least, pig may be used for purposes other than eating; in life and death situations, Kosher rules are set aside.

Xenotransplantation

This topic raises a number of scientific and ethical considerations. Should transgenic animals be created as a source of organs? Proponents claim that harvesting an animal for its organs is not any different than the current practice of harvesting animal tissues for food. Because a pig's lifespan is shorter than a human's, would a pig organ be genetically programmed to senesce sooner than the human body in which it was transplanted?

Technically, the procedure has many advantages over established methods. For example, animal organs are resistant to some human infections which might, as in the case of liver transplants following destructive hepatitis B infections, destroy the transplanted organ as well. But xenotransplantation also carries certain risks. Organ transfer from nonhuman primates into humans requires a high degree of vigilance to prevent the transfer of viruses such as endogenous retroviruses and herpesviruses. While acknowledging the existence of risks, many people suggest that the potential for infections should not halt progress. Clinical experience with xenografts, although limited, has not yet revealed an actual problem with introduction of infections, either to transplant patients or to family or health-care providers. Sensitive, biotechnology-based screening procedures such as DNA amplification by polymerase chain reaction, which allow detection of exceedingly small numbers of microbial pathogens, may help to eliminate potential transplant organs carrying human pathogens.

Xenotransplant organs from pigs may be more suitable than those from nonhuman primates. Large differences between the hosts might be expected to lower the chance of pathogen transfer from pigs to humans. Other potential advantages of pigs over baboons as a source of transplant organs include comparable size and physiology of pig organs with human organs, as well as ease in growing pigs. Some clinicians feel that the use of pigs would address many important ethical issues. The use of organs from nonhuman primates has been protested due to the intelligence and socialisation of these animals, and the strong right-to-life feeling of many animal rights activists towards them. Pigs, on the other hand, are commonly raised for food, minimising issues of supply and ethics.

Finally, would the public accept animal organs for transplantation? In a survey of attitudes of Australian nurses towards organ donation, two thirds were opposed to the use of animal organs for transplant. Although successful xenotransplantation may represent a breakthrough for medical science, the procedure will be of limited value if people are unwilling to accept animal organs.

Integration of a transgene into a breeding population

The production of a useful transgenic animal is only the first step towards introducing the transgene into a production population. Prior to becoming available for commercial production herds, the transgene must first be transferred to nucleus breeding herds and undergo selection to optimise the performance for the production traits of interest. This will be particularly important for transgenes affecting quantitative traits such as growth, body composition, or reproduction and for transgenes that modify intermediary metabolism. The introgression of a transgene into a nucleus herd has a number of associated costs. Gama et al. (1992) suggested that the best strategy for introgressing a transgene into a nucleus swine herd would involve three generations of backcrossing prior to initiating selection of a herd and characterisation of the phenotype. Thus, the net economic merit of the transgene affecting a production trait or production efficiencies would need to be sufficiently high to compensate for these costs. Also, it should not be assumed that the transgene will necessarily yield the same phenotype when placed in different genetic backgrounds.

Genetic diversity and inbreeding

Another potential concern is whether or not the use of cloning or genetically engineered animals will lead to a reduction in genetic diversity or increased rates of inbreeding. If cloned animals, which by definition exhibit virtually no genetic variation, are properly used within the context of a selective breeding programme, then inbreeding should be minimised. The same is true for transgenic animals, which also are more inbred than the population at large whether produced by microinjection or cloning. In either case, the reliance on a limited number of founder animals could lead to increased inbreeding, while the selection by industry of a limited number of production genotypes, like breeds today, could lead to reduced genetic diversity in the gene pool over a prolonged period.

Industry acceptance

The acceptance of genetically engineered animals by industry, as with the use of cloning to enhance the genetic contribution of exceptional females, will depend on economic incentives. If the cost of stock or the loss in selection progress is greater than the return to the producer through increased efficiencies or income over a reasonable period, then these technologies will not be used. In the case where the transgene results in a new product, such as antimicrobial milk or moth-resistant wool, the producer will probably require a premium to convert the production flock or herd to the new genotype. In the end, if scientists have done a good job in the selection of traits to be manipulated, the acceptance of genetically modified animals by industry will come down to whether or not consumers are prepared to buy the resulting products.

Consumer acceptance

There is every reason to assume that the introduction of genetically modified livestock will engender vigorous public debate. Concerns range from decreasing genetic diversity and the safety of genetically modified foods to animal welfare issues, although the latter case is not specific to genetically engineered or cloned animals.

Animal biotechnology has contributed to genetic improvement in the past through artificial insemination and embryo transfer. Transgenic technology and cloning can, and indeed should, be successfully used in the future as tools to increase the genetic merit of agriculturally-important animals. However, as we move into the 21st Century, we need to engage in two debates: one with the industry to determine the most important areas to be targeted for manipulation, and the other with the public so that consumers fully understand the nature of the genetic changes that have been introduced.

Priorities for Ireland

The following are some of the applications of transgenic animals that merit attention in the Irish context:

▶ Agriculture spplications:

- disease resistance

- improved productivity, milk and meat quality
- reduced fat
- nutrition (e.g. phytase gene to eliminate phosphate supplements)

❱ Medical applications

- production of valuable proteins, recombinant vaccines and therapeutics in milk, blood or urine

❱ Industrial applications

- production of industrial products such as spider silk in milk

❱ Marker assisted selection

Other important research areas of Animal Biotechnology should be in the production of valuable pharmaceutical products (molecular pharming), marker assisted selection, and technologies associated with influencing livestock fertility, offspring gender ratios etc.

Further Reading

Cibelli, J.B., *et al.* (1998). Cloned transgenic calves produced from nonquiescent fetal fibroblasts. Science 280: 1256-1258.

Schnieke, A.E., *et al* (1997). Human factor IX transgenic sheep produced by transfer of nuclei from transfected fetal fibroblasts. Science 278:2130-2133.

Brinster, R.L. (1993) Stem cells and transgenic mice in the study of development. *Int. J. Dev. Biol.* 37:89-99.

Cappechi, M.R. (1989) Altering the genome by homologous recombination. *Science 244*:1288-1292.

Castilla, J. *et al.* (1998). Engineering passive immunity in transgenic mice secreting virus-neutralising antibodies in milk. Nature Biotech. 16:349-354.

Chan A.W.S. *et al.* (1998). Transgenic cattle produced by reverse-transcribed gene transfer in oocytes. Proc. Natl. Acad. Sci. USA 95:14028-14033.

Dunham , R A. and Devlin, RH, Comparison of traditional breeding and transgenesis in farmed fish with implications for growth enhancement and fitness (1999). *Transgenic animals in agriculture*. JD Murray, GB Anderson, AM Oberbauer and MM McGloughlin (Eds.) CABI, London. pp. 209-230.

Gordon, J.W., and Ruddle, F.H. (1981). Integration and stable germline transmission of genes injected into mouse pronuclei. Science 214:1244-1246.

Gurdon, J.B. (1977). Nuclear transplantation and gene injection in amphibia. Brookhaven Symposia in Biology 29:106-115.

Hammer, R.E. *et al.* (1985). Production of transgenic rabbits, sheep and pigs by microinjection. Nature 315:680-683.

Kato Y. *et al.* (1998). Eight calves cloned from somatic cells of a single adult. *Science* 282:2095-2098.

Maga, E.A. and Murray, J.D. (1995). Mammary gland expression of transgenes and the potential for altering the properties of milk. Bio/Technology 13:1452-1457.

Palmiter, R.D. *et al.* (1982). Dramatic growth of mice that develop from eggs microinjected with metallothionein-growth hormone fusion genes. Nature 300:611-615.

Perry, M.M. and Sang, H.M. (1993). Transgenesis in chickens. Transgenic Res. 2:125-133.

Pinkert, CA and Murray, JD (1999). Transgenic farm animals. *Transgenic animals in agriculture*. JD Murray, GB Anderson, AM Oberbauer and MM McGloughlin (Eds.) CABI, London. pp. 1-18.

Pinkert, C.A. (1994). Transgenic pig models for xenotransplantation. Xeno 2:10-15.

Pinkert, C.A. (1997). The history and theory of transgenic animals. *Lab Anim.* 26:29-34.

Pinkert, C.A., Irwin, M.H., and Moffatt, R.J. (1997). Transgenic animal modelling. In: *Encyclopedia of Molecular Biology and Molecular Medicine* (R.A. Meyers, Ed.), 6:63-74. VCH Publishers, NY.

Pursel, V.G. (1989). Genetic engineering of livestock. *Science* 244:1281-1288.

Rogers, G.E. (1990). Improvement of wool production through genetic engineering. Trends in Biotechnology 8:6-11.

Schnieke, A.E. *et al.* (1998). Human factor IX transgenic sheep produced by transfer of nuclei from transfected fetal fibroblasts. Science 278:2130-2133.

Shuman, R.M. (1991). Production of transgenic birds. Experientia 47:897-905.

Thomson, J. A. *et al.* (1998). Embryonic Stem Cell Lines Derived from Human Blastocysts. Science: 282: 1145-1147.

Wall, R.J., Hawk, H.W. and Nel, N. (1992). Making transgenic livestock: Genetic engineering on a large scale. J. Cellular Biochem. 49:113-120.

Wilmut, I. *et al.* (1997). Viable offspring derived from fetal and adult mammalian cells. Nature 385:810-813.

Chapter 4

BIOTECHNOLOGY & THE ENVIRONMENT

Biotechnology & The Environment

The quality of life on Earth is linked inextricably to the overall quality of the environment. In response to growing pressures on air, water, and land resources, global attention has focused in recent years on finding new ways to sustain and manage the environment. Biotechnology is an essential tool in this endeavour because it can provide new approaches for understanding, managing, preserving, and restoring the environment.

Biotechnology can be used to assess the well-being of ecosystems, transform pollutants into benign substances, generate biodegradable materials from renewable sources, and develop environmentally safe manufacturing and disposal processes. Researchers are just beginning to explore biotechnological approaches to problem solving in many areas of environmental management and quality assurance, such as:

▶ Restoration ecology (which involves reestablishing the nutrient balance and the structure and function of ecosystems)

▶ Diagnostics, epidemiology, and dispersal monitoring related to human disease agents

▶ Disease, pest, and weed control in agriculture

▶ Contaminant detection, monitoring, and remediation

▶ Toxicity screening

▶ Conversion of waste to energy.

Developments in molecular biology, ecology, and environmental engineering now offer opportunities to modify organisms so that their basic biological processes are more efficient and can degrade more complex chemicals and higher volumes of waste materials. While some success has been achieved in this area, the potential benefits of the new environmental biotechnology are far from fully realised. Only knowledge acquired through basic research can provide the foundation for new environmental applications of biotechnology, facilitate the development of these technologies by the commercial sector, and ensure adequate evaluation and safe application of products without blocking innovation with regulatory requirements.

Bioremediation

Bioremediation involves the use of living organisms to degrade organic pollutants contaminating soils, groundwater, and sludges. Oil and oil products, gasoline and its constituents, polycyclic aromatic hydrocarbons, and solvents such as trichloroethylene and perchloroethylene are hazardous chemicals commonly attempted in bioremediation efforts. The bioremediation may be performed *in situ*, or the contaminated material may be removed from the site for treatment. Different types of organisms can be bioremediation agents. However, microorganisms (primarily bacteria and fungi) are nature's original recyclers. Their capability to transform natural and synthetic chemicals into sources of energy and raw materials for their own growth suggests that expensive chemical or physical remediation processes might be replaced or supplemented with biological processes that are lower in cost and more environmentally benign.

Research continues to verify the bioremediation potential of microorganisms. For example, a recent addition to the growing list of bacteria that can sequester or reduce metals is *Geobacter metallireducens*, which removes uranium, a radioactive waste, from drainage waters in mining operations and from contaminated groundwaters. Some of the current systems promote the growth of indigenous degrading microorganisms by incorporating fertiliser (nitrogen and phosphorus) into the contaminated medium. Other technologies may add naturally occurring microorganisms or, in the future, genetically modified microorganisms that have been selected for their degrading efficiency.

The bioremediation of oil spills involves the application of nitrogen and phosphorus to stimulate the indigenous microorganisms after removal of the excess oil from beaches. In the future, microorganisms might be applied to the site. This technology is, of course, totally "uncontained", and large populations of bacteria may be carried with water or in aerosols to distant aquatic sites, and to terrestrial ecosystems inland.

Bioremediation of various hazardous chemicals, or of industrial waste streams may also be accomplished in "contained" bioreactors. Although the containment of bioreactors varies with the design and the inactivation system used, releases of microorganisms to the environment would probably be small and/or unintentional.

Heavy metals

One of the principle areas of concerns with respect to environmental pollutants is heavy metal contamination. The use of poplar trees to remove mercury contamination has already been addressed on page 67. There are a number of other approaches to amelioration of heavy metal contamination under consideration. Heavy metals in aquatic systems are of particular concern because of the potential for broad-based exposure. Accumulation of heavy metals may result in concentrations which are toxic to living organisms or which may cause commercial species to become unsuitable as food. In an effort to develop a model system for the bioremediation of heavy metals, Erbe *et al*, at the University of Alabama have expressed a strong metal binding protein, mouse metallothionein, in the freshwater cyanobacterium, *Anacystis nidulans*. *A. nidulans* expressing recombinant mouse metallothionein was found to be resistant to cadmium concentrations exceeding the maximum permissive concentration of the wild type organisms and to sequester more cadmium from the growth media than wild type organisms. A research group at Oxford University is working on microbial bioremediation of metal ion contamination of the environment. A strain of *Citrobacter* sp. (a bacterium), isolated from metal-contaminated soil, has been particularly promising in the removal of low concentrations of ions which may escape chemical treatment. Removal of metal ions is achieved by two general methods, including adsorption of ions, a passive process in which ions attach to substances on the microbial surface, and accumulation, an active process.

Hydrocarbons

TCE (trichloroethylene), a widely used degreaser and a highly toxic carcinogen, is a particularly commonly encountered pollutant. Unfortunately, there are no known bacteria that will use TCE as their food source. One solution is to take a structural gene for a TCE-degrading enzyme from *Pseudomonas mendicina* and put it into a host vector system, allowing it to turn the gene on or off.

Scientists working at Oak Ridge National Laboratory (ORNL) recently started an ambitious project aimed at the degradation of polyaromatic hydrocarbons (PAHs) in soil using a genetically modified bacterium. The study facility at ORNL provides a high level of containment since it was originally designed to study uranium leaching. The PAHs naphthalene, phenanthrene, and anthracene are considered priority pollutants; their occurrence in soils typically is due to spills or leaks of fossil fuels. Strains of *Pseudomonas fluorescens* possessing a metabolic pathway for degradation of naphthalene were isolated from PAH- contaminated soil and genetically engineered with the lux genes from *Vibrio fischeri*, a bacterium that lives in specialised light-generating organs of certain deep sea fish. The lux gene was fused with a promoter normally associated with the naphthalene degradation pathway. The modified strain responds to naphthalene (or salicylate, a degradation product) by luminescing.

The current phase of the research project simulates bioremediation of landfill disposal and leaching scenarios. The project is the first to entail release of a GMO into the environment for the purpose of enhancing biodegradation and bioremediation. It examines *in situ* GMO activity, movement, and process optimisation, using bioluminescent sensing technology. Initial results from the Oak Ridge study show that the bacteria have a low level of fluorescent activity even though the population remains fairly steady at about 1 million per gram of soil, probably because little naphthalene remains. The investigators have found that the modified strain is useful for detecting naphthalene in the simulated spill site. The next step is to add a new mixture of PAHs to the soil along with some nutrients (nitrogen and phosphorous) which should result in a pronounced increase in degradative activity and light production. In the long run, the investigators hope the work will be a positive stimulus for further development of safe and effective utilisation of GMOs in the environment.

Rhizobia for bioremediation?

The broad-host-range plasmid RP4::TOL has been transferred from *Escherichia coli* to a *Rhizobium meliloti* strain by researchers at Howard University. RP4::TOL carries the benzene, toluene, and xylene degradative gene cluster. These toluene-based compounds include fuels, solvents and similar hydrocarbons which become contaminants when in the soil. The project was funded primarily by the U.S. Army and involved cooperation with researchers at the USDA/ARS lab in Beltsville, Maryland. The advantages of using a legume symbiont as a bioaugmentation agent is twofold. First, the legume host will feed and provide a home for the bacteria in the soil; second, the alfalfa legume is deeply rooted which hopefully will carry the rhizobia deep into the contaminated soil. Bioremediation experiments still need to be done under field conditions, not just in the greenhouse as has been the case to date, and the EPA must approve the safety of the organism before commercial release.

Alternatives to Chemical Application in Agriculture

The environmental value of the biotechnological approach to pest and disease control has been covered in detail in Chapter 2. However, microbial inoculants can also contribute to a reduction in agrochemical application. For example, they can be used as "natural" fertilisers. The Office of Pollution Prevention and Toxics (OPPT) of the U.S. Environmental Protection Agency approved an intergeneric *Sinorhizobium meliloti* strain for use as an alfalfa seed inoculant in September 1997. *S. meliloti* is an indigenous soil bacterium that forms a symbiosis with alfalfa in nodules that develop on the alfalfa roots. The beneficial results of this symbiosis are that the bacteria receive nutrition from the plant and in turn contribute or "fix" nitrogen for the host plant.

The genus *Sinorhizobia* is one of a number of genera referred to as "rhizobia". Commercial production of rhizobia inoculants began in Germany in 1895. In 1985, the BioTechnica Company of Cambridge, Massachusetts decided to develop better rhizobia by genetic manipulation. The strategy for improvement was to modify the regulatory components of the genome that produce the nitrogenase enzyme, and increase the amount of energy substrate supplied to the rhizobia by the host plant.

In addition to nitrogen, phosphorous is another important plant nutrient, and is the most limiting compared to nitrogen and potassium. Many soils are low in phosphorous and even when it is abundant, uptake of this nutrient by plants can be tricky. Countries such as India spend an enormous amount of their precious foreign exchange in importing phosphate fertiliser which is derived from rock phosphate found in a few areas such as the U.S., Russia, Morocco and Tunisia. Global reserves of high quality rock phosphate are limited and may run out in about 100 years according to one estimate.

A logical way to address this problem is by developing plants which can efficiently draw phosphate (a common form of phosphorous) from soil. A research group led by K. G. Raghothama at Purdue University were the first to clone phosphate transporter genes in plants from *Arabidopsis* in 1996. More recently such genes have also been found in tomato, potato, *Medicago* and *Catharanthus* identified by other researchers, appear to be similar in structure and function to the *Arabidopsis* genes. Predictably, expression of these genes appears to be localised in the root epidermis, the site of phosphate uptake. Changes in the cellular concentration of phosphorous apparently induce their expression. Raghothama's team is now developing transgenic plants to overexpress transporter genes to test whether this would result in a higher efficiency uptake of phosphorous.

Identification of genes involved in phosphate uptake is a major first step towards the eventual development of plants which can absorb phosphorous from soil in an efficient manner. Strategies like this may play an increasingly important role in the future to deal with the problems of poor soil fertility and to reduce the dependency on fertiliser application. This would be particularly welcome by resource-poor farmers in developing countries.

No-till agriculture

Thanks to biotechnology an older, more environmentally friendly, technology is enjoying a major resurrgance. This cultivation technique termed no-till agriculture is a system in which the soil is disturbed only along the slit or in the hole into which the seeds are planted which reserves detritus from previous crops covers and protects the seedbed. The practice is one of several primitive farming methods that have been revived as conservation measures in the 20th century.

Unlike conventional tillage, which controls weed growth by ploughing and cultivating, till-less agriculture uses quantities of selective herbicides to kill weeds and the remains of the previous crop. The vegetation detritus protects seedlings when they are most vulnerable to the ravages of nature. This makes the use of herbicide tolerant crops most attractive.

A primary benefit of the protection and minimal disturbance of topsoil is a decreased rate of soil erosion. In addition thanks to the use of insect-resistant crops it allows the growth and protection of beneficial insects in the debris. The no-till technique reduces equipment, fuel, and fertiliser needs and, significantly, the time required for tending crops. The method improves soil-aggregate formation, microbial activity in the soil, and water infiltration and storage, while enabling cultivation on slopes of up to 15 per cent. Crops suited to the technique include maize, pigeon pea, cowpea, and soybean.

Farmers have adopted this reduction of soil tillage - thereby using less tractor fuel while increasing earthworm numbers and building soil organic matter levels from photosynthesised carbon dioxide. This is in contrast to the traditional organic practice of using tillage in place of herbicides for weed control. But in order to go further in reducing both pesticide usage and soil tillage, farmers need better technology. One of the best new approaches is biotechnology which dramatically reduces pest damage and pesticide needs.

Biomass Conversion

Plant biomass, which represents the cellulosic materials that compose the cell walls of all higher plants, is the most abundant source of fermentable carbohydrates in the world. When biologically converted to fuels, such as ethanol and various other low-value high-volume commodity products, this vast resource can provide environmental, economic, and strategic benefits on a large scale, with some, such as reduced release of greenhouse gases, unparalleled by any other sustainable resource. Cellulase enzymes provide a key opportunity for achieving the tremendous benefits of biomass utilisation in the long term because of the high glucose yields possible and the opportunity to apply the modern tools of biotechnology to reduce costs. Production of diesel fuel from oil seeds is probably the best known industrial application of a "renewable" oil; the hydroxy fatty acids from oil seeds can be used in a wide range of products, including cosmetics, waxes, nylons, plastics, and coatings.

Fuels and chemicals can be produced not only from oil seed crops (e.g., soybeans, canola, and crambe), but also from unicellular algae and waste fats from animals. The substantial fractions of oils in these resources can be transformed through a chemical process that changes the large molecules in fats and oils into smaller molecules.

Presently, the use of microorganisms for biomass conversion has dealt with the conversion of plant biomass into many commercially valuable products. In particular, there is considerable interest in genetically modified microorganisms that can degrade cellulose, lignin, and hemicelluloses which account for much of the carbon in plant biomass. Organisms featuring the necessary genes for cellulose, hemicellulose or lignin-degrading enzymes include species of Cellulomonas, Bacillus, *Clostridium, Aeromonas, Streptomyces*, or *Phanerochaete*. Often, *Escherichia coli* is the organism in which the genes are cloned and expressed. The biomass conversion process first involves using the organism, a crude enzyme preparation derived from it, or sometimes mineral acids, to hydrolyze the raw materials to yield sugars. Yeasts or bacteria are then added to convert the sugars or other simple molecules to fuels, or other commercially valuable products. The process may be carried out under "semi-contained" conditions since commercially feasible volumes may be too large for bioreactors. Under these conditions, release of large numbers of microorganisms would be expected with aeration and agitation. Biomass conversion may also be "contained" in bioreactors or in fermentation plants for other uses such as fuel production.

Microorganisms can be used to produce fuel products such as ethanol, hydrogen, methane and other hydrocarbons. The raw material may be plant biomass, human wastes, or animal wastes or, when photosynthetic microorganisms are used, sunlight. In particular, ethanol production using maize starch, crop plants, trees, agricultural wastes, or urban wastes as carbon sources has generated commercial interest. Large scale production would probably be commercially viable only without stringent containment. The ecosystems affected and the exposure scenarios for ethanol production are similar to those for biomass conversion. Methane production is essentially a two step process whereby anaerobic microorganisms are used to convert cellulose and other polysaccharides to simple organic acids, carbon dioxide and hydrogen gas, and then these substances are converted to methane. The raw materials are animal feedlot wastes, sewage or sludge, or food crop biomass. This technology is most likely semi-contained and releases would be small and continuous.

Mining and Metals Recovery Industry

Biotechnology for mining and metals recovery can be divided into two major technologies: bioleaching (biorefining)/minerals biooxidation and metals bioremediation and recovery. Biorefining involves the use of microbes in mineral processing systems. Biorefining is environmentally friendly and in some cases enables the recovery of minerals and use of resources that otherwise would not be possible. For example, a significant amount of copper is biorefined from slag heaps. Research now underway addresses the use of microorganisms to bioleach oxide and sulphide ores, and to concentrate metals such as manganese, nickel, cobalt, and precious metals. Increased understanding of metabolic pathways will open the door to the manipulation of parameters such as kinetics and metal selectivity, with the aim of enhancing mineral recovery.

An intriguing potential use of biotechnology is *in situ* bioleaching of ore deposits or waste piles. Bacteria used are mainly *Thiobacillus ferrooxidans* and *Leptospirillum ferrooxidans* and certain high- temperature bacteria, to leach metals of value (e.g. copper, zinc and cobalt) from a sulphide mineral. The principal advantages of this process are shorter timescale, and absense of production of noxious gases or toxic. Research is needed to develop a mechanistic understanding of the bioleaching process and to identify environmental and process factors affecting biosystem performance. In addition, bioprocess monitoring schemes and cell-free leaching systems should be developed. Cell-free or cell component systems eliminate the need to provide an environment conducive to survival of a microorganism and enhance control over the reaction.

Biosorption and metal recovery from dilute aqueous solutions is an emerging field of interest, from both a resource conservation standpoint and an environmental remediation standpoint. Metals bioremediation and recovery replaces the traditional alkaline degreasing process that creates a large volume of wastewater containing heavy metals. The new method operates at a reduced temperature, reuses tensides, prolongs life of degreasing and pickling baths, reduces water and acid consumption, generates less waste and produces better process performances. Microbes, algae, cell wall material, proteins, and other types of biomass have been investigated for use in this application, but economical methods for selective metal recovery have yet to be developed. Use of microorganisms to remove fine particles from aqueous process streams is also of interest. Laboratory-scale studies have shown that certain microorganisms can cause flocculation of fine mineral suspensions, while others can function as flotation collectors or depressants. Extensive research will be needed before the use of extracellular colloidal molecules (such as polysaccharides and exopolymers released by live biomass) can become a viable alternative to current chemical-based systems.

Biosensors

Currently, *in situ* degradation processes cannot be measured or validated directly; researchers must rely on tracers and gas generation to assess bioremediation processes. Increased investment in biosensor research could lead, over the long term, to improved tools for efficacy assessment. The development of biosensors promises to revolutionise the way pollutants are detected and monitored in the environment.

Unlike standard methods, which rely on analytical chemistry in measuring the total concentration of a pollutant, biosensors can detect the fraction available to microorganisms. Biosensors also have the advantage of being nondestructive and located on-line, meaning that samples do not have to be removed and transported to a laboratory for analysis. Biosensors may utilise either whole bacterial cells or specific molecules (e.g., enzymes or biomimetics) as a detection system. Combinations of biosensors in arrays can be exploited to deal with a diversity of toxicants and pollutants.

One type of biosensor involves linking a gene such as the mercury resistance gene (mer) or the toluene degradation (tol) gene to genes that code for bioluminescence within living bacterial cells. The biosensor cells can signal that extremely low levels of inorganic mercury or toluene are present in contaminated waters and soils by emitting visible light, which can be measured with fibre-optic fluorometers.

A second type of biosensor employs molecular detectors, which consist of enzymes, nucleic acids, antibodies, or other "reporter" molecules attached to synthetic membranes. Antibodies specific for an environmental contaminant can be coupled to changes in fluorescence to increase sensitivity of detection. Fluorescent or enzyme-linked immunoassays have been derived for a variety of contaminants, including pesticides and PCBs. With sustained long-term research, molecular arrays could be constructed on synthetic membranes and other matrices that would allow the simultaneous detection of a range of contaminants in a variety of environmental substrates.

Safety Concerns

Concerns over the release into the environment of genetically modified microorganisms remain a major obstacle to the use of bioremediation and biopesticides.

One company, GX BioSystems Inc. is working on programmed killing systems that eliminate microorganisms once they have done their job. The modified microorganisms are killed using lethal genes that are controlled by specific factors either present or absent in the environment. The company, for example, has developed an organism that degrades toluene and dies after the toluene concentration falls below a certain level. Survival rates of only one organism out of 100 million have been documented, significantly reducing the risk of persistence in the environment of the engineered microbe.

Before the tremendous potential of bioremediation can be realised, gaps in scientific knowledge must be closed and more field experience and data acquired.

Priorities

A number or priority areas of research into the development of microorganisms for bioremediation can be identified:

▶ Develop an understanding of the structure of microbial communities and their dynamics in response to normal environmental variation and novel anthropogenic stresses.

▶ Determine the biochemical mechanisms, including enzymatic pathways, involved in aerobic and particularly anaerobic degradation of pollutants.

▶ Expand understanding of microbial genetics as a basis for enhancing the capabilities of microorganisms to degrade pollutants.

▶ As a standard practice, conduct microcosm/mesocosm studies of new bioremediation techniques to determine in a cost- effective manner whether they are likely to work in the field, and establish dedicated sites where long-term field research on bioremediation technologies can be conducted.

▶ Develop, test, and evaluate innovative biotechnologies, such as biosensors, for monitoring bioremediation in situ; models for the biological processes at work in bioremediation; and reliable, uniform methods for assessing the efficacy of bioremediation technologies.

Further Reading

King, J.M.H. et al. (1990). Rapid, sensitive bioluminescent reporter technology for naphthalene exposure and biodegradation. Science 249:778-781.

Heitzler, A. et al. (1994). Optical biosensor for environmental on-line monitoring of naphthalene and salicylate bioavailability with an immobilised bioluminescent catabolic reporter bacterium. Appl. & Environ. Microbiol. 60:1487-1494.

Heitzler, A. et al. (1992). Specific and quantitative assessment of naphthalene and salicylate bioavailabillity by using a bioluminescent catabolic reporter bacterium. Appl. & Environ. Microbiol. 58:1839-1846.

Chapter 5

Industrial Biotechnology

INDUSTRIAL BIOTECHNOLOGY

The Technology

Industrial biotechnology applies the techniques of modern molecular biology to improve the efficiency and reduce the environmental impacts of processes in industries like food production, textiles, paper and pulp and speciality chemicals. Today up to 90 per cent of the enzymes used in large scale for commercial applications result from the exploitation of rDNA methods in the manufacturing process or for the improvement of the catalysts themselves (see Appendix 4). Industrial biotechnology companies develop biocatalysts, such as enzymes, to be used in chemical synthesis, and manufacture them in fermenters.

In industrial processes, the specific action of enzymes allows high yields to be obtained with a minimum of unwanted by_products. Enzymes are very efficient catalysts, and being formed to function in living cells, they can work at atmospheric pressure and in mild conditions in terms of temperature and acidity. Most enzymes function optimally at a temperature of 30-70°C and at pH values which are near pH 7. Enzyme processes are therefore potentially energy saving and save investing in special equipment resistant to heat, pressure or corrosion.

Companies involved in industrial biotechnology are constantly striving to discover and develop high-value enzymes and bioactive compounds that will enhance current industrial processes. The opportunity to identify unique bioactive molecules is vast. Less than 1 per cent of the microorganisms in the world have been cultured and characterised.

Advantages of genetic engineering

Many enzymes are now produced by fermentation of genetically modified microrganisms They offer several advantages, including:

▶ Enzymes with a higher specificity and purity can be produced

▶ New and improved enzymes can be developed, which would otherwise not be available for economical, occupational health or environmental reasons

▶ Due to higher production efficiency there is an additional environmental benefit through reducing energy consumption and waste from the production plants

▶ For enzymes used in the food industry there are particular benefits, for example: better use of raw materials (juice industry), better keeping quality of a final food and thereby less wastage of food (baking industry), and a reduced use of chemicals in the production process (starch industry)

▶ For enzymes used in the feed industry a particular benefit is a significant reduction in the amount of phosphorus released to the environment from farming.

Due to an efficient separation process the final enzyme product does not contain any GMOs. The enzyme is produced by fermentation of the genetically modified microorganisms (the production strain) in closed fermentation tank installations, and is then separated from the production strain, purified and mixed with inert diluents for stabilisation.

Progress To Date

Food industry

Enzymes were important agents in food production long before modern biotechnology was developed. They were used, for instance, in the clotting of milk to prepare cheese, the production of bread and the production of alcoholic beverages. Nowadays, enzymes are indispensable to modern food processing technology and have a great variety of functions. They are used in almost all areas of food production including grain processing, milk products, beer, juices, wine, sugar and meat.

In almost all cases the enzymes are used as processing aids in food. This means that they only have a function during the food production process. In the final food they are either not present, or they have no function. Over the past ten to fifteen years an increasing variety of food enzymes have been produced using genetically modified microorganisms and this trend is set to continue until virtually all new food enzymes will be produced by using genetically modified microorganisms.

Starch and sugars

Biotechnology enzymes are used for the liquefication and saccharification of starch into glucose and isomerisation into fructose. Maize and other grains can be converted enzymatically to sweeteners, such as high-fructose maize syrup and maltose syrup. Other important applications are in the production of ethanol from grain.

The DE (dextrose equivalent) value is used as an indication of the degree of hydrolysis of a syrup. The DE value of starch is zero and that of dextrose is 100. Using traditional methods (acid hydrolysis) it is difficult to produce low-and high-DE syrups of a high quality. In the last 30 years, as new enzymes have become available, starch hydrolysis technology has been transformed and today virtually all starch hydrolysis is performed using enzymes. Furthermore, in the 1970s an enzyme technique made possible the production of a syrup as sweet as sucrose - high fructose syrup. The production of this syrup has significantly boosted the growth of the starch industry in many countries.

Depending on the enzymes used, syrups with different compositions and physical properties can be obtained from starch. The syrups are used in a wide variety of foodstuffs: soft drinks, confectionery, meats, baked products, ice cream, sauces, baby food, canned fruit, preserves, etc. There are three basic steps in enzymatic starch conversion. Firstly, there is a liquefaction process. By using bacterial-amylase on its own, a 'maltodextrin' is obtained which contains many different oligosaccharides and dextrins. Maltodextrins are only slightly sweet and they usually undergo further conversion. Most starch treated with bacterial-amylase is made sweeter in a second step called saccharification using amyloglucosidase. This can theoretically hydrolyse starch completely to glucose, but in practice a little maltose and isomaltose are produced too. Pullulanases are debranching enzymes that can also be used to aid saccharification. Fungal-amylases can also be added in order to produce syrups with a higher maltose content, which means high fermentability and a relatively high degree of sweetness. A high maltose content can also be obtained by using-amylase and Maltogenase® in combination with a pullulanase. The third step is isomerisation. A proportion of the glucose can be isomerised into fructose, which is about twice as sweet as glucose, using a glucose isomerase. In the 1970s, Novo Nordisk developed the glucose isomerase Sweetzyme® - the first immobilised enzyme to be produced on an industrial scale. Immobilising the isomerase makes it possible to use it continuously for several months.

Starch is a natural component of sugar cane. When the cane is crushed, some of the starch is transferred into the cane juice. Some of this starch is degraded by natural enzymes but, to speed up the degradation of the starch, it is now standard practice to add enzymes during the evaporation of the cane juice. An example is Novo Nordisk's Termamyl® which is extremely thermo-stable and therefore may be added at an earlier stage of the multi-step evaporation process than conventional enzymes. This enzyme is also used in the production of the biofuel ethanol.

Another polysaccharide, dextran, is not a natural component of sugar cane or sugar beet. However, it is sometimes formed in cane when it is stored under adverse conditions (high temperatures and high humidity) allowing bacterial growth, and in beet that has been damaged by frost. Dextrin has several detrimental effects on sugar processing but can be removed by adding a dextrin-splitting enzyme at a suitable stage of the process. Novo Nordisk supplies a fungal enzyme called Dextranase for this application

Alcohol

The choice of raw material for the production of spirits differs around the world, but in all cases, starch is the basic ingredient. Starch is composed of long chains of glucose molecules and these have to be broken down into smaller molecules that the yeast can transform into alcohol. This enzymic process involves the steps of liquefaction and saccharification discussed in the previous section.

Enzymes have traditionally been provided by adding malt. However, since the late 1960s there has been a dramatic change and in many countries malt has been totally displaced from distilling operations by the use of industrial enzymes. The advantages of using industrial enzymes instead of malt are many. A few litres of enzyme preparation can be used to replace 100 kg of malt. Enzymes are therefore much easier to handle and to store. In terms of raw material costs, savings of 20-30 per cent can be expected when switching to commercial enzymes. Furthermore, industrial enzymes are supplied with a uniform, standardised activity so distilling becomes more predictable and there is a better chance of obtaining good yields from every fermentation. Finally, industrial enzymes perform better than those found in malt. Microbial amylases are available with better activity at the low pH values found in the mash. Extremely thermo-stable amylases are available that go on liquefying starch at 100°C long after malt enzymes have been destroyed.

In countries with surplus agricultural capacity, ethanol produced from biomass may represent a sensible substitute, extender or octane booster for traditional motor fuel. While sugar-based raw materials such as cane juice or molasses can be fermented to produce fuel alcohol directly, this is not possible for starch-based raw materials. They have to be broken down into fermentable sugars first. Though the equipment is different, the principle of using enzymes from starch is exactly the same as when producing alcohol for drinking purposes.

Bread

For decades, enzymes such as malt and fungal-amylase have been used in bread making. Advances in biotechnology have made a number of new enzymes available to the baking industry. Wheat flour consists of gluten, starch, non-starch polysaccharides, lipids and trace amounts of minerals. As soon as the bread dough is made, the yeast starts to work on the fermentable sugars, transforming them into alcohol and carbon dioxide, which makes the dough rise. Starch is the largest component of wheat flour. Amylases can degrade starch and produce small dextrins for the yeast to act upon.

Bread staling is responsible for significant financial losses for both consumers and bread producers. Staling is associated with the loss of freshness in terms of increased crumb firmness and decreased crumb elasticity and is believed to be due to changes in starch structure during storage. A bacterial maltogenic-amylase has been found to have a substantial anti-staling effect. It modifies the starch during baking at the temperature when most of the starch starts to gelatinise. The resulting modified starch granules remain more flexible during storage.

Gluten is a combination of proteins which form a large network during dough formation. This network holds the gas in during dough proofing and baking and its strength is therefore very important for the quality of all bread raised using yeast. Normal wheat flour contains 1-1.5 per cent lipids, both polar and non-polar. Some of these lipids, especially the triglycerides, are bound with gluten, impeding its functionality. The addition of a functional lipase modifies the triglycerides and their interaction with gluten, yielding a gluten network with improved strength. Flour contains 2.5-3.5 per cent non-starch polysaccharides which are large polymers (mainly pentosans) that play an important role in bread quality due to their water absorption capability and interactions with gluten. Although the mechanism is unclear, it is well known that the addition of certain types of pentosanase or xylanase at the correct dosage can improve dough machinability, yielding a more stable dough that gives better ovenspring during baking, resulting in a larger volume and improved crumb texture. Chemical oxidants such as bromates, azodicarbonamide and ascorbic acid have been widely used to strengthen the gluten for bread making. Oxidative enzymes (e.g. glucose oxidase) can partially replace the use of these chemical oxidants and achieve better bread quality.

Each of the enzymes mentioned above has its own specific substrate in the wheat flour dough. Because the interaction of these substrates in dough and bread is rather complex, the use of enzyme combinations can have synergistic effects that are not seen if only one enzyme is used - not even at high dosages. Quite often an overdose of one enzyme will have a detrimental effect on either the dough or the bread, so a careful balance must be found to achieve optimum dough consistency, stability and bread quality.

Brewing

In the traditional brewing process, malt acts both as a raw material providing starch and protein and as a source of enzymes. However, malting is a relatively expensive way of producing enzymes. Considerable savings can be made by replacing at least part of the malt with industrial enzymes and unmalted cereals such as barley. Apart from the financial savings, the brewing process can be more precisely controlled because of the uniform quality and activity of industrial enzymes. Furthermore, the wide selection of industrial enzymes available makes it possible to meet specific needs in the brewing process.

Unmalted barley is a natural and inexpensive substitute for barley malt since it contains the same basic components. The main difference is that barley has a low enzyme content, with the exception of ß-amylase - the enzyme that forms maltose. A large amount of the malt can be replaced by unmalted barley. All it takes is the addition of extra satisfactory breakdown of polysaccharides and protein. Protein plays a vital role in fermentation by providing soluble nitrogen compounds that the yeast needs in order to thrive. By adding a protein-splitting enzyme, more protein can be solubilised from the malt and made available to the yeast.

Slow filtration is often a problem when the mash is run off in the lauter tun and when the final beer is filtered. This is due to the presence of certain polysaccharides, mainly ß-glucans and pentosans which form a layer of gel which blocks the tiny holes of the filters. Though normally soluble, ß-glucans become insoluble in certain concentrations of alcohol and form a precipitate. This can happen during fermentation and lagering of strong beers. A simple solution is to break down the ß-glucans using a ß-glucanase added during mashing or at the start of the fermentation process.

Under normal brewing conditions, malt's own enzymes cannot break down all the starch into fermentable sugars. About one third of the starch is converted into non-fermentable dextrins, which are carried over into the finished beer. Enzymes can be added during either mashing or fermentation in order to break down these dextrins into glucose. The glucose is almost completely transformed into alcohol and carbon dioxide by the yeast leading to a beer with normal alcohol strength but significantly fewer calories.

During the primary stage of fermentation, acetolactate is formed by the yeast. This substance is slowly converted into diacetyl - a chemical with a very unpleasant flavor. At the end of fermentation and during maturation, the yeast converts most of the diacetyl to acetoin, which has a much more neutral flavor. An enzyme called an acetolactate decarboxylase significantly reduces the production of diacetyl and thereby makes it possible to reduce the beer maturation time.

Wine and juice

All types of fruit and berry of nutritional and industrial significance contain varying amounts of a substance called pectin which acts as a kind of glue holding plant cell walls together. Some of the pectin passes into the juice during pressing, leading to an increase in viscosity and difficulties in obtaining optimal juice yields. The extracted juice is low in colour and flavour components. Furthermore, it is difficult to clarify and filter. These difficulties can be overcome by adding pectinases to the fruit pulp (or mash) prior to pressing. This enzymatic mash treatment facilitates the release of the juice and leads to considerably improved juice yields and press capacity.

Apple juice is one of the juices that can contain considerable amounts of starch, particularly at the beginning of the season. The starch must be degraded in the production of clear juices and/or concentrates. This is achieved by adding starch-splitting enzymes together with the pectinase during depectinisation of the juice. In some cases, the addition of other enzyme preparations such as cellulases may also lead to improved juice yields and better colour extraction. The polysaccharide araban (a polymer of the pentose arabinose) is an important part of fruit cell walls and may cause haze in fruit concentrates. With modern fruit juice technology pushing yields higher and higher, considerable amounts of araban are often extracted from the cell walls and the risk of araban haze has increased. To safeguard against the formation of haze in the concentrate pectinase preparations recommended for juice depectinisation contain sufficient arabanase activity.

Special pectolytic enzyme preparations are used in the citrus industry. Tailor-made pectolytic enzymes are used for the clarification of citrus juices (particularly lemon and lime juice), for the recovery of essential oils and the production of highly turbid extracts from the peels of citrus fruit. These cloudy concentrates are used in the manufacture of soft drinks. The enzymatic peeling of citrus fruit is a relatively new application for the production of fresh peeled fruit, fruit salads and segments. Enzymatic treatment with Peelzym™ results in citrus segments with improved freshness as well as texture and appearance compared with the traditional process using caustic soda.

The ideal enzyme preparations for winemaking are different to those for fruit juice processing. In fruit juice processing, the enzymes are inactivated very shortly after they have done their job, for example by pasteurisation. In winemaking, no such heat treatment takes place. The enzymes therefore maintain their activity over a longer period. Side activities that may be beneficial for fruit juice processing can be less desirable for winemaking as they may negatively influence wine quality during storage. Specific enzyme preparations for winemaking have been developed in order to improve wine quality while at the same time bringing about the desired technological advantages. In winemaking, one aim is to extract as many flavour compounds as possible. In the case of red wine, colour extraction is also very important.

Research into the chemical composition of grapes is opening up new enzyme applications. One example is an enzyme for aroma liberation a glycosidase which hydrolyses terpenyl glycosides (also known as bound terpenes). Terpenes are released and these are one of the important constituents of the bouquet. Winetasters can usually detect a noticeable improvement in the bouquet after treatment with this glycosidase.

Food functionality

Food functionality covers a very diverse group of applications, including Nutrition/Infant food, Protein hydrolysis, Extraction of GAGs (Glucose-Amino-Glucans), Dairy and Pet food. Common to most of these applications is that they are based on the application of proteases and other enzyme groups (e.g. lipases and carbohydrases).

The basic feature of a protease is the ability to convert proteins into peptides and free amino acids. There are two main groups of proteases: endoproteases, which cleave peptide bonds within the protein structure, yielding peptides, and exopeptidases, which work from the ends and tend to yield free amino acids. Proteases have been used for more than 50 years to produce infant milk formulae from cow's milk. Non-degraded cow's milk protein can induce sensitisation in infants when they are fed the but this risk is minimised when the milk is degraded. The nutritional value of the milk is also increased when the proteins are degraded into smaller peptides. When producing low-allergenic infant formulae, the type of enzymes used is very important. Endoproteases hydrolyse hydrophobic amino acids, and they can be used for this application provided the process is sufficiently controlled.

Protein hydrolysates cover a very broad range of applications from gelatin hydrolysis to functional meat extracts and soy sauce. The gelling ability of gelatin is quickly eliminated by partial hydrolysis and the protein becomes soluble, even at low temperatures. Hydrolysed gelatin is used as a nutritional protein supplement for people needing extra protein. Increased solubility is a general effect of hydrolysis and is often utilised for other protein products, such as supplements based on casein, whey protein, soya protein, meat protein, etc.

The main challenge in the production of these products is to achieve a sufficiently neutral taste. This requires an in-depth knowledge of the specificity of different enzymes and the nature of different raw material sources. Many protein raw materials have a tendency to develop a bitter taste, or other taste defects, after hydrolysis, whereas others are by nature bland-tasting, even after extensive hydrolysis. Gelatin seldom develops a bitter taste - in contrast to casein which yields a bitter taste even at a very low degree of hydrolysis. The bitter taste is related to the amino acid sequence and the structure of the peptides. It is known that hydrophobic amino acids in the end-position of a peptide yield a bitter taste. When the hydrophobic amino acid is cut off, the mixture achieves a non-bitter taste. Thus the careful selection of enzymes and optimal processing can prevent most of these problems.

A range of raw materials from the meat industry can be utilised and processed into valuable ingredients for the food industry. An example is the meat left on the bones after cutting off the lean meat parts. In order to utilise this the meat has to be made soluble, separated from the bone and fat material, and then dried to obtain the extracted protein. By using proteases for the process the protein can be made soluble by a gentle hydrolysis process, and products with different properties can be produced, mainly by varying the enzyme composition and dosage. Protein extracted with a relatively low degree of hydrolysis possesses some very good functional properties, making it ideal for use as a marinade for meat products like ham or bacon. These functional extracts can be used to improve the meat products with respect to flavor, cooking loss and sliceability. Other important applications for meat extracts are as flavour improvers in soups, sauces, snack food and pot-noodles. Depending on the choice of enzymes it is possible to control the flavour of the extract.

Another important application of proteases is to break down protein tissue in order to be able to extract a particular substance, such as heparin, from the lining of pig intestines. Heparin is a poly-carbohydrate that is widely used to prevent blood clotting during surgery. Heparin extraction is a good example of how a by-product from one production is used for the production process of another valuable product.

The most important application of enzymes in pet food production is in the production of digest, which is coated onto or mixed into dry pet food to improve its palatability. Digest is produced using proteases that hydrolyse meat or meat by-products, so liquefying the raw material and creating a good flavour.

Animal feed

Animal feed is predominantly composed of plant material, much of which cannot be fully digested and utilised, especially by monogastric animals (those with one stomach). It is however possible to break down plant cell wall materials, phytic acid and nutrients such as proteins and starch using a range of microbial enzymes. In this way, feed utilisation and digestibility are enhanced. As animals retain more of what they eat, less manure is produced, including substances such as nitrogen and phosphates that can harm the environment

The largest single cost in the raising of poultry is the feed, which is mainly cereal-based. Maize has a low content of soluble non-starch polysaccharides (NSPs), and is considered to be an ideal cereal. It is used widely where it is available and the cost can be justified. Other cereals, such as barley, contain higher amounts of NSPs that normally impair feed utilisation, and are therefore generally avoided in feed formulations. However, by adding microbial enzymes to barley-based feed, the NSPs can be degraded, resulting in improved litter appearance, better feed utilisation and faster growth rate.

Cleaning industry

To most people, the best known application of enzymes is in the manufacture of enzymatic washing agents ('biological' detergents). Proteases are the most widely used enzymes in the detergent industry. They remove protein stains such as grass, blood, egg and human sweat. These organic stains have a tendency to adhere strongly to textile fibres and can act as glues, preventing the water-borne detergent systems from removing some of the other components of the soiling, such as pigments and street dirt.

Although protein stains can easily be digested by enzymes, oily and fatty stains have always been troublesome to remove. The trend towards lower washing temperatures has made the removal of grease spots an even bigger problem but in 1988 Novo Nordisk launched Lipolase® for the detergent industry - the first industrial enzyme developed by the application of genetic engineering. Lipolase is capable of removing fatty stains such as lipstick, frying fats, butter, salad oil, sauces and the tough stains on collars and cuffs and has now been incorporated into a great number of major detergent brands around the world, and a second-generation Lipolase called Lipolase Ultra with enhanced wash performance was launched in 1994. In 1998 LipoPrime® was launched as a protein-engineered variant of Lipolase which shows superior fat-removing efficacy.

Amylases are used to remove residues of starchy foods such as mashed potatoes, spaghetti, oatmeal porridge, custards, gravies and chocolate. This type of enzyme can be used in laundry detergents as well as in chlorine-free automatic dishwashing detergents. The development of detergent enzymes has focused mainly on enzymes capable of removing stains. However, a cellulase complex from Novo Nordisk called Celluzyme® has properties enabling it to modify the structure of cellulose fibrils such as those found on cotton and cotton blends. When added to a detergent, it has three major effects: enhancing colours, softening the fabric, and removing soil particles. The effect of celluzyme on the fabric is cumulative. In other words, each time a garment is washed, the enzyme produces a further improvement in its appearance.

Traditionally, detergents used for washing dishes have not depended on the inclusion of enzymes, but this too is changing, as microbial enzymes are increasingly being incorporated into these products.

Textiles industry

Enzymes are being used increasingly in textile processing, mainly in the finishing of fabrics and garments. Desising is an enzyme application dating back to the beginning of the 20th century. In the case of fabrics made from cotton or blends of cotton and synthetic fibres, the warp (longitudinal) threads are coated with an adhesive substance known as a 'size'. This is to prevent the threads breaking during weaving. The most common sizes are starches and starch derivatives. After weaving, the size must be removed again in order to prepare the fabric for finishing (bleaching, dyeing, printing, water-or crease-proofing, etc.). This process (desising) may be carried out by treating the fabric with strong chemicals such as acids, bases or oxidising agents. However, starch-splitting enzymes (amylases) have been preferred for many years due to their high efficiency, specific action and harmlessness to the environment.

Cotton and other natural fibres based on cellulose can be improved by an enzymatic treatment known as Bio-polishing, which removes 'fuzz' and gives the fabric a smoother and glossier appearance. Many 'casual' garments are subjected to a wash treatment to give them a slightly worn look. A prime example is the stonewashing of denim jeans. In the traditional stonewashing process, the blue denim was faded by the abrasive action of pumice stones on the garment surface. Nowadays, denim finishers are using a special cellulase to accelerate the abrasion. The cellulase works by loosening the indigo dye on the denim in a process known as 'bio-stoning'. A small dose of enzyme can replace several kilograms of stones.

Natural fabrics such as cotton are normally bleached with hydrogen peroxide before dyeing. Bleaches are highly reactive chemicals and any peroxide left on the fabric can interfere with the dyeing process. That's why a thorough 'bleach cleanup' is necessary. The traditional method is to neutralise the bleach with a reducing agent, but the dose has to be controlled precisely. Enzymes present a more convenient alternative because they are easier and quicker to use. A small dose of catalase is capable of breaking down hydrogen peroxide into water and oxygen.

Biotechnology can also produce genetically engineered cotton that has the texture of cotton, but is warmer and has increased strength, improved dye uptake and retention, enhanced absorbency and wrinkle- and shrink-resistance.

Pulp and paper industry

Driven largely by market and environmental demands for less-chlorinated products and byproducts, the pulp and paper industry is cited as the fastest growing market for industrial enzymes. Existing pulping operations are polluting. Biopulping, which is a cleaner process, involves treating lignocellulosic materials with lignin-degrading fungi to manufacture the pulp. Enzymes also are used to improve physical properties of fibres, enhance pulp fibrillation and ultimately improve paper strength.

De-inking of waste paper is an area with large potential for enzymes. This technology appears to be well suited for mixed office waste. The current de-inking methods mostly use an alkaline environment. Moving to a neutral de-inking system which can employ neutral/alkaline enzyme classes requires some change in the chemistry of the system, but can result in improvements in both the process and the final product.

Chlorine and derivatives of chlorine have been the cheapest and most versatile bleaching agents available for the bleaching of chemical pulps. This class of compounds has the disadvantage of forming chlorinated organic substances (some of which are toxic) during bleaching. The pulp and paper industry is under growing pressure from authorities, consumers and environmental groups to reduce the use of chlorine-based bleaching chemicals and the discharge of chlorinated organic compounds. This can be achieved by the use of enzymes during pulping, in a technique is called 'bleach boosting', which gives a significant reduction in the need for chemicals in the subsequent bleaching stage.

Pitch and deposit problems are common in paper mills. Pitch agglomerates form on the processing equipment and can cause holes in the paper so it has to be recycled or downgraded in quality. A commercial lipase has been developed for use in mill operations. This enzyme has proved its ability to reduce pitch deposits significantly on rollers and other equipment.

In the manufacture of coated papers, a starch-based coating formulation is used to coat the surface of the paper. The coating provides improved gloss, smoothness and printing properties compared to the uncoated product. Raw starch is unsuitable for this application, since the flow properties would be unsuitable. In one case, chemically modified starch with a much lower solution viscosity is used. As an economical alternative to modifying the starch with aggressive oxidising agents, the starch can be treated with enzymes (-amylases) to obtain the same viscosity reduction. Modified starch is available from starch producers or can be produced on site at the paper mill using a batch or continuous process.

Leather tanning

One of the oldest applications of industrially produced enzymes is in the processing of hides and skins for leather. Hides and skins contain proteins and fat in between the collagen fibres. Before the hides and skins can be tanned, these substances must be partially or totally removed. The proteins can be removed by proteases and the fat can be removed by lipases, as well as by tensides and solvents.

When preparing hides and skins for liming and unhairing, proper soaking of the rawstock is essential for obtaining good quality leather. For some raw materials, notably dried stock, satisfactory rehydration may be a difficult and time-consuming process. By degrading interfibrillary protein using proteolytic enzymes, water absorption is significantly facilitated and the soaking operation can be shortened. The conventional way to remove hair from bovine hides is to use lime and sodium sulphide in a hair-burning process. They dissolve the hair and open up the fibre structure. Novo Nordisk markets a protease that assists in the removal of hair. It is a unique protease because it is active at the very high pH of 12-13 found in the liming process.

Oils and fat

The use of enzymes in the oils and fats industry is still in its infancy, but some commercial enzymes have already become well established.

Traditionally, oil and fat processors have changed the fatty acid structure of their materials by blending different triglyceride mixtures (combination of natural fats), by chemical modification of the fatty acids (such as by hydrogenation) or by re-arrangement of the fatty acids on the glyceride backbone of the fat (interesterification). Specific enzyme catalysts such as Lipozyme® IM may now be used for interesterification. Unlike other catalytic agents that cannot distinguish between the 1, 2 and 3 positions on the triglyceride, some enzymes can select some fatty acids and leave others alone. Using a 1,3-specific lipase, a particular fatty acid can be incorporated into the two outer positions of the triglyceride structure without changing the fatty acid residue in the middle position. Alternatively, the 1,3-specific lipase can randomly rearrange the fatty acid residues at the outer positions without touching the one in the middle - a process called transesterification.

This enzyme technology allows processors to produce 'tailor-made' fats. For example cocoa butter fats required for the production of chocolate are often in short supply and the price can fluctuate widely. Palm oil, however, can be upgraded in a reaction with stearic acid using enzymatic interesterification. The resulting fat has similar properties to cocoa butter. Low-value fats in overabundant supply, such as palm oil, can be upgraded by enzymatic modification and used in a wider variety of applications. In margarine production, the melting point, spreadability, shelf-life or nutritional properties of a natural fat or oil can be modified.

Traditionally, the production of fatty esters has been carried out by chemical catalysis. In certain cases, side-reactions occur which are considered undesirable, either because of poor product yield or due to the hazardous nature of the by-products. Enzymes offer the advantage of catalysis under mild reaction conditions. This is especially important because the mild conditions reduce the side reactions and the resulting formation of by-products to a minimum. As well as being used in the production of flavors and fragrances, esters are used as surfactants in cosmetic products such as moisturising creams and shampoos. For these end-uses, purity is vital. The specificity of the lipase enzyme reaction results in esters with virtually no unwanted by-products.

Food diagnostics

The growing concern over food safety is having a positive impact on biotechnology. Biotechnology-based diagnostic systems offer more rapid and lower cost alternatives to slower and more costly traditional methods. Rapid, accurate, non-invasive tools of biotechnology can help improve the detection and control of food-borne human pathogens as well as chemical contaminants.

DNA probe kits have been developed for *Salmonella*, *Listeria*, *E.coli* 0157:H7, and *Staphylococcus aureus*. Compared to traditional culture-plating methods, these new diagnostic kits offer greater precision, shorter turnaround times, and reduced need for highly trained personnel. DNA diagnostic techniques for Norwalk viruses, a leading cause of gastroentiritis, for which conventional culture techniques are not available, have also been developed. In addition to detecting food contaminants, DNA probes and other tools of biotechnology can help reduce levels of naturally occurring toxicants in foods. DNA probes can be exploited in research and plant breeding to isolate genes associated with the biosynthesis of major toxicants, facilitate understanding of the genetic regulatory mechanisms for toxicants in plants, and develop lines of plants with reduced levels of toxicants.

Mycotoxins in food are a periodic threat to food safety. DNA probes could help detect the presence of mycotoxin-producing fungi that grow under certain conditions in plant materials such as improperly dried maize and peanuts. DNA probes could also be used to learn more about the sources of fungal contamination in the environment and as a means to develop management strategies under field conditions. Given the expanding nature of these markets, a growing number of companies are developing biotechnology-based diagnostics for food and agriculture. These include: Agdia, BioControl Systems, Chromagen, Diagnostix, Editek, Gene-Trak Systems, Idetek, IDEXX Laboratories, International Diagnostics Systems, ImmunoSystems, Neogen, Organon Teknika, Promega Corporation, and Vicam.

As the industry matures, some people believe that competition will thin out the sector, resulting in larger companies, but fewer of them. Survival will likely be based on traditional pillars of successful commercialisation, including effective innovation, collaboration, and globalisation.

Biosensors

The development of biosensors offers great promise for improving food processing, analysis, and safety assurance. The highly specific actions of biological molecules can be exploited for use in biosensors that can measure the concentration of specific components in complex mixtures. Enzymes, antibodies, and microbial cells can be immobilised on solid surfaces, and the specific reactions they mediate can be detected by various physical and chemical means. Biosensors are commercially available to detect a variety of sugars, alcohols, esters, peptides, amino acids, cell types, and antibiotics. Development of tailor-made membranes capable of separating molecules based on size, electrical charge, or solubility will accelerate biosensor development as well as the exploitation of biomimetic systems.

Miniaturisation and mass production of biosensors could increase their availability and decrease their unit cost. Technologies such as microlithography, ultrathin membranes, and molecular self-assembly have the potential to facilitate the miniaturisation of molecular and cellular processes for enrichment, detection, and analysis of chemical and microbiological contaminants in food. Advances in the semiconductor industry have made it possible to combine chemical and biological components and integrated circuits in miniaturised systems (See Chapter 1). Biosensors can be inserted directly into food processing streams to obtain on-line, real-time measurements of important food processing parameters. Miniature biosensors could also be incorporated into food packages to monitor temperature stress, microbial contamination, or remaining shelf life, and to provide a visual indicator to consumers of product state at the time of purchase.

The Future

The enzyme industry

A revolution has taken place in biotechnology over the last decade with the growing understanding of gene technology. This has had a big impact on the enzyme industry. Techniques such as genetic engineering have enabled enzyme manufacturers to produce large quantities of almost any enzyme no matter what the source. Protein engineering allows the properties of the enzymes to be adjusted prior to production. These tools mean that enzyme technology is at a very exciting phase of development.

The biotechnology industry has a long-standing interest in stabilising proteins. Key objectives are stability against temperature, chemical denaturants, oxidation, and proteolysis (autolysis). The tools used for these purposes have all met with success: site-directed mutagenesis; homology-based designs, and the newer directed evolution approaches. Structure-based modelling has assisted mutagenesis and homology modelling, whereas directed evolution has been useful in screening random libraries. *In silico* design methods combine these ideas by using computational models to generate and screen sequences against mathematically defined criteria to find those with optimal folding energies.

A prime focus area is protein engineering. A highly pure, crystalline sample of the enzyme is first obtained and a very accurate three-dimensional structure of the enzyme molecule based on the position of individual atoms is then determined using X-ray crystallography. This information, including the sequence of the amino acid chain, is then entered into a computer programmed to carry out molecular modelling and to predict the structural changes that take place if one or more of the amino acids are changed. Using this approach, it may be possible to foretell how to improve the performance of an enzyme or even give it new, desirable characteristics. Properties that scientists are eager to study are primarily those of substrate specificity and affinity, pH and temperature dependence, and stability over time. Industrial enzymes improved by protein engineering are already on the market, for example Novo Nordisk's Everlase™ (a protease) and Duramyl™ (an amylase) for use in detergents.

The advent of genetic engineering, and the knowledge amassed on strains of three genera of microorganism - *Bacillus* (a bacterium), *Aspergillus* (a fungus) and *Saccharomyces* (a yeast) - have transformed the nature of industrial enzyme production. These microorganisms are well understood and have proved safe to handle, quick to grow and capable of producing a high yield of enzyme, often by excreting it into the fermentation medium. Today, once a useful enzyme has been identified in a new microorganism, the genetic material coding for its structure can be quickly transferred into one of these microorganisms. With improvements in promoter identification and codon usage the production of the enzymes in ever higher yields is becoming possible. A further benefit of genetic engineering is that enzymes can now be produced with a much higher degree of purity and free from contaminating enzyme activity. This allows for greater control over processes catalysed by enzymes and, in turn, leads to higher quality end-products.

There is a rapidly growing interest in the industrial use of enzymes for synthesising organic chemicals. Enzymes can either be used to build more complex molecules from simple ones or to break down selectively a mixture of larger molecules. For example, specific glycosyltransferases called cyclodextrin glycosyltransferases can be used to create cyclodextrins from simple starch molecules. These cyclodextrins are useful carriers of certain fragile compounds such as vitamins and flavours. No chemical means exists for creating this class of substances, so the enzymatic route is unique.

As with every other biotech field the rapidly advancing technologies of functional genomics, bioinformatics, domain shuffling etc. are providing new tools for the rapid identification of new targets for industrial enzymes research. Research priorities include:

▶ **Use genomics to optimise trait discovery and manipulation of** industrial enzymes

▶ Investigate methods to enhance the efficiency and expand the utility of upstream processing technology

▶ Develop capabilities to recover and purify products from dilute bioprocess streams and develop predictive models to facilitate the design of downstream separations

▶ Develop methods for monitoring and control of commercial bioprocessing including reliable and robust real-time sensors.

Priorities in food biotechnology

Ireland has considerable potential in the food industry, with strong programmes at Univerity College Cork, and Teagasc, Moorepark.The key research priorities of this industry that are targeted for the next decade include:

▶ Increase processing efficiencies with a reduction of environmental impact

▶ Expand development of value-added technologies

▶ Understand and utilise component interactions in formulated food systems

▶ Develop and promote strategies to control food borne illnesses

▶ Increase development of foods that promote health and well being.

Issues and topics of food microbiology are paramount throughout this group of research priorities. Among these, the exploding area of functional foods and probiotics shows considerable promise to expand the industry into new arenas. The economic impact of the projected functional foods market is significant and spans foods including natural functional foods (e.g. cranberry juice, green tea), foods and ingredients for specified health use, formulae for infants and the elderly, nutraceuticals, and drug foods. Within this continuum between food and drug, there are seemingly unlimited niches for the development of food systems that promote optimal nutrition, health, and general well being.

Concerns Addressed

Microorgamisms genetically modified for the production of enzymes are typically grown in large-scale fermentation facilities where there is equipment to minimise releases from the facility, and thus, these systems are considered "contained". The containment measures include practices such as separation of the microorganisms from the enzyme product, inactivation/sterilisation of the fermentation broth, inactivation of the filter cakes before disposal, HEPA filters to minimise aerosols during off-gassing, etc... The releases of microorganisms from these facilities are generally small, and are followed by some sort of treatment of the waste water from the facility.

Chapter 6

ANIMAL & HUMAN HEALTH

ANIMAL & HUMAN HEALTH

Animal Health

One of the most promising areas for applications of genetic engineering is in health care, primarily in the development and production of pharmaceuticals, therapeutics and diagnostics for disease detection and treatment. Many of the systems developed for human applications are first tested in animals and animals are the collateral beneficiaries of much of this research. Before covering the application of biotechnology for human health, animal health applications will be addressed.

Therapeutics

Animal health biotechnology is creating new vaccines, therapeutics and other products to treat and vaccinate animals for cancer, leukemia, rabies, allergies, distemper, heartworm and various other diseases. Farm animal recombinant products include tests for feline leukemia, vaccines for preventing diarrhoea in piglets and calves, rabies in pigs and neurological disease in chickens.

Genetically engineered strains of *Brucella abortus* strain RB51 may be suitable for vaccination of wild animals (specifically elk and bison in the Yellowstone Park region, U.S.A). A vaccinia-vectored vaccine for rabies has been successfully used in bait to vaccinate raccoons and wild foxes for rabies, greatly reducing the likelihood of zoonotic spread of rabies from wild life to domesticated animals and humans. "Suicide vectors" are being developed for vaccine use. These bacteria or viruses are not able to replicate in the host animal but are able to deliver therapeutic or prophylactic genes or proteins into animal cells. These strains die when they begin a replication cycle. These are useful for gene therapy, toxic drug delivery (targeting specific organs) and vaccination.

Designer strains of nonpathogenic (nondisease-causing) bacteria can be used to colonise the intestinal tract of poultry, swine and other food animals. These strains competitively inhibit pathogenic pathogens, like *Salmonella* spp., resulting in fewer opportunities for food poisoning or food toxicity.

Diagnostics

Numerous rapid, simple methods for diagnosis, many based upon detection of genes or gene products through probes or polymerase chain reaction, and enzyme immunoassays, are either in place or in development.

DNA-based probes and amplification systems

These techniques have many diagnostic applications, such as detecting genetic diseases, detecting infectious agents, determining parentage, and "DNA fingerprinting". DNA detection methods utilise probes which are labelled with an easily detectible marker, such as a radioscope or a substance such as biotin that can be coupled to a colourimetric or photometric response by methods similar to those on which ELISA (see below) is based. Both radioactivity and colourimetric methods are capable of nanogram or picogram sensitivity of detection, but the colourimetric methods have obvious advantages.

For greater sensitivity the polymerase chain reaction (PCR) can be applied. In the polymerase chain reaction two short, chemically synthesised DNA fragments, called primers, are hybridised to the DNA which is then amplified through a repeated cycle of reactions. Vanishingly small amounts of DNA can be amplified to concentrations sufficient for detection by gel electrophoresis and staining. The specificity of both hybridisation reactions and PCR often can be adjusted by altering conditions, so that assays have been developed for a single DNA sequence or for a family of related DNA sequences, using the same probe or primers.

For detection of microbes, hybridisation methods have many advantages over the more traditional methods for detecting infectious disease agents. They eliminate cultivating the organism (shorter time to detection, less danger of "missing" the microbe in question because some critical condition of growth was not met or is even available, and less danger of infecting technical personnel). Often they provide greater specificity than microscopic analysis, and eliminate the need for maintaining animal cell cultures or doing immunoassays.

An example of the development of probes for veterinary diagnosis is that of swine dysentery, a common disease of pigs. Diagnosis requires detection of the causative agent, *Serpulina (Treponema) hyodysenteriae*. Bacteriological culture can be time consuming and some veterinary diagnostic laboratories are not equipped to examine specimens for this organism. A problem which can interfere with the diagnostic process is the existence of a similar, but nonpathogenic bacterium, *Serpulina innocens*. Another diagnostic difficulty is presented by animals that have recovered from the disease. They can continue to shed *S. hyodysenteriae* for long periods at levels which are not detectable by selective culture. The ability of these animals to transmit the infection to susceptible pigs often results in introduction of the disease into previously non-affected herds.

Nucleic acid probes increase the sensitivity and rapidity of detection of *S. hyodysenteriae*. Dr. Lynn Joens of the Department of Veterinary Science, University of Arizona, Tucson, AZ, and Dr. Thad Stanton, USDA National Animal Disease Center, Ames, IA, have taken different approaches. Joens began with nonchromosomal (plasmid or phage) DNA from *S. hyodysenteriae* and was able to identify a fragment which does not, under appropriate conditions, hybridise with DNA from *S. innocens*. This fragment has been used as a probe for detection of S. hyodysenteriae in feces of acutely ill and carrier pigs. Stanton developed a probe based on the 16S rRNA gene of *S. hyodysenteriae*.

A Tucson-based company, Arizona Biotechnology Corporation, has developed methods to extend the use of Joens' probe to take advantage of the increased sensitivity provided by PCR. Under conditions of lowered stringency, DNA segments from *S. innocens* are amplified along with those from *S. hyodysenteriae*, but by adjusting these conditions, only the latter is detected.

Immunological methods

These methods are based on the high specificity of binding to proteins and other antigens that certain proteins exhibit. The proteins of consequence here are of course antibodies, which may be obtained commercially, for example from immunised rabbits. In recent years, immunologists have developed "monoclonal" antibodies (Mab). A Mab differs from the usual "polyclonal" antibody obtained from the serum of an immunised animal because the Mab has a reliable and high specificity. The immunologist fuses the antibody producing cell, which is terminally differentiated and incapable of cell division with a cell from an "immortalised" mammalian cell line, thus producing a cell that both divides and generates the Mab, so that large quantities of highly specific binding proteins can be produced for molecular diagnostics. Mabs are commercially available and are widely available in diagnostic kits. The ELISA, enzyme-linked immunosorbent assay has been widely applied in diagnostics using either polyclonal or monoclonal antibodies and can be used to quantify amounts of a substance.

Monoclonal antibody probes for detection of intestinal parasites are now common. Organisms of the genera *Cryptosporidium* and *Giardia* are reported with increasing frequency as causes of intestinal disease in man and domestic animals. Both cryptosporidiosis and giardiasis have traditionally been diagnosed by microscopic examination of fecal specimens. Dr. Charles Sterling of the University of Arizona and his research group have developed monoclonal antibody-based probes for detection of these organisms. The resulting indirect fluorescent antibody (IFA) test kits are produced and distributed by Meridian Diagnostics, Cincinnati, OH.

Caseous lymphadenitis (CL), a chronic disease of small ruminants, is characterised by abscessation of superficial lymph nodes. CL has been difficult to diagnose in the live animal, because chronic abscesses are not always detectable. Sheep and goats infected with *Corynebacterium pseudotuberculosis*, the bacterium which causes CL, produce antibodies against many of this organism's antigens, some of which are shared by other bacteria found in the animals. A collaborative project between workers at the Ontario Veterinary College, University of Guelph, and the Department of Veterinary Science, University of Arizona has led to the development of a sensitive and specific diagnostic assay for CL using a recombinant antigen. The structural gene for an antigen, a protein toxin, unique to *C. pseudotuberculosis* was cloned and expressed in *E. coli*, and recombinant toxin was used as the antigen in an enzyme-linked immunosorbent assay (ELISA).

Vaccines

Modern methods for animal production often lead to increased risk of disease occurrence due to the intensive nature of housing and frequent lack of individual animal care. The use of antibiotics and drugs for disease prophylaxis and/or growth promotion is the subject of increasing disfavour due to the consumer issues generated by real or perceived residue problems.

The advent of genetic engineering brought with it great hope for animal vaccines of greater efficacy and a lower cost:effectiveness ratio. Although there have been some successes, the technology holds more promise than payoff at present. Research into the pathogenesis of a disease, including developing a clear understanding of the host immune response to the specific infecting agent, should allow definition of the point or points of attack for prevention and control strategies. Using this information, one can often apply techniques for genetic manipulation of organisms to production of immunoprophylactic materials. A simple example might be the cloning of a gene which expresses an important immunogenic protein, allowing overproduction of that protein by some expression system. The recombinant protein could then be administered directly to animals in a conventional manner.

Genes expressing important immunogenic proteins can also be cloned into vectors which can be readily cultivated *in vitro* but which are subject to limited multiplication *in vivo*, often due to amino acid auxotrophy. An example is the use of aro mutants of *Salmonella* sp. which are incapable of synthesising aromatic amino acids. When transformed with a plasmid containing the gene of interest, these vectors can be used to stimulate the immune system of naive animals, often by the gastrointestinal route. During limited multiplication, the antigenic protein is produced and the animal produces an immune response and is subsequently protected against natural challenge. In addition to the bacteria-based systems for delivery of recombinant antigens, viruses may be used in a similar capacity. An added benefit of this approach, when it is successful, is that multiple immunogenic products can be delivered at once. This system was used for the first approved recombinant vaccines for animal applications. The first vaccine was genetically engineered rabies vaccine. It was prepared by inserting a gene from the rabies virus into the live vaccinia virus. Consequently, it carried a protein identical to the one on the rabies virus and the vaccinated animal develops antibodies that attack the protein, disabling the virus. The vaccine cannot spread the disease because it does not contain the parts of the virus that cause rabies. The vaccine was available for commercial use in 1994.

Another recombinant vaccine based on the vaccinia vector system has been developed by Tilahun Yilma at UC Dvais, CA for prevention of rinderpest, a fatal disease of cattle that occurs widely in Asia and Africa. Rinderpest is an acute viral disease, in which affected animals develop hemorrhagic inflammation and necrosis of the intestinal tract, with bloody diarrhoea, rapid weight loss, and death. Although there is an effective, tissue-culture prepared vaccine for rinderpest, there are many problems with its production and use in the field, including transport, lack of refrigeration, and lack of a simple system for administration. The recombinant product, on the other hand, can be freeze-dried, abating problems with transportation and handling, and can be administered effectively to scarified skin to regenerate the serum. Vaccination of cattle with this recombinant vaccine results in a high level of immunity, affording protection against test inoculations of 1000 times the lethal dose of rinderpest virus. The methods for field production and administration of the vaccine are similar to those developed and refined during the worldwide campaign to eradicate smallpox. The results of this work are encouraging, both in the promise for control of rinderpest and in the suggestion that other diseases can be attacked by similar methods.

Scientists at Syntro Corporation have used genetic technology to construct a strain of pseudorabies virus for controlled immunisation of pigs against this disease. Beginning with a virulent and highly immunogenic field strain of pseudorabies virus, they reduced its virulence by genetic manipulation and then deleted a gene for an expendable glycoprotein apparently produced by all field strains. Swine immunised with this engineered virus are protected against development of the clinical signs of pseudorabies, but their immune response, in that it does not contain antibodies against the glycoprotein, is differentiable from that to wild-type field strains. Animals with antibodies to the glycoprotein are presumed to have been infected and are culled as part of the eradication programme.

Another important animal disease into which genetically engineered vaccines may soon make inroads is poultry coccidiosis. Coccidiosis is a source of immense economic loss to the poultry industry, costing more than US$250 million annually for anticoccidial drugs alone. In addition to the cost, two factors - drug resistance and consumer concerns regarding residues - are driving the search for other methods of control. The genes for parasite products which have been shown to be naturally immunogenic are being cloned and the value of the resulting recombinant antigens examined.

An important problem with genetically engineered vaccines is their cost relative to other available immunoprophylactic or therapeutic products. A company investing a large amount of money in a recombinant vaccine may be successful in preparing an efficacious product, only to find that producer acceptance is low due to the availability of an equally effective (or even less effective) product of nonrecombinant origin. One company, which developed an excellent product for prevention of enteritis in neonatal swine, was unable to market it effectively due to its cost, which was more than 10 times that of competing nonrecombinant products.

Using a live virus as a vector for introducing vaccines into animals has won approval for commercialisation from the U.S. Department of Agriculture's Animal and Plant Health Inspection Service (APHIS). The viral vector technology was developed by Syntro Corporation of Lenexa, Kansas and promises a precise and safe method of introducing vaccines into animals while eliminating risks associated with mutant strains of viruses.

The first step in developing a viral vector vaccine is identifying and removing disease causing genes from the "transport" virus. Then "immunity-inducing" genes are removed from other disease causing viruses and inserted into the disarmed virus vector vehicle for introduction into the animal. The vaccine approved by APHIS uses the fowl pox virus as a disarmed vector for the transport of genes that induce immunity to fowl pox and Newcastle disease in poultry. Syntro has filed several broad patents covering its viral vector system.

DNA vaccines

Using DNA as a vaccine is a new approach that has the potential to eliminate many of the problems associated with traditional vaccines. These vaccines are unique in their ability to elicit a long-term immune response similar to that elicited by modified live vaccines, but without the danger of exposing the vaccinate to live pathogenic agents.

The manufacture of DNA vaccines is often easier than that of regular vaccines. Plasmids, containing an antigen gene from the pathogen, are inserted into nonpathogenic bacteria for mass production in fermentation tanks. The plasmids are subsequently purified from the bacteria and administered to the animal. A review article by Clayton Beard and Peter Mason describes recent trials of DNA vaccines for cattle, pigs, sheep, and chickens. In all cases, antibody was produced in response to the DNA vaccine. However, most vaccines yielded only partial protection when the organism was challenged with viable pathogens. Only some DNA vaccines produced complete protection. For example, chicken influenza viral DNA vaccine worked as well as the traditional vaccine.

DNA vaccines do not produce transgenic animals. Although "foreign"

DNA is being introduced into animal cells, testing has shown that the DNA does not integrate into the cellular genome. Also, the cells are targeted by the immune system and usually killed.

DNA vaccines have the potential to solve many of the logistical and economic problems of traditional vaccines. They are more stable at room temperature than traditional vaccines. No pathogens that might cause disease are used in production and vaccines can be created against pathogens that do not grow well in culture. Future development areas include identifying ideal DNA fragments for use as vaccines, improving vaccine delivery systems, and determining dosage-potency requirements.

Human Health

The results of investment in biotechnology are having a profound impact on medicine and health care, providing improved approaches to the diagnosis, treatment, and prevention of disease. There are more than 350 biotechnology drug products and vaccines currently in human clinical trials and hundreds more in early development in the United States. These medicines are designed to treat various cancers, Alzheimer's, heart disease, diabetes arthritis, multiple sclerosis, AIDS, obesity and other conditions. Biotechnology is responsible for hundreds of medical diagnostic tests that keep the blood supply safe from the AIDS virus and detect other conditions early enough to be successfully treated. Home pregnancy tests are also biotechnology diagnostic products.

In clinical genetics, deletions, substitutions and rearrangements, that are the basis of genetic disorders can be detected by either probing or PCR. In DNA fingerprinting, restriction endonucleases are used to fragment the DNA. The specificity of cutting of the DNA, combined with the specificity of probes for particular DNA sequences, often easily detects, "repetitive" sequences, and provides, if the analysis is carried far enough, the potential for distinguishing the DNAs of any two individuals on earth. This has obvious application to forensics.

The technology

Recombinant DNA technology

Recombinant DNA Technology provides the health industry with new and more efficient ways to produce/ create vaccines and therapeutics such as complex pharmaceuticals including insulin for diabetes sufferers and human growth hormone to allow dwarf children to achieve normal growth rates. Human growth hormone previously was available only in very small quantities but became a pharmaceutical agent because of the power of genetic engineering. The products currently on the market based on this technology are listed in Appendix 5.

Genomics and the application to therapeutics

cDNA databases and elementary informatic tools provide instantaneous glimpses of gene families or tissue-restricted expression patterns as a means of new target identification. In addition, cDNA microarrays and two-dimensional gel electrophoresis unmask the expression of genes with unassigned or unexpected functions. Depletion of mRNA with ribozymes or neutralisation of proteins with intracellular antibodies enables investigators to reject or embrace new molecular hypotheses about the determinants of disease, pharmacology or toxicology.

Several trends are fueling interest in the application of cell-based assays for drug discovery:

▶ **The pharmaceutical industry needs to shorten the time between target validation and lead discovery during a period when the numbers of both targets (from genomics) and compounds (from combinatorial chemistry) are increasing dramatically. Cell-based screens meet this need because they can be miniaturised to increase screening throughput and reduce costs while delivering 'information-rich' data**

▶ **Information about target biology is encouraging development of assays for specific, often subtle effects on target function. For example, screens for modulators of ion channel kinetics, allosteric regulators of receptor agonist efficacy and protein interactions are possible using functional assays**

▶ Advances in biology, chemistry and instrumentation are providing user-friendly tools for the development and execution of increasingly sophisticated assays. Among the more important of these advances are the continued development of optical indicators of cell function and the use of molecular biology to create customised optical biosensors. Many of these new methods allow direct detection of target function in living cells.

EST database mining

Efforts to map, sequence and analyse the human genome are accelerating the pace of disease gene discovery and revolutionising pharmaceutical research. High-throughput DNA sequence analysis has increased the rate of discovery of new, biologically relevant target molecules. The focus of high-throughput sequencing has been on identifying and tagging each expressed gene in the human genome. These tags, in some instances, reveal the functional or disease-related importance of newly identified genes. Efforts to obtain expressed sequence tags (ESTs) for each gene in the human genome are proceeding in public and private sectors and are generating massive databases for drug discovery purposes.

Figure 3: Genomics & its application to therapeutics

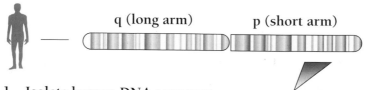

q (long arm)   p (short arm)

1. Isolate human DNA sequence

...G A G A A C T G T T T A G A T G C A A A A T C C A C A A G T... ..

2. Translate DNA sequence
   into AMINO ACID SEQUENCE
   (*the building blocks of protein*),
   using computer program.

...E N C L D A K S T S... ..

3. Look for similar sequences in
   databases of model organism
   proteins (*lighter areas reflect great
   differences; darker, smaller variations*).

HUMAN ...E N C L D A K S T S...

FRUIT FLY
(Drosophila
melanogaster) ...E N S L D A Q S T H...

**NEMATODE
WORM** ...E N S L D A G A T E...
(Caonorthabolitis
elegans)

4. Model human
   protein based on
   known structure
   of a similar
   protein from a
   model organism.

**BAKER'S
YEAST** ...E N S L D A N A T M...
(Saccharomycos
cerevislae)

BACTERIA .E N S L D A G A T R...
(Escherichia Coli)

**POSSIBLE
DRUG**

5. Find drug that binds
   to modeled protein.

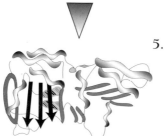

 *This area is encoded by
the sequence data shown.*

Early efforts to extract molecular targets from EST databases have relied on two strategies. First, these databases are extending existing families of target proteins. This is accomplished by searching the newsequences for structural features that are shared with known target proteins. This approach has been particularly productive in identifying new proteins that regulate cell death and inflammatory responses. New findings in this area include novel cytokines related to tumor necrosis factor (TNF), a well known inflammatory mediator, and counterpart receptors that bind these new TNF-like ligands (see below for application of this target in rheumatoid arthritis). Each new cytokine opens the possibility for new pharmacological intervention points that modulate immune responses or cell death pathways in cancer, inflammation, metabolic diseases and neurologic disorders. The newly identified receptors, and their associated signaling molecules, also provide new pharmacological targets.

A second strategy for distilling targets from the data contained in large EST collections relies on differential gene expression. As databases grow in depth and encompass diverse tissue types, electronic surveys can define genes that are preferentially expressed in a limited number of tissues or confined to specific diseased tissues. The discovery of cathepsin K as an osteoclast-specific protease, through EST sequencing of a human osteoclast cDNA library, exemplifies this approach. As databases grow larger, it is certain that we will see more examples of target selection based on specific expression in diseased tissues.

2D gel electrophoresis

One technology that promises to advance our selection of targets and target lead compounds is termed 'proteomics' which was described in detail in Chapter 1. The aim of proteomics is the comprehensive description of cellular proteins and how cellular protein expression is altered in diseased states. Protein fingerprints of diseased and normal tissues are generated by fractionating cellular components on two-dimensional gels, quantifying the resolved proteins and comparing the two patterns qualitatively and quantitatively. Specific proteins within the gels can be identified by extraction followed by mass spectroscopy.

Microarray expression analysis

Micoarray techniques are described in Chapter 1 (page 13). They allow comprehensive analysis of transcriptional expression occurring in diseased or drug-treated tissues. A comparison of the message profiles of two different cell or tissue sources permits identification of the genetic expression differences between the experimental conditions. Because a single microarray can currently contain thousands of distinct genes, a large portion of the expressed genome can be surveyed in a single experiment.

Optical biology

New optical assay methods promise to accelerate the use of living cells in screens for drug discovery. Most of these methods employ either fluorescent or luminescent read-outs and allow cell-based assays for most targets, including receptors, ion channels and intracellular enzymes. Furthermore, genetically encoded probes offer the possibility of custom-engineered biosensors for intracellular biochemistry, specifically localised targets, and protein–protein interactions.

In addition to labelling proteins with fluorescent molecules, protein–protein interaction assays could possibly be detected using enzyme complementation strategies. Other detection methods, such as fluorescence polarisation, fluorescence correlation spectroscopy, and time-resolved detection, which are still primarily used in biochemical or binding assays, will also undoubtedly migrate into cells and acquire more functional applications. The scientifically and economically motivated trends toward assay automation and miniaturisation will force the new tools to be generic and simple. A premium will be placed on assays which can be developed rapidly and require little or no sample manipulation during screening.

Target validation

Using the approaches outlined above, investigators will be able to expand their molecular target options significantly. A project team can often use pragmatic and subjective considerations to refine the options but the number of targets will remain unmanageable by current discovery strategies. At most pharmaceutical companies, intramural competition for project resources (e.g. medicinal chemistry, drug metabolism, toxicology support and funding) require an additional demonstration of technical feasibility and biological significance before advancing. Targeted gene disruption to produce 'knockout' or transgenic animal models is the most sophisticated approach available, but it is not necessarily well aligned with the sense of urgency in drug discovery enterprises. Methods that allow modulation of genes and proteins on a normal background, preferably human, and in a timely manner, are better for decisions about the fate of a drug development project.

Antisense

Antisense technology involves the inactivation of transcripts (mRNA) from native genes, through binding to complimentary RNA sequences. What made antisense a reasonable proposition were two innovations of the 1980s: automated solid-phase oligonucleotide synthesis, and phosphorothioates. The substitution of a sulphur for one of the phosphate oxygens makes the phosphorothioate nucleotide chain largely resistant to the nucleases that would otherwise degrade it.

Stanley Crooke founded Isis to exploit this technology in 1989. It led to the development of cytomegalovirus (CMV) inhibitor fomivirsen, a phosphorothioate antiviral for the AIDS-related condition CMV retinitis. Their next objective is an inhibitor of intercellular cell adhesion molecule 1 (ICAM1). This drug is in both a phase III trial for Crohn's disease (an autoimmune condition), and phase II trials for several other indications.

In selecting the site to attack on any mRNA - no simple task given the secondary structure in many mRNAs - Isis has rejected prediction programmes and opted for high-throughput screening fed by a 96-well synthesiser. Within three days they can go from identification of the candidate gene, to screening of fifty sites with first and second-generation chemistry, to confirmation of active constructs, to filing a patent. Isis claim that having automated patenting so the data drops into the patent format they will identify antisense to approximately 100 RNAs and file thr corresponding patents.

Ribozymes

Ribozymes are catalytically proficient RNA molecules that hybridise to and cleave mRNA. Sequences of ~200 nucleotides are sufficient to design ribozymes that deplete cells of a 'target' mRNA. Depletion of the proto-oncogene HER-2/neu mRNA, by Juhl and co-workers, exemplifies the contemporary use of ribozymes in functional genomics. Ribozyme expression diminished the cellular content of the HER-2/neu mRNA and protein by >90 per cent allowing the modulation of HER-2/neu expression on tumours in experimental animals. This provided insights into the susceptibility of the tumour at different stages of tumourigenicity and validated a role for HER-2/neu as a rate-limiting component in ovarian cancer growth.

Although ribozymes may be valuable therapeutic tools for repairing cellular RNAs transcribed from mutated genes or for destroying unwanted viral RNA transcripts in the cell, targeting ribozymes to the cellular compartment containing their target RNAs has proved a challenge. Now, Samarsky and colleagues have demonstrated that a family of small RNAs in the nucleolus (snoRNAs) can readily transport ribozymes into this subcellular organelle. They chose yeast for their experiments because the requirements for trafficking of a specific snoRNA (called U3) are well understood in this organism. The investigators appended a test ribozyme to the 5' end of U3, and then inserted its RNA target sequence into the same location in a separate U3 construct. The snoRNA-ribozyme molecule (called a snorbozyme) and its U3-tethered target were transported into the nucleolus. Here the ribozyme cleaved its target RNA with almost 100 per cent efficiency.

There should be plenty of applications for snorbozymes, particularly as the nucleolus is proving to be more than just the place where rRNA is synthesised. For example, precursor transfer RNAs, RNA encoding the enzyme telomerase, signal recognition particle RNAs, and U6 snRNAs all pass through the nucleolus where they are either processed or receive base and/or backbone modifications. SnoRNA chimeras harbouring ribozymes or protein-binding elements should prove valuable not only therapeutically but also for elucidating why certain RNAs and proteins traffic through the nucleolus.

Antibodies and intrabodies

Monoclonal or polyclonal antibodies directed against macromolecular epitopes on the exterior of vertebrate cells can reveal the functional roles of the corresponding macromolecule. Macromolecules in the cell interior are now also accessible to immunochemical neutralisation through the use of intrabodies (intracellular antibodies). Intrabodies are single-chain antibodies (scFvs) with a variable domain of the heavy chain linked to a variable domain of the light chain using recombinant methods. They can be produced intracellularly through transfection with cDNA constructs encoding scFvs. Direct neutralisation of intracellular molecular targets is particularly advantageous for proteins with longer half-lives that are poor candidates for RNA depletion approaches because of slow protein turnover. Curiel and colleagues have exemplified the use of intrabodies in their investigations on the determinants of apoptosis in breast cancer cells.

If one can eventually target gene delivery of intrabodies to tumour cells it may provide a novel component for combination therapy with conventional antineoplastic agents.

Genentech is one of the few companies who have a flourishing Mab business based on humanised Mabs. Their most successful therapeutic to date is Herceptin targeted against metastatic breast cancer tumours which over express the HER2 (human epidermal growth factor receptor2) protein. In addition in clinical trials they have seven other Mabs including ones targeted against IgE to reduce allergenic response, antiVEGF to prevent tumour angiogenisis, rituxan antibody against lymphoma, anti-CD18 to help blood flow and treat myocardial infarctions, anti CD11 for psoriasis. All of these are being produced in Chinese hamster ovary cells in 12K litre bioreactors.

A summary of target validation methods

The use of genomic technologies, EST databases, quantitative two-dimensional gel and microarrays are leading to the rapid expansion of the list of new therapeutic targets. The expansion so far has been primarily limited to extension of existing target protein families. On the near horizon, however, we can predict a tremendous influx of truly novel targets that will require rapid and convincing validation before undertaking a drug discovery effort. Emerging technologies involving ribozymes and intrabodies are attractive for filtering molecular target options. These new developments in target validation approaches are summarised in Table 6.

Drug delivery

Liposomes, which are spherical bilayers of phospholipids, have become increasingly useful as delivery vehicles for drugs and other therapeutants. Specific delivery allows reduction in nonspecific toxicity of drugs and use of lower doses. Now polysaccharide-coated liposomes can be constructed, which possess greater stability and can be more easily directed to specific cells. Liposomes have been targeted to tumours of the brain and other tissues, and may be used to potentiate the immune response against tumours (such as melanomas) and against infectious disease of various types.

Diagnostics

Clinically important human genetic variation is most frequently observed as point mutations or other small DNA variations that alter gene function. The number of point mutations needed for a particular DNA-based diagnostic test varies from one (e.g. sickle cell anaemia) perhaps up to 10,000 (e.g. the hereditary breast and ovarian cancer gene BRCA1 analysis). For inherited mutations and polymorphisms, there are always two, one or no copies of the mutation in each diploid cell. Cancer cells, which carry acquired mutations, however, may be mixed with a large excess of normal cells. The level of this type of mutation within the total cell population can vary, therefore, from 100 per cent to less than 0.1 per cent. From these considerations it follows that for maximum efficacy the choice of a point mutation analysis system should be dependent on the specific clinical need.

Without gene amplification

Within a typical sample for a DNA-based diagnostic test the numbers of target molecules may range from 10 to 10^5. Traditionally, a target amplification method has been employed to increase the number of molecules to a detectable level. There is, however, much interest in eliminating the need for an amplification step altogether by using hypersensitive detection techniques. Some possible approaches are as follows:

▶ Amplification of the signal as opposed to the target DNA. Branched DNA and dendrimers can hybridise to the target, which then provides multiple hybridisation sites for the detection probe. They have been applied successfully to problems of detection of infectious agents where as few as 50 molecules/ml are present.

Table 6: Comparison of molecular target validation approaches

APPROACH	INFORMATION NEEDED	INFORMATION SOURCE	SELECTIVITY	SPEED & ADAPTABILITY	LIMITING FEATURES
Ribozymes	Partial cDNA 200 bases.	cDNA databases (e.g. Genbank)	Good 20 candidate ribozymes)	Fast; adaptable to many cell types.	Synthesis of metabolically stable ribozymes; half-life of target protein.
Antisense	Partial cDNA 200 bases.	cDNA databases (e.g. Genbank)	Poor to good, depending upon sequence.	Fast; adaptable to many cell types.	Synthesis of metabolically stable ribozymes; half-life of target protein.
Aptamers or nucleotide translation	Protein/peptide.	Direct amino acid equencing or nucleotide translation.	Good	Slow to moderate; adaptable to many cell types.	Synthesis.
Intrabodies	Protein/peptide.	Direct amino acid sequencing or nucleotide translation.	Good	Moderate; adaptable to many cell types.	**(scFv).** Antibody engineering and expression.
Knockout and transgenic	Genomic sequence.	Scientific literature or proprietary.	Good	Slow from beginning of process to creation of useful model.	Technical proficiency and facilities.

▶ Surface-enhanced resonance Raman scattering provides spectral information which allows the identification of different individual chromophores either separately or in mixtures with detection down to single molecule levels.

▶ Fluorescence correlation spectroscopy is also capable of detecting single molecules in solution. It records spatio-temporal correlations among fluctuating light signals, coupled with devices for trapping single molecules in an electric field. It allows fast screening of spectra in which targets are labelled by specific fluorescent ligands.

▶ Single-molecule electrophoresis involves the determination of electrophoretic velocities by measuring the time required for individual fluorescently tagged molecules to travel a fixed distance between two laser beams. With appropriate controls the technique indicates changes in base composition.

Polymerase chain reaction (PCR)

PCR remains the dominant technique amongst those that amplify the target DNA and has been systematically improved in many ways. One of the first improvements was the adaptation for use in an allele-specific manner (one allele is amplified specifically and so ends up being in excess of the other alleles, giving a good signal:noise ratio) to permit genotyping of DNA directly without the need to probe PCR products after the reaction. Further improvements have been in the instrumentation, which have allowed the reaction volume and time to be reduced significantly. For example, PCR has been adapted to run in a continuous flow system on a chip described as a micromachined chemical amplifier that moves the sample through thermostated temperature zones on a glass microchip. Using this technique, reaction times have been reduced to as little as 90 seconds.

Mini sequencing or single nucleotide primer extension involves the single base extension of an immobilised primer where the incorporated base corresponds to the allelic variation of interest. Recently, the use of all four bases, each labelled with a different fluorophore, allows the scoring of allelic variation according to the fluorescent emission wavelength. Fluorescent analysis coupled with multiplex PCR and DNA chip technology may be a potential candidate for high-throughput mutation detection and genotyping.

There has been much interest in the development of PCR amplification procedures in combination with high-density oligonucleotide arrays, so called DNA chips, which have applications in analysis for potential mutations. This technology may provide the ability to scan any given gene rapidly to determine the zygosity (i.e.

discrimination between homozygotes, heterozygotes and compound heterozygotes) for all possible allelic variations in patient samples.

The clinical requirements and context in which diagnostics are to be applied will be decisive in the selection of which of the recent advances will actually translate into DNA diagnostics. For the future, complexity reduction of the genome to allow direct, unamplified, detection will become a key area of interest.

The Human Genome Project

The ultimate goal of the Human Genome Project (HGP) is to discover all the more than 80,000 human genes and render them accessible for further biological study. Information obtained as part of the HGP will dramatically change medical research and dwarf the catalogue of current knowledge of human genetics. Both the methods and data developed through the project are likely to benefit investigations of many other genomes, including a large number of commercially important plants and animals.

Rapid progress and technology developments during the first half of the project have affirmed researchers' optimism that the task can be completed ahead of time and within budget. A final 5-year set of U.S. goals was presented to Congress in the fall of 1998. Priorities through to 2003 include the following:

▶ **Clone and sequence full-length cDNAs of humans and model organisms, especially mouse**

▶ **Develop and improve software for determining and assembling sequences and recognising expressed genes**

▶ **Identify single-nucleotide polymorphisms as measures of human variation**

▶ **Continue to study ethical, legal, and social issues related to the project.**

The plan calls for generating a "working draft" of the human genome DNA sequence by 2001, which was infact achieved by June 2000 and obtaining the complete and highly accurate reference sequence by 2003.

Although initially controversial in the scientific community, the genome project's value has been proved beyond question. The wider biological and scientific communities around the world are developing tools and applications for the new data in such wide-ranging fields as medicine, agriculture, bioremediation, and industrial enzymology. International efforts have played a critical role in the project's success, with at least 18 countries now supporting programmes for analysing the genomes of a variety of organisms ranging from microbes to economically important plants and animals, as well as humans. Already revolutionising biology, genome research provides a vital thrust to the increasing productivity and pervasiveness of the life sciences.

Disease targets

Biotechnology companies are currently working on treatments and cures for diseases that affect large numbers of people.

Influenza virus

Influenza, or flu, is an acute respiratory infection caused by a variety of influenza viruses. The use of current influenza treatments has been limited due to a lack of activity against all influenza strains, adverse side effects, and rapid development of viral resistance. Although inactivated influenza vaccines are available, their efficacy is suboptimal partly because of their limited ability to elicit local IgA and cytotoxic T cell responses. Clinical trials of cold-adapted live influenza vaccines now under way suggest that such vaccines are optimally attenuated, so that they will not cause influenza symptoms but will still induce protective immunity. Aviron (Mountain View, CA), BioChem Pharma (Laval, Quebec, Canada), Merck (Whitehouse Station, NJ), Chiron (Emeryville, CA), and Cortecs (London), all have influenza vaccines in the clinic, with some of them given intra-nasally or orally.

Meanwhile, the team of Gilead Sciences (Foster City, CA) is one of the first biotechnology companies to come out with an anti-flu therapeutic. Tamiflu™ (oseltamivir phosphate) is the first flu pill from this new class of drugs called neuraminidase inhibitors (NI) that are designed to be active against all common strains of the influenza virus. Neuraminidase inhibitors block viral replication by targeting a site on one of the two main surface structures of the influenza virus, preventing the virus from infecting new cells. Neuraminidase is found protruding from the surface of the two main types of influenza virus, type A and type B. It enables newly formed viral particles to travel from one cell to another in the body.

Outside of the U.S., Tamiflu has also been approved for the treatment of influenza A and B in Argentina, Brazil, Canada, Mexico, Peru and Switzerland. Regulatory review of the Tamiflu MAA by European authorities is ongoing.

Tamiflu's main competitor, Zanamivir, marketed as RelenzaTM, was one of a group of molecules developed by GlaxoWellcome and academic collaborators using structure-based drug design methods targeted, like Tamiflu, at a region of the neuraminidase surface glycoprotein of influenza viruses that is highly conserved from strain to strain. Glaxo filed for marketing approval for Relenza in Europe and Canada.

Influenza A virus has recently been reconstructed entirely from cloned cDNA segments. Until now, the virus had been notoriously difficult to alter *in vitro* because the genome is distributed among eight subgenomic segments of negative-stranded RNA. Researchers have relied on the use of helper viruses to study the pathogen, but such approaches allow alteration of only a small subset of influenza virus genes. Led by Yoshihiro Kawaoka in Wisconsin, scientists developed a new reverse-genetics system that allows one to efficiently generate influenza A viruses entirely from cloned cDNAs. They transfected human cell lines with eight separate plasmids, each carrying the cDNA of a subgenomic segment in front of an RNA polymerase I promoter. The approach yielded highly concentrated virus stocks, and the cDNA plasmids were amenable to alteration by standard recombinant DNA techniques. The authors claim that this new reverse-genetics system will likely enhance the use of influenza viruses as vaccine vectors. Influenza induces strong mucosal immunity and does not integrate into the host genome, making it a potentially useful vector for both vaccines and gene therapy.

HIV

One of the most insidious of all viruses and one that has so far remained recalcitrant to vaccination methods is human immunodeficiency virus, HIV. Probably about 20 million people worldwide are infected by the virus and it is estimated that between 50 and 110 million people may have died from AIDS. HIV stimulates programmed cell death (apoptosis) of T cells, a key component of our immune system. The reduction in the T cells now is seen not as the prime cause of AIDS but as an indicator of the destruction of the lymph nodes, leaving the patient defenseless against all manner of opportunistic diseases. With the aid of biotechnology, biomedical researchers have been able to identify the virus quickly, understand it and mount a counter attack. It is probably the most intensely studied virus in history.

HIV therapeutics

Many strains of HIV occur, some more deadly than others. Immune components such as interferon and interleukin-2, which stimulate the body's immune response, are being used experimentally in conjunction with AZT, ddC and ddI, which are therapeutics that interfere with the virus replication. The problem with these drugs is that the virus' replication machinery is faulty so it mutates very rapidly.

With the right chemical cocktail of antiretroviral drugs including protease and replicase inhibitors, it is now possible to reduce HIV blood levels almost completely, keeping HIV infection in check and slowing or preventing the development of AIDS. But some HIV remains hidden in various parts of the immune system. Even a couple of viral particles can reinfect T-cells and start the whole disease process over again. Researchers are looking at a number of ways of boosting the immune system's tools for dealing with these stray pathogens.

Scientists at the University of Pittsburgh Graduate School of Public Health believe that boosting the virus-killing capability of a small group of immune cells, CD8 T cells, also referred to as killer T cells, may be the key to establishing long-term immunity against HIV-1. Boosting the patient's immunity to HIV in this way might eventually allow discontinuation of the complex regimens of drugs required for treatment of HIV infection.

Encouraging macrophages to fight infections and restore immune system function may provide another way to eliminate small amounts of HIV from the system following drug treatment. Researchers at the University of California, San Francisco reported that a new compound called WF10 (tetrachlorodecaoxygen) boosts macrophage activity. Preliminary clinical research shows that WF10 activation of macrophages may encourage the immune system to better fight AIDS and opportunistic infections. The studies showed that WF10 decreased the blood levels of CD38, a marker that is a possible predictor of AIDS progression, and increased the blood levels of CD8 cells. Furthermore, WF10 did not increase the amount of HIV in the blood or cause reoccurrence of resistant strains of the virus, one of the major disadvantages of immune stimulation.

Scientists have found that, unless the replicating HIV is integrated into the T cell DNA, it is degraded. Therefore, they are working on a strategy to prevent that integration. For example it was recently found that the virus Shanghis a T-cell protein called cyclophilin could get into the cells and replicate so researchers are attempting to stop it in its tracks from doing this. Antiviral therapies are also being examined which should interfere with other steps in the life cycle of the virus. Success to date is limited, but provides some hope.

HIV vaccines

Development of a vaccine has resulted in little success in combating HIV. However, some animal model systems have shown success. A mutated simian immunodeficiency virus (SIV) has been found to cause a low level infection in rhesus monkeys, which produces a strong immune response and no disease symptoms. Perhaps the same can be done for humans. Feline immunodeficiency virus (FIV) was discovered at the University of California at Davis in 1987. Since that time FIV has been recognised not only as an infection in cats worldwide but also as a valuable model for AIDS. In 1990, UC Davis reported the development and successful testing of a vaccine the succeeded in protecting laboratory cats from FIV. These researchers used virus-infected white blood cells rather than killed virus or virus particles as their vaccine. This system now is being used as a model for AIDS studies.

A new three-dimensional map of a protein called gp120 found on the surface of HIV cells could be an important guide to the development of new AIDS vaccine candidates. In order for HIV to enter a human cell this protein must interact with a key human immune system receptor (CD4), and with certain co-receptors (a common one is CCR5). A collaborative effort by scientists at the Dana Farber Institute, Columbia University and the Howard Hughes Medical Institute have uncovered the three-dimensional crystal structure of the HIV gp120 core in a complex with CD4 and a neutralising antibody. The researchers then designed a series of mutant gp120 proteins that could provide insight into how gp120 interacts with the co-receptor CCR5. They identified a region of gp120 that binds to CCR5. They were excited to find that this region was highly conserved, meaning it appears on a wide variety of strains of HIV. Equally important, this conserved region was recognised by antibodies capable of neutralising diverse HIV strains. Several vaccine candidates utilising gp120 have already been tested, and other trials are now getting underway. The early candidates were limited by the fact that they could not overcome the variability of the gp120 regions found in different strains of the virus. The newly identified conserved region of gp120 gives vaccine researchers the kind of target they have lacked previously.

Gene modification

The genetic modification of T cells for use in HIV infection has focused on the generation of HIV-specific CTLs as well as the introduction of genes into CD4 cells that confer resistance to HIV infection.

An alternative approach to the isolation and expansion of HIV-specific CTL clones is the engineering of T cells with MHC-unrestricted specificity for HIV through the introduction of antigen-specific chimeric T-cell receptors. In one study, a chimeric immune receptor composed of the human CD4 extracellular and transmembrane domains fused to the chain of the TCR (CD4) was introduced into primary human T cells and a human natural killer cell line using an efficient retro-viral transduction system. CD4-expressing CD8 human T cells proliferated, secreted activating cytokines, and demonstrated cytolytic activity in response to target cells transfected with the HIV envelope protein gp120 as well as cultured T cells infected with primary and laboratory isolates of HIV-1. A phase I clinical trial of the adoptive transfer of CD4-expressing CD8 T cells from HIV-uninfected twins into their HIV-infected twin counterparts is underway and a phase II pilot study of autologous CD4-modified T cells in HIV-infected patients has been initiated. All of these adoptive immunotherapy approaches are limited by the need to isolate and gene-modify autologous cells from each individual patient. To circumvent this restriction the researchers are attempting to create 'universal donor' cells by engineering T cells with reduced expression of class I MHC molecules, thereby rendering them less immunogenic.

Rather than augmenting the immune response to HIV infection, an alternative approach is the use of various gene therapy strategies targeting different stages of the retroviral replication cycle. These include the introduction of genes for transdominant HIV proteins, ribozymes, RNA decoys, and intracellular antibodies.

DNA vaccines

DNA vaccines were discussed extensively in the Animal Health section (page 153). The efficacy of DNA vaccines has now been shown in several models of human infectious disease caused by pathogens such as viruses, bacteria, and parasites. In addition, the scope of the utility of DNA vaccines has been extended to noninfectious diseases such as cancer, autoimmunity and allergy, and significant advances have been made during the past few years on some of the underlying processes involved in the induction of immune responses.

Studies have shown that DNA vaccines against hepatitis B surface antigen induce antibodies in strains of mice that respond poorly to the antigen in other forms, including recombinant protein, as is used in the licensed vaccine. Other DNA vaccines also have compared favourably to corresponding licensed vaccines. For example, influenza DNA vaccines provided superior effectiveness against virus shedding compared to the corresponding whole inactivated virus vaccine, in ferrets against an antigenically drifted strain of virus. In addition, DNA vaccines encoding single *Mycobacterium tuberculosis* or *M. leprae* antigens conferred protection against *M. tuberculosis* challenge in mice similar in magnitude to that conferred by the *M. bovis* BCG vaccine itself.

Vical Inc. (San Diego) announced in January 2000 the initiation by Merck & Co. Inc. of a Phase I clinical trial testing a naked DNA vaccine to prevent infection with the human HIV. Merck is developing the vaccine using Vical's patented naked DNA gene delivery technology. The trial, which began in late December 1999, is designed to test the safety of the experimental vaccine and to evaluate immune responses in human volunteers. Merck also holds a license to use Vical's naked DNA technology for a therapeutic vaccine against HIV, and for vaccines against several other infectious diseases.

DNA vaccines have enjoyed much success in preclinical animal models, thereby demonstrating the robustness of the technology, and this has led to their rapid progression into human clinical trials. However, there may be a need for improved formulations of DNA vaccines that can lower the dose of DNA required for efficacy, that are more stable, or that can transfect a greater number of cells or deliver a greater amount of DNA into cells. In addition, as mechanisms of induction of immune responses

Figure 4:   Patient specific vaccine production using plants.

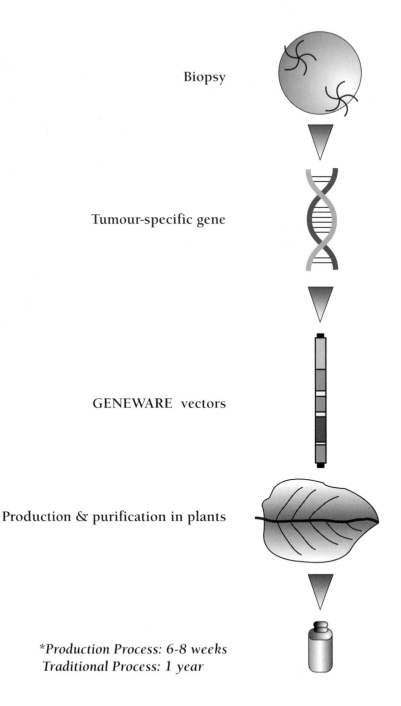

Biopsy

Tumour-specific gene

GENEWARE vectors

Production & purification in plants

*Production Process: 6-8 weeks
Traditional Process: 1 year*

after DNA vaccination are better understood, the targeting of certain tissues or cells for transfection by DNA vaccines may be desirable, particularly for cellular and mucosal responses.

Heart disease

Few medical specialties have made more progress in the diagnosis, treatment and prevention of disease than cardiology. Several major advancements were made in 1999, demonstrating the important role of genetic research in finding solutions for cardiovascular disease.

Hypertension, or high blood pressure, is a risk factor for heart attack, stroke and kidney disease. Researchers discovered a gene that makes the protein for the mineralocorticoid receptor. The protein is a master regulator of the body's handling of salt. The mutation leaves the receptor stuck in the "on" position. This causes the kidney to retain too much salt, ultimately leading to high blood pressure. This discovery helps us to understand the cause of an inherited form of high blood pressure in children, and could open the way for new treatments for high or low blood pressure. Another gene, UFD1, has been identified that appears to contribute to the congenital heart defects associated with DiGeorge syndrome, a common disorder marked by heart and face defects. The discovery of UFD1 followed the identification of other genes, including some involved in forming a normal heart. This research promises to speed the development of interventions that could prevent many deaths from congenital heart defects.

New genetic probe technologies are accelerating the search for disease genes. Using these techniques, researchers reported the discovery of a gene defect responsible for Tangier disease. Although this disease is rare, the discovery has broader implications. Patients with the disease have dangerously low levels of HDL, the "good" cholesterol, and a high risk of heart attack. Their blood vessel walls fail to pump out excess cholesterol for removal by the body. After analysing 60,000 genes from Tangier patients, scientists linked the disease to a gene called ABC1. When they added the protein that the gene makes to cells grown in the laboratory, the cells ejected significantly more cholesterol. This finding could lead to drugs to treat not only Tangier patients, but also millions of others with dangerously low levels of HDL.

Myocardial "stunning" - severely weakened contractions of the heart that limit the amount of blood pumped through the body - can strike people who suffer a heart attack or undergo heart surgery. Innovative animal research has confirmed that myocardial stunning results from an abnormality in troponin I, a protein vital to ensuring that the heart muscle contracts properly. Scientists demonstrated a link between stunning and a partial breakdown in troponin I by breeding a line of mice that have had a malfunctioning troponin I gene inserted into their own gene. The mice with the altered gene developed myocardial stunning. The discovery may eventually lead to new drugs that can prevent or reverse myocardial stunning.

Using a technology called tissue engineering (covered in more detail on page 19), a team of researchers reported that it had grown the first complete *in vitro* heart valves and implanted them in sheep, with promising early results. The team used autologous cells, which are cells derived from the blood vessel walls of the recipient sheep, to grow trileaflet pulmonary valves in a device with a chamber that simulates the flow of blood in the body. The research signals a new option for treatment of damaged valves that may overcome some of the problems of current approaches.

Cancer

Cancer is one of the prime candidates for medical biotechnology research. Cancer results from the accumulation of a series of genetic errors. Some mutations affect the control of cell proliferation, others endow cancerous cells with the ability to move from their normal location and survive at distant sites (metastasis), or stimulate the growth of new blood vessels (angiogenises) necessary for tumour growth. In recent years, the rapid increase in the number of sequenced human genes, the combined use of genomics and array-based expression analysis, as well as a deeper understanding of many signal transduction pathways, has lead to a dramatic expansion in the number of potential cancer targets. The challenge is thus shifting from gene identification to rational selection and validation of those disease-relevant targets that provide the best opportunities for development of specific therapeutics.

Many biotechnology-based cancer therapies are being investigated. Lymphokines (such as interferon) appear to attack cancer cells directly, or trigger the body's immune system to attack the cancer. Other proteins, called growth factors, appear to push cancer cells to respond properly to developmental signals, slowing their rampant production. Lymphokines and growth factors have been produced by genetic engineering for research and clinical purposes.

Genome instability

A common mechanism by which cancer cells obtain a growth advantage is through deregulation of cell-cycle checkpoints. Until recently, those that control the G1 phase of the cell cycle were the most well understood, and included oncogenes such as Ras, as well as tumour suppressors such as p53 and retinoblastoma protein Rb. Recent studies have suggested, however, that additional checkpoints function during mitosis to ensure proper alignment and segregation of chromosomes, and so the delivery of the correct complement of genetic material to each daughter cell.

Recently, several oncogenes and potential tumour suppressors have been identified including serine/threonine kinases that function in a normal cell during mitosis. Alteration of such genes may be responsible for the abnormal chromosome content (aneuploidy) and chromosomal deletions prevalent in many cancers, particularly those of colourectal origin. Aneuploidy may be one mechanism by which defective cells acquire an increased rate of mutation, enabling them to adapt and evolve toward tumour progression. Targeting enzymes involved in the control of genetic stability and chromosome segregation may define a potential new strategy for cancer therapy.

A new family of mammalian mitotic serine/threonine kinases was described recently, and named aurora1 and aurora2. The human aurora2 protein is localised to centrosomes and the mitotic spindle apparatus of dividing cells, but is rapidly downregulated prior to anaphase. Not only is aurora2 overexpressed in most human tumor cell lines, and in many primary tumours, but chromosomal localisation studies showed that it lies on the 20q13 amplicon and is amplified, overexpressed, and activated in >50 per cent of primary colon cancers and 10 per cent of primary breast cancers. Overexpression of aurora2 results in the transformation of Rat1 fibroblasts, suggesting that it can have an impact on key regulatory pathways. In addition, preliminary target validation studies suggest that abation of aurora2 leads to growth arrest of tumour cells. These features make aurora2 an attractive target for developing enzymatic inhibitors for cancer therapy.

Yet another interesting mitotic serine/threonine kinase is Bub1, the mammalian orthologue of *Saccharomyces cerevisiae* Bub1. In yeast, Bub1 appears to function as a sensor for properly aligned chromosomes during metaphase, and regulates the mitotic checkpoint prior to initiation of anaphase. Disruption of murine Bub1 with a dominant negative reagent results in premature exit from mitosis in the presence of a damaged spindle and subsequent apoptotic cell death. These findings support a conserved role for Bub1 in yeast and mammals as an important regulator of a mitotic spindle assembly checkpoint. Bub1 has been proposed to be a target for mutational inactivation in some colon tumours, specifically those displaying chromosomal instability.

The finding that several mitotic serine/threonine kinases are inappropriately regulated in human tumour cells, and are associated with chromosomal instability, suggests that aneuploidy may be causally involved in tumourigenesis. Based on these findings, new therapeutic interventions are suggested, including the development of small molecule inhibitors of the mitotic kinases aurora2 or Plk1. In addition, it may be possible to exploit the differences in mitotic checkpoints between normal and tumour cells to improve the selectivity of currently available chemotherapy.

Apoptosis

For more than two decades, scientists have known that normal cells have a quality-control system that signals them to detect and repair genetic damage or commit suicide (termed programmed cell death, or "apoptosis") if that damage is irreparable. When this control system fails to function, cells carrying genetic mutations continue dividing unchecked and can eventually progress to cancer. Several new contributions in this field have been made recently, including the roles of two kinases, Akt, the insulin-like growth factor 1 (IGF1) receptor (IGF1R), new *Caenorhabditis elegans* death genes, and telomerase.

Akt is a mammalian proto-oncogene related to the retroviral oncogene v-akt, and encodes a serine/threonine kinase. Recent progress has advanced our understanding of how Akt is regulated by phosphatidylinositol 3-kinase and has led to the identification of several of its upstream and downstream signaling partners. These data point to activated Akt as a key survival signal protecting cells from apoptosis, and suggest that its deregulation would provide a growth advantage to tumour cells. A related kinase, Akt2, is amplified and overexpressed in a subset of pancreatic, ovarian, and breast carcinomas (many of which express an activating Ras mutation). These observations suggest that an inhibitor of Akt or Akt2 might be of therapeutic benefit.

Implication of IGF1R signaling in tumour progression is based in part on the pleiotropic activities of its ligand IGF1, and overexpression of the receptor in solid tumours. This signal plays an important role in mitogenesis, cell survival, motility, and adhesion. These diverse activities have prompted studies of its efficacy for treating diseases including osteoporosis, growth deficiency, catabolic disorders, diabetes, and neurodegenerative diseases, such as amyotrophic lateral-sclerosis.

Additional cell survival targets are likely to come from analysis of invertebrate genomes. The genetic composition of the first metazoan organism became available in 1998, with the complete sequencing of the 100 megabase genome of the nematode *C. elegans*. As ~70per cent of all human genes have homologues in worms, and are often functionally interchangeable with the worm counterpart, one can use worm genetics to implicate human genes that are suspected to lie in apoptotic signaling pathways. A recent example comes from the cloning of the C. elegans ced-5 gene, whose mutation affects cell death. Ced-5 protein is related to a human SH3-domain containing protein DOCK180 and a *Drosophila* protein myoblast city. Ced-5 is the first to be sequenced from a list of at least six worm genes involved in the engulfment of dying cells. Dissection of the signaling pathways utilised by ced-5 will probably enhance our understanding of cell death in humans and possibly provide additional cell survival targets with relevance to cancer.

A survival tactic of tumours may be the extension of a normal cell's lifespan. Telomerase is an RNA-dependent DNA polymerase that synthesises the telomeres (guanine-rich tandem repeats) at the end of chromosomes. Telomeres function to protect chromosomes from degradation and inappropriate recombination. Studies on human cells in culture suggest that cell lifespan is determined by telomere length. Furthermore, telomerase activity is observed in the majority of human tumours, suggesting that reactivation of this enzyme in somatic cells (which do not normally have telomerase activity) is a major step in the progression of human cancers. The recent cloning of telomerase has allowed such hypotheses to be tested. It has been shown that telomerase transcription is upregulated in tumour cells, and that overexpression of telomerase results in a prolonged lifespan. Formal target validation will be required to test whether inhibition of telomerase in an already established tumour can inhibit growth or survival of the tumour. Nevertheless, the available evidence suggests that telomerase will be an attractive candidate for drug development.

A number of drugs which effect the cell cycle by triggering apoptosis, have been found and shown to have therapeutic possibilities in cancer treatment. Two of the best known are taxol (isolated from the bark of *Taxus*, the yew tree) and -la pachone (derived from Pao D'arco tree, a South American plant). In animal tests it was shown that these drugs work best in concert. In mice that received both drugs together, or -la pachone ahead of taxol, all the tumour masses disappeared, and the mice survived without complications. This demonstrates that drug combinations that target the cell cycle at critical points can cause cell death. The next step is a clinical trial to test the therapy in human patients.

Tumour environment

The spread of cancer cells from a primary tumour to secondary sites (metastasis) involves diverse processes, including invasion, migration, adhesion, proliferation, and angiogenesis. Studies on the molecular basis of metastasis have primarily focused on three general classes of molecules: proteases, metastasis suppressors, and adhesion molecules.

Many of the adhesive and migration aspects of metastasis are attributed to cell-surface adhesion molecules, such as integrins, cadherins, selectins, and their ligands. While much effort has focused on blocking these extracellular interactions, it is now recognised that many of these proteins use similar intracellular signaling pathways, suggesting alternative strategies for intervention.

One intriguing receptor tyrosine kinase that may play an important role in tumour invasion is the discoidin domain receptor (DDR). This receptor was originally cloned from human breast carcinoma cells. Detailed analysis revealed that it is overexpressed in breast tumours when compared to normal tissue, and a role in tumour invasion was suggested. Recently, the extracellular matrix protein collagen was identified as a ligand for DDR. Collagen also binds the integrins leading to signals that control cell migration and proliferation. This potential link between DDR and integrin signaling and possibly with tumour metastasis is intriguing, and deserves to be explored further. These examples highlight the complexity of cellular interactions that allow tissues, or tumours, to receive cues from their local environment. A better understanding of the molecular nature of cellular communication may provide additional targets for blocking tumour growth.

Cadherin and catenin are frequently downregulated or mutated in cancers, and are believed to play an important role in the decreased cell adhesion and metastatic potential of tumour cells. These molecules influence gene expression, cell migration, and cell adhesion. An interesting recent addition to this signal transduction pathway has come from characterisation of integrin-linked kinase (ILK), a serine/threonine kinase that binds to the beta1 and beta3 integrin cytoplasmic domains. Overexpression of ILK enhances fibronectin matrix assembly, decreases E-cadherin expression, and induces anchorage-independent cell-cycle progression. Overexpression of ILK also results in epithelial cell transformation, as measured by growth as tumours in nude mice. These studies support ILK as another possible target for therapeutic intervention, although it will first be important to determine if it is overexpressed in any human tumours.

A relatively new discovery which inspires some hope for developing an anti-cancer vaccine is that of immunostimulating molecules. One of these, called B7, when inserted into the cells of a tumour, can convert uncontrollable cancer cells into ones that T cells attack and destroy. There are also a group of normal cell proteins called mucins that are altered in tumour cells. Vaccines could be constructed from these altered proteins to induce the immune systems to attack cancerous cells containing them. The big problem with a cancer vaccine is again the one of mutation, by which the tumour cells may avoid destruction by changing their antigens.

Angiogenesis

Folkman's famous paper of 1995 brought angiogenesis (novel blood vessel growth) to center stage as a target to battle cancerous tumours. He stated that discoveries of endogenous negative regulators of angiogenesis, thrombospondin, angiostatin and glioma-derived angiogenesis inhibitory factor, all associated with neovascularised tumours, suggest a new paradigm of tumourigenesis. It is now helpful to think of the switch to the angiogenic phenotype as a net balance of positive and negative regulators of blood vessel growth. The extent to which the negative regulators are decreased during this switch may dictate whether a primary tumour grows rapidly or slowly and whether metastases grow at all.

Indeed research from many labs provide compelling data that implicate angiogenesis and tumour-associated neovascularisation as a central pathogenic step in the process of tumour growth, invasion, and metastasis. These complex processes involve multiple steps and pathways dependent on the local balance between positive and negative regulatory factors, as well as interactions among the tumour, its vasculature, and the surrounding extracellular tissue matrix. A tumour remains in a dormant state, the cellular proliferation rate balanced by the apoptotic rate, unable to grow in size beyond a few millimeters in the absence of the acquired angiogenic phenotype. The mechanism by which tumours switch to the angiogenic phenotype is unknown.

The inhibition of angiogenesis is considered to be one of the most promising strategies that might lead to the development of novel antineoplastic therapies. This concept is supported by the dramatic results of gene inactivation experiments in mice that have identified several vascular endothelium related molecules as rate limiting for embryonic angiogenesis. Likewise, a number of recent animal studies have shown that angiogenesis inhibitors can prevent metastasis and shrink established experimental tumours to small dormant microtumours.

Conclusion

Cancer therapeutics has entered the molecular age. Potential oncology targets are now routinely identified by screening gene and protein expression in tumour cells compared with their normal cellular counterparts, by dissecting the biological processes, such as growth control or survival, and by comparing genomes from simple and complex organisms. Detailed molecular characterisation and target validation (using tools such as antisense, dominant negative alleles, or gene knockouts) are used to prioritise these targets prior to target-based high-throughput screens. Several new therapeutics that were identified by such a rationale have already entered the clinic, including anti-proliferatives, metalloprotease inhibitors, and specific inhibitors of angiogenesis. It is anticipated that future cancer therapies will not only include cytotoxics and anti-proliferatives, but will also rely on specific drugs designed to combat these aspects of the tumour life cycle.

Auto-immune diseases

While the immune system can be harnessed for good in medicinal diagnostics and therapeutics, when it goes wrong it can be a daunting adversary. In allergies and in autoimmune disease such as multiple sclerosis (MS) and rheumatoid arthritis (RA) and some forms of diabetes, the immune system acts on body tissues as if they were foreign invaders.

Autoimmune diseases may be considered the result of failed homeostasis in the immune system, leading to the activation of autoreactive T cells and/or antibodies. Many chronic inflammatory diseases (e.g. arthritis) of humans are ascribed to autoimmunity but, despite decades of intensive study, the primary underlying causes of most remain uncertain. Perhaps the best-characterised human autoimmune disease is myasthenia gravis, caused by auto-antibodies specific for the acetylcholine receptor, and sometimes treated by thymectomy. Other human diseases thought to be autoimmune are more common, and exact a heavy toll of mortality. Such diseases may attack single cell types: beta cells in pancreatic islets in insulin-dependent diabetes mellitus (IDDM), single organ systems: the central nervous system (CNS) in MS, or they may devastate many tissues: e.g. systemic lupus erythematosus (SLE).

A diabetic person can be immunised against the T cell receptor that sees insulin producing pancreatic cells as antigen. Their new antibodies can then reduce the ability of such a receptor to bind and direct destruction of such pancreatic cells. The rejection of transplanted organs is mechanistically a similar problem to this kind of diabetes, and can be tackled in a similar way. For example, the very first monoclonal antibody to be registered as a drug was one that targets the T cells that cause rejection of kidney transplants.

New classes of immunomodulatory and anti-inflammatory drugs represent a new era is the treatment of arthritis. One of these is Etanercept, also known as TNF receptor P75 Fc fusion protein, or Enbrel. It is a biological response modifier that regulates production of the inflammatory protein TNF (tumour necrosis factor) by inhibiting the binding of TNF to TNF-receptor sites. TNF is known to be involved in the inflammatory process that characterises rheumatoid arthritis. In a large clinical trial of etanercept, significant improvements were seen in signs and symptoms among patients receiving etanercept compared with placebo. Similar results were reported with another immunomodulator that also interferes with the actions of TNF, but by a different mechanism. The drug, called infliximab (or Remicade), is a chimeric monoclonal anti-TNF alpha antibody. The antibody binds with TNF, interrupting the inflammatory process. Treatment benefit was observed within the first week of treatment, and persisted throughout a long-term trial.

These new drugs are a welcome addition to the current armoury against rheumatic disease, representing new hope for patients who cannot tolerate or do not respond fully to current treatments. There is concern, however, that treatment with immunomodulatory agents may make some patients vulnerable to serious infection, malignancy and autoimmune disease. While there is little indication of risk at this point, only long-term studies can clear up these concerns.

During the last few years, specific autoantibodies have been found in

Rasmussen disease and other epileptic syndromes. Immunomodulatory treatments (IVIg, plasmapheresis) have been used with significant success in refractory epilepsies, and IVIg is considered by most epileptologists as the first-choice treatment in Rasmussen syndrome. Recent work has shown that autoantibodies directed against some brain components might interact with ion-gated channels or neurotransmitters and therefore affect the stability of neuronal membranes. Autoimmune mechanisms are considered possible in the process of epileptogenesis. Taking this hypothesis further, immunomodulatory treatment at the time of brain injury (such as by trauma, prolonged seizures or stroke) could offer a preventive approach against epileptogenesis and therefore prevent recurrent seizures.

Stimulated by the successful introduction of interferon as treatment for relapsing-remitting multiple sclerosis (MS) and based on an improved knowledge of the immunopathology of MS, a vast array of treatment options is currently under investigation for disease course modification. The different approaches comprise mostly recombinant biotechnical agents, but also conventional immunosuppressants.

Aside from the therapeutic approaches now already introduced for clinical use, newer agents and treatment concepts include monoclonal antibodies, intravenous immunoglobulins, modulators of trimolecular complex and agents that interact with co-stimulatory molecules. Cytokine modulators and inhibitors of cell adhesion are promising candidates but their effect on the disturbed immunological network associated with MS has to be investigated thoroughly. In the future, simultaneous or sequential combinations of agents with different targets may significantly improve the efficacy of treatments for MS. The clinical evaluation of new treatment approaches will be difficult given the hetoregeneity and unpredictable course of the disorder.

Interesting future therapeutic approaches include intracellular signal transduction modulators, vitamins and newer immunosuppressants. Gene therapy, vaccination with naked DNA or dendritic cells may also turn out to be useful. Besides developing new immunotherapies it seems indispensable to improve delivery of symptomatic treatment and rehabilitation aiming at the quality of life of individual MS patients. Identification of disease course predictors or treatment response will improve accuracy of therapeutic decision-making.

Future medical developments

Gene therapy

There are many diseases whose molecular pathology is well understood, but for which no satisfactory treatments have yet been developed. Gene therapy offers new opportunities to treat these disorders both by restoring gene functions that have been lost through mutation and by introducing genes that can inhibit the replication of infectious agents, render cells resistant to cytotoxic drugs, or cause the elimination of aberrant cells. Genes can, therefore, be viewed as medicines, and their development as therapeutics should embrace the issues facing the development of small-molecule and protein therapeutics such as bioavailability, specificity, toxicity, potency, and the ability to be manufactured at large scale in a cost-effective manner. One form of gene therapy is 'DNA vaccines', discussed on page 152. This section will focus on other forms of gene therapy.

An ideal gene therapeutic should, therefore, be stably formulated at room temperature and amenable to administration either as an injectable in a vial or aerosol or by oral delivery in liquid or capsule form. The therapeutic should also be suitable for repeat therapy, and when delivered, it should neither generate an immune response nor be destroyed by tissue-scavenging mechanisms. When delivered to the target cell, the therapeutic gene should then be transported to the nucleus, where it should be maintained as a stable plasmid or chromosomal integrant, and be expressed in a predictable, controlled fashion at the desired potency in a cell-specific or tissue-specific manner.

Defective or missing genes are responsible for an assortment of genetic disorders. The main area that gene therapy is focused on is the use of genetic engineering to replace deleted or abnormal genes with normal ones. An encouraging example of this approach is in treatment of severe combined immunodeficiency disease (SCID) - the "boy in the bubble" disorder. In one form of this disease, the gene that codes for the enzyme adenosine deaminase (ADA) is defective. Without ADA, the body's bone marrow cells are unable to make functioning white blood cells to fight infection. Therefore, an individual with this single gene defect has a severely impaired immune system.

By inserting the normal ADA gene into some of the patient's bone marrow cells, it becomes part of the patient's cells' genetic makeup and, when injected back into the bone marrow of the patient, the missing enzyme (ADA) is produced and restores immune function. Two groups have recently reported the longer term results of adenosine deaminase (ADA) gene transfer into T cells from a total of four children with SCID. In one of these studies, transduced bone marrow progenitor cells were also reinfused. Successful gene transfer and the prolonged *in vivo* survival of gene-marked cells was reported in all four patients. ADA-modified T cells persisted *in vivo* for up to three years and were associated in most patients with increases in T-cell number and ADA enzyme levels, and an improvement in immune function. In two patients receiving gene-modified PBLs and bone marrow, T cells derived from transduced PBL were progressively replaced by marrow-derived T cells, confirming successful gene transfer into long-lived progenitor cells.

The cystic fibrosis (CF) gene was identified a couple of years ago. This gene, called the CF transmembrane conductance regulator, codes for an ion channel protein that regulates salts in the lung tissue. The faulty gene prevents cells from excreting salt properly causing a thick sticky mucus to build up and destroy lung tissue. Scientists have spliced copies of the normal genes into disabled cold viruses that target lung tissues and have used broncoscopes to deliver them to the lungs. The procedure worked well in animal studies, but clinical trials in humans were of limited success. Because the cells lining the lungs are continuously being replaced the effect is not permanent and must be repeated. Studies are underway to develop gene therapy techniques to replace other faulty genes for example to replace the genes responsible for factor VIII and factor IX production whose malfunctioning causes haemophilia A and B respectively; and to replace the faulty gene in dopamine production that results in Parkinson's disease.

Although more cell than gene therapy, cloning bovine foetal cells might be a useful way to simplify an experimental new treatment for Parkinson's disease involving the transplantation of foetal cells into the brains of patients with the disease. Researchers recently reported the first successful transplantation of foetal brain cells from pigs into humans to treat Parkinson's disease. The preliminary results indicated that most of the 11 patients showed some improvement in the 12 months following the surgery. This method of treatment has the potential to help not only Parkinson's patients, but also patients with other degenerative brain diseases like Alzheimer's, Huntington's, and Lou Gehrig's Diseases. There is however concern that non-human foetal cells could carry unknown infectious agents that could be introduced into the human genome.

Gene therapy is also being considered for neoplastic diseases, using mutation compensation (which relies on strategies to ablate activated oncogenes or augment tumour-suppressor gene expression) or molecular chemotherapy (which uses delivery of a toxin gene to tumour cells for eradication).

Prostate cancer is the most common neoplasm in men and a significant cause of mortality in affected patients. Gene therapy offers hope of using the differential characteristics of normal and malignant tissue in constructing treatment strategies. Several clinical trials in prostate cancer gene therapy are currently under way, using anti-oncogenes, tumour suppressor genes and suicide genes. A continued understanding of the etiological mechanisms involved in the establishment and progression of prostate cancer, along with advances in gene therapy technology, should make gene therapy for prostate cancer therapeutically valuable in the future.

Brain tumours are the most difficult of all cancers to treat, because they are generally inoperable and chemotherapy is ineffective.

Researchers are now taking advantage of gene therapy. This time rather than inserting a gene to replace a faulty one they are inserting a gene into patients' tumour cells that will mark these cells for death. The gene is part of the replication machinery of the herpes virus that is targeted by a drug called Ganciclovir, which impairs DNA synthesis. To get the gene into the tumour's DNA it was spliced into a harmless carrier virus that could only get incorporated into cells that are replicating. Normal brain cells do not replicate, so the virus, and the gene it carries, were inserted only into the target tumour cells. To ensure a continuous supply of this virus to tumours, virus first was placed in mouse cells, and cells were injected into the tumour to give a continuous supply of virus inserting in the tumour cells. Subsequently, patients were treated with Ganciclovir. This has yet to be proven as a successful therapy.

Rational drug design

Rational drug design is basically using the structure of the target to deduce which one chemical key will fit the protein lock. That ideal cannot yet be met, but using combinatorial chemistry, rational drug design can certainly produce a family of 10,000 compounds that it would be good to make. Computer modelling indicates the rough shape for the key, and custom programmes generate a list of chemicals that might fit that description.

After chemicals are made they must be tested which takes time and money. Smaller libraries are more suited to the later stages of drug discovery. The first chemical that shows promise in drug testing rarely ends up being the final drug. Instead there is a period of optimisation, in which hundreds of variants of the original 'lead' chemical are made and tested. Combinatorial chemistry can be used to make more variants more rapidly. Usually one or more of the variants is an improvement on the original lead chemical.

At the company CombiChem's, a scientist Anido and a team of researchers have programmed their computers with every chemical building block they can come up with, and the known laws of chemical reactions, and let the computer come up with it's own trillion-member chemical library.

Anido initially does a standard screen for lead chemicals, however poor, in a diverse 10,000-member library. Computers tell him what common hole, protrusion, or corner in all these chemicals might have made them all stick to the same target protein. The computer then searches the trillion-member library for other chemicals with that common shape. Anido's team makes these new chemicals, and the whole process is repeated. Four to six repetitions, each taking approximately three months, usually yields a chemical that is good enough to hand over to a large pharmaceutical company for animal and human testing. That is where things slow down. Combinatorial chemistry has sped up lead discovery dramatically, but to get a drug on the market a company must do toxicology, animal and human testing, and these take just as long as before.

Probiotics

As we become more aware of the necessity of being proactive in maintaining health rather than reactive in treating illhealth the field of probiotics is gaining renewed interst. A probiotic is a live microbial feed supplement which beneficially affects the host animal by improving its intestinal microbial balance. There are approximately10^{12} bacteria, comprising several hundred species per gram of contents in the large intestine. It is widely accepted that this microbial population has a powerful influence on the host in which it resides. It is implicit in the definition of probiotics that consumption of probiotic cultures positively affect the composition of this microflora and extends a range of host benefits including:

▶ Pathogen interference, exclusion, and antagonism

▶ Immunostimulation and immunomodulation

▶ Anticarcinogenic and antimutagenic activities

▶ Alleviation of symptoms of lactose intolerance

▶ Reduction in serum cholesterol

▶ Reduction in blood pressure

▶ Decreased incidence and duration of diarrhoea (antibiotic associated diarrhoea, *Clostridium difficile*, traveller's, and rotaviral)

▶ Prevention of vaginitis

▶ Maintenance of mucosal integrity.

Many of the specific effects attributed to the ingestion of probiotics, however, remain convoluted and scientifically unsubstantiated and it is rare that specific health claims can be made. Over decades of work, the science supporting the probiotic concept remains remarkably weak.

Nevertheless, industrial interest in developing probiotics and probiotic-functional foods is thriving, driven largely by the market potential for foods that target general health and well being. Given the developments in molecular techniques over the past decade, many of the key issues which have hindered scientific progress in probiotics are now removed. Exacting methods for the identification, tracking, and analysis of probiotic cultures within complex microbial ecosystems are now available and promise to revolutionise our understanding of their functional roles, and *in vivo* effects. Moving the probiotic field into the functional genomics area will yield a mechanistic view of the potential for probiotic cultures to be used in both traditional and novel roles. In this regard, molecular tools and gene transfer systems will be needed to advance genetic analysis and modification of probiotic cultures.

There will be many opportunities to enhance existing traits and develop novel properties by genetic modification of probiotic cultures. Targets for genetic modification and improvement include:

▶ **Immunostimulation and oral vaccine development**

▶ **Antimicrobials and bacteriocins**

▶ **Vitamin synthesis and production**

▶ **Adhesions and colonisation determinants**

▶ **Production and delivery of digestive enzymes**

▶ **Metabolic engineering to alter products (e.g. polysaccharides; organic acids) or link cultures with specialty probiotics designed to enhance the performance of a probiotic *in vivo*.**

Ageing

A wide range of genetic models with postponed ageing are now available, from selected mice and *Drosophila* to mutant *Caenorhabditis elegans* and *Saccharomyces cerevisiae*. These systems allow efficient testing of alternative mechanistic hypotheses for aging. Genetic analysis is forging stronger connections between particular alleles and susceptibility to particular 'diseases of ageing'. For example, two different genes for Alzheimer's disease have been identified.

Recent progress has been made in understanding age related changes at two cellular loci: telomeres and the nucleolus. The idea that shortening of telomeres could account for the gradual loss of replicative capacity of cultured cells (cellular senescence) arose from the inability of DNA polymerases to fully replicate the ends of linear DNA duplexes. This 'telomere hypothesis' was eventually supported by the observation that fibroblast telomeres decreased in length during both serial culture *in vitro* and ageing *in vivo*. The recent demonstration that artificial lengthening of telomeres in cultured human cells extends their replicative capacity establishes the importance of telomere shortening in human cellular senescence.

Some human diseases are distinguished by their late onset or their superficial resemblance to accelerated forms of normal ageing. Some of them have genetic aetiology in at least a minority of cases (e.g. amyotrophic lateral sclerosis [ALS]), whereas others appear to be exclusively monogenic in origin (e.g. Huntington's disease [HD]). There is no reason to think that these so-called diseases of ageing are, in fact, disorders related to the ageing process in normal humans. Nonetheless, they probably arise for the same reason as normal ageing, the attenuation of natural selection at later ages.

Alzheimer's disease (AD) is one of the signature diseases of ageing. AD is a progressive neurodegenerative disease. Most cases occur sporadically, but familial forms of the disease have been most widely studied because of the insight they give into disease etiology. Genetic causes of the disease are heterogeneous and include mutations or variants in several genes, including the amyloid precursor protein (APP), the presenilin (PS) and apolipoprotein E (ApoE) gene. The disease phenotype is remarkably consistent and includes the accumulation of ß-amyloid (A) and its deposition into senile plaques, the formation of intracellular inclusions (tangles) of an abnormally phosphorylated form of the tau protein, a change in the morphology and biochemical properties of astrocytes (reactive gliosis), neurodegeneration, cholinergic deficit and cognitive impairment.

The first transgenic mouse to develop a robust AD-related phenotype was created in 1995 by the Exemplar/Athena Neuroscience group. This mouse, known as PDAPP in reference to the platelet-derived growth factor (PDGF) promoter-driven APP cDNA, overexpressed mutant APP at high enough levels to generate sufficient A peptide for extracellular deposits (plaques) to form in relevant regions of the brain. In 1996, a second mouse (Tg2576) was created by Karen Hsiao and co-workers, that also made sufficient amyloid for deposits to form and, in addition, this mouse was reported to show age-related cognitive impairments. Several groups have created transgenic mice that overexpress mutant PS but these mice do not show amyloid deposition, most probably because they have insufficient levels of the A peptide.

In July, 1999, a team at Elan Pharmaceuticals in South San Francisco reported in Nature that, in mice genetically engineered to develop an Alzheimer's-like condition, immunisation with b-amyloid (Ab), the protein fragment that forms ß-amyloid plaque, reversed or prevented plaque formation and neural damage. The finding raises the possibility that immunisation with Ab may eventually be used as a treatment, or prophylactically, for Alzheimer's disease.

Another disease that provides with insight into the ageing process is Werner's disease. Patients who have this rare hereditary condition begin ageing dramatically while still very young. Researchers in 1996 reported that they had identified the gene at fault in Werner's syndrome (WS), which apparently encodes a DNA-unwinding enzyme called a helicase. Four mutations in WS patients were identified. The identification of a mutated putative helicase as the gene product of the WS gene suggests that defective DNA metabolism is involved in the complex process of ageing in WS patients.

Mitochondria are the major intracellular source and target sites of reactive oxygen species that are continually generated as by-products of aerobic metabolism in animal and human cells. Work by the Nobel laureate Paul Berg has implicated these essential organelles in the ageing process. It has been demonstrated that mitochondrial respiratory function declines with age in various human tissues and that a defective respiratory chain results in enhanced production of reactive oxygen species and free radicals in mitochondria. Furthermore, accumulating evidence now indicates that lipid peroxidation, protein modification and mitochondrial DNA (mtDNA) mutations are concurrently increased during ageing. On the basis of these observations it has recently been postulated that oxidative stress is a major contributory factor in the ageing process.

As we gain more knowledge of the parameters of ageing related degenerative diseases we can establish antiageing biomarkers and have individuals undergo "biochemical" check-ups like today's dental check-ups.

Replacement parts

With the May 1999 announcement of Geron buying out Ian Wilmut's company Roslin BioMed, they declared it the dawn of a new era in biomedical research. Geron's technologies for deriving transplantable cells from human pluripotent stem cells (hPSCs) and extending their replicative capacity with telomerase will be combined with the Roslin Institute nuclear transfer technology, the technology that produced Dolly the cloned sheep. The goal is to produce transplantable, tissue-matched cells that provide extended therapeutic benefits without triggering immune rejection.

Although the term "stem cell" is commonly used to refer to the cells within the adult organism that renew tissue (e.g., haematopoietic stem cells, a type of cell found in the blood), the most fundamental and extraordinary of the stem cells are found in the early-stage embryo. These embryonic stem (ES) cells, unlike the more differentiated adult stem cells or other cell types, retain the special ability to develop into nearly any cell type. Embryonic germ (E.G) cells, which originate from the primordial reproductive cells of the developing foetus, have properties similar to ES cells.

It is the versatility of the ES and E.G cells that presents such unusual scientific and therapeutic promise. Geron Corporation and its collaborators at the University of Wisconsin - Madison and John's Hopkins University announced in November 1998 the first successful derivation of hPSCs from human embryonic stem cells and human embryonic germ cells. These represent a tremendous scientific advancement in two ways: first, as a tool to study developmental and cell biology; and second, as the starting point for therapies to develop cures to treat some of the most deadly diseases. The derivation of stem cells is fundamental to scientific research in understanding basic cellular and embryonic development. Observing the development of stem cells as they differentiate into a number of cell types will enable scientists to better understand cellular processes and ways to repair cells when they malfunction. It also holds great potential to yield revolutionary treatments by transplanting new tissue to treat heart disease, atherosclerosis, blood disorders, diabetes, Parkinson's, Alzheimer's, stroke, spinal cord injuries, rheumatoid arthritis, and many other diseases. By using stem cells, scientists may be able to grow human skin cells to treat wounds and burns. And, it will aid the understanding of fertility disorders. Many patient and scientific organisations recognise the vast potential of stem cell research.

Another possible therapeutic technique is the generation of "customised" stem cells. A researcher or doctor might need to develop a special cell line that contains the DNA of a person living with a disease. By using a technique called "somatic cell nuclear transfer" the researcher can transfer a nucleus from the patient into an enucleated human egg cell. This reformed cell can then be activated to form a blastocyst from which customised stem cell lines can be derived to treat the individual from whom the nucleus was extracted. By using the individual's own DNA, the stem cell line would be fully compatible and not be rejected by the person when the stem cells are transferred back to that person for the treatment.

In the longer term, it may be possible to use sophisticated genetic modification techniques to eliminate the major histocompatibility complexes and other cell-surface antigens from foreign cells, prepare master stem cell lines with less likelihood of rejection. This could lead to the development of a bank of universal donor cells or multiple types of compatible donor cells of invaluable benefit to treat all patients.

Stem cells also show great potential to aid research and development of new drugs and biologics. Now, stem cells can serve as a source for normal human differentiated cells to be used for drug screening and testing, drug toxicology studies and to identify new drug targets. The ability to evaluate drug toxicity in human cell lines grown from stem cells could significantly reduce the need to test a drug's safety in animal models.

Geron have also established a procedure for extending the replicative potential of transplantable cells. Normal ageing of cell lineages is associated with the gradual erosion of the telomeres at the ends of the chromosomes. It has been shown that this can be prevented by reactivating the enzyme telomerase, which maintains the lengths of the telomeres. The reactivation was accomplished by means of gene transfer (inserting a recombinant telomerase gene into the cell and thereby expressing the active enzyme). Geron believes that by using this method, large quantities of homogenous cell populations can be produced in the laboratory and when transplanted, will last the lifetime of the patient. In other words, degenerating organs could be repaired using normal, perpetually young, healthy cells.

The research collaboration between Geron Corporation and the Roslin Institute will focus at its most fundamental level on understanding the molecular mechanisms used by egg cell cytoplasm to reprogram adult cells. A key objective of the work is to confer reprogramming capability (which normally resides only in relatively undifferentiated egg cell cytoplasm) to the cytoplasm of any somatic cell in order to eliminate reliance on harvested eggs. In this way, they believe that transplantable tissue-matched cells could be derived from cells taken from the intended transplant recipient. Such cells would not trigger immune rejection because they would exactly match the tissue antigens of the transplant recipient.

The implications of these studies, taken together, are truly profound. They may make organ regeneration therapies available for every patient with any chronic degenerative disease that is treatable with cell or tissue transplantation. Stem cell therapy could make it possible to store tissue reserves that would give health care providers a wholly new and virtually endless supply of:

▶ **Cardiac muscle cells to treat heart attack victims and degenerative heart disease**

▶ **Skin cells to treat burn victims**

▶ **Spinal cord neuron cells for treatment of spinal cord trauma and paralysis**

▶ **Neural cells for treating those suffering from neurodegenerative diseases**

▶ **Pancreas cells to treat diabetes**

▶ **Blood cells to treat cancer anemia, and immunodeficiencies**

▶ **Neural cells to treat Parkinson's, Huntington's and Amyotrophic Lateral Sclerosis (ALS)**

▶ **Cells for use in genetic therapy to treat 5,000 genetic diseases, including Cystic Fibrosis, Tay-Sachs Disease, schizophrenia, and other diseases**

▶ **Blood vessel endothelial cells for treating atherosclerosis**

▶ **Liver cells for liver diseases including hepatitis and cirrhosis**

▶ Cartilage cells for treatment of osteoarthritis

▶ Bone cells for treatment of osteoporosis

▶ Myoblast cells for the treatment of Muscular Dystrophy

▶ Respiratory epithelial cells for the treatment of Cystic Fibrosis and lung cancer

▶ Adrenal cortex cells for the treatment of Addison's disease

▶ Retinal pigment epithelial cells for age-related macular degeneration

▶ Modified cells for treatment of various genetic diseases.

Tissue engineering

Tissue engineering - a term coined in 1987 referring to the development of biological substitutes to restore, maintain, or improve human tissue function - employs the tools of biotechnology and materials science as well as engineering concepts to explore structure-function relationships in mammalian tissues. This emerging technology could provide for substantial savings in health care costs and major improvements in the quality and length of life for patients with tissue loss or organ failure.

A company called Advanced Tissue Sciences started by producing a skin substitute, called Skin, to measure drug and cosmetic toxicity. This soon evolved into Dermagraft a fine biodegradable mesh seeded with cells taken from neonatal foreskins which have an advantage over adult cells in that the skin grows more rapidly and does not scar. This is being used to replace skin destroyed by leg ulcers but promises to have much broader application. They are now developing matrices for seeding with cartilage cells called Chondrocytes to replace cartilage in damaged joints. It is important that these matrices dissolve over time so they are constructing them of polylactic glycolic acid (same as sutures) to which an amino acid that serves as an attachment site for other molecules is added. The biodegradable plastic, polyhydroxybutyrate has applications in this area for both biocompatible dissolvable matrix production and drug delivery systems.

Scientists also are beginning to explore the potential to grow many tissues in culture. Using stromal cells from human tissue, researchers are developing blood vessels, bone, cartilage, nerve, oral mucosa, bone marrow, liver, and pancreatic cells.

Encapsulated cell therapy is an example of a technique under development by industry that employs biomaterials in the treatment of certain serious, chronic diseases. The goal of this approach is to replace cells within the body that have been destroyed by disease in order to augment circulating or local levels of the deficient molecules. Targets for replacement include insulin-producing cells in diabetics and dopamine-secreting cells in patients with Parkinson's disease. An encapsulated cell implant consists of cells that secrete the desired hormones, enzymes, or neurotransmitters, enclosed within a polymer capsule and implanted into a specific site within the host. Studies suggest that the transplanted cells are protected from destruction and perhaps even recognition by the host's immune system, allowing the use of unmatched or even genetically altered tissue without systemic immunosuppression.

One branch of medical research is examining the development of alternatives to animal testing especially in areas of cosmetics and chemical testing. Now thanks to biotechnology, there is product called Corrositex made by In Vitro International that consists of a vial filled with a mixture of chemical detectors, capped by a cellulose membrane that supports a gel-like artificial skin three centimeters thick. Corrosives that destroy skin change the colour of the detection fluid. Another advantage of the artificial skin technique is that it costs US$300 and takes one day; rabbit tests cost US$1,200 and take a month. The procedure received government approval in May, 1993. The company also produce *in vitro* tests to replace eye and skin irritant tests used by cosmetics companies.

Concerns

Gene therapy and genetic engineering: the biological medicines of tomorrow, was the subject of two days of discussions by some 200 professionals working in the area of medicines at a meeting organised by the European Department for the Quality of Medicines (EDQM) of the Council of Europe, held in Strasbourg, France, in October 1999. The participants, who included some from Australia, Canada, the USA, Japan and Taiwan, examined the advantages and risks associated with the use and production of medicines by means of genetic engineering and biotechnology, and also covered the development of new vaccines and blood products.

It was agreed that the production of new medicines has resulted in new challenges, and there is a need to develop appropriate techniques for quality control. It was proposed to set up a framework for exchanges between all the partners (scientists from universities, manufacturers, licensing and pharmacopeial authorities) to keep up with developments in these new technologies and to determine all their implications.

It was also agreed to repeat these exchanges every two to three years to maintain a global dialogue to keep up with advances in the biological and medical sciences and, from the outset, to build a harmonised regulatory framework involving the various partners. Also at the instigation of the EDQM, representatives of national control laboratories from the 18 members of the European Union and the European Economic

Area met to examine the programme of market surveillance of medicines that have received an EU authorisation. The programme consists of quality tests on medicines authorised in 1996 and 1997, as well as certain other drugs selected by the European Medicines Evaluation Agency. Appropriate procedures have been established and will be set up as the initial studies progress. These procedures describe how to coordinate the sampling of products marketed in the various countries of the EU and how to divide up their testing among the laboratories.

It has also been announced that the CD-ROM 2000 version of the European Pharmacopeia is now available. It has been supplemented with 200 new or revised standards entering into force on January 1, 2000, in the territories of the 28 parties that have signed the EP Convention. New European standards have been elaborated not only to harmonise monographs but also to standardise products or new technologies such as gene amplification.

Confidentiality

With the increasing computerisation of medical records and the consolidation of the health care system, people have become more concerned about the potential threat to the confidentiality of individual health information. The biotechnology industry and the health community believe that it is of paramount importance to provide strong protections for sensitive patient health information. Patients do not want sensitive health information about them to be inappropriately disclosed or used against them. Patients also want access to their medical records and to have procedures in place to inspect and correct information in these records.

While it is critical to ensure confidentiality, most patients are comfortable with and support the use of health information to undertake important medical research. Biotechnology research relies on medical information to perform the studies that identify new treatments and cures. Individual privacy can be protected without burdening biotechnology research with onerous authorisation requirements and additional layers of review that do not enhance confidentiality. For example, it would be virtually impossible to recruit patients to participate in a clinical trial of a product to treat a small sub-population with a specific genetic disease if a researcher could not use biological samples to identify the subset of people whom the product might benefit.

People's privacy can be protected by utilising coding and encryption, by security laws and careful restriction of the codes, and by strong penalties for unauthorised use of any such code or de-encryption device to reveal the individual's identity. Furthermore, genetic information should be given the same strong protection as all medical information. As our understanding of science progresses, we recognise that virtually all medical facts have a genetic component. All medical information, including information about infectious or genetic diseases, is extremely sensitive and deserves strong protection.

Gene therapy

Arguments in favour of gene therapy

The central argument in favour of gene therapy is that it can be used to treat desperately ill patients, or to prevent the onset of horrible illnesses. Conventional treatment has failed for the candidate diseases for gene therapy, and for these patients, gene therapy is the only hope for a future. Many commentators liken somatic cell gene therapy to other new medical technologies, and argue that we have an obligation to treat patients if we can.

While the development of germ-line gene therapy techniques will undoubtedly place some embryos at risk in the laboratory, once the successful techniques are developed, the therapy could help parents and researchers avoid the moral dilemma of disposing of "defective" embryos in the lab if the embryos could be repaired.

Arguments against gene therapy

Many persons who voice concerns about somatic cell gene therapy use a "slippery slope" argument against it. They wonder whether it is possible to distinguish between "good" and "bad" uses of the gene modification techniques, and whether the potential for harmful abuse of the technology should keep us from developing more techniques. Other commentators have pointed to the difficulty of following up with patients in long-term clinical research. Gene therapy patients would need to be under surveillance for decades to monitor long-term effects of the therapy on future generations. Some are troubled that many gene therapy candidates are children too young to understand the ramifications of gene therapy treatment.

Others have pointed to potential conflict of interest problems pitting an individual's reproductive liberties and privacy interests against the interests of insurance companies, or society not to bear the financial burden of caring for a child with serious genetic defects. Issues of justice and resource allocation have also been raised: in a time of strain on health care systems, can we afford such expensive therapy? Who should receive gene therapy? If it is made available only to those who can afford it, the distribution of desirable biological traits among different socioeconomic and ethnic groups would become badly skewed.

Embryonic stem cells

In November 1998, President Clinton charged the National Bioethics

Advisory Commission, in the United States with the task of conducting a thorough review of the issues associated with human stem cell research, balancing all ethical and medical considerations. The President's request was made in response to three separate reports that brought to the fore the exciting scientific and clinical prospects of stem cell research while also raising a series of ethical controversies regarding federal sponsorship of scientific inquiry in this area. Scientific reports of the successful isolation and culture of these specialised cells have offered hope of new cures for debilitating and even fatal illness, while at the same time renewing an important national debate about the ethics of research involving human embryos and cadaveric foetal material. The following is a summary of the report.

Recent developments in human stem cell research have raised hopes that new therapies will become available that will serve to relieve human suffering. These developments also have served to remind society of the deep moral concerns that are related to research involving human embryos and cadaveric foetal tissue. Serious ethical discussion will (and should) continue on these issues. However, in light of public testimony, expert advice, and published writings, substantial agreement has been found among individuals with diverse perspectives that although the human embryo and foetus deserve respect as a form of human life, the scientific and clinical benefits of stem cell research should not be foregone. Authorities have been persuaded that carrying out human stem cell research under federal sponsorship is important, but only if it is conducted in an ethically responsible manner.

Cloning

In the UK, the Human Genetics Advisory Cormmission and the Human Fertilisation & Embryology Authority published a joint report on 'Cloning issues in Reproduction, Science and Medicine' on 7 December, 1998. The report recommends that there should be a continued ban on all 'reproductive cloning' but gives cautious support to the cloning of human cells for therapeutic purposes. It recognises the very large potential for human cells in the treatment of a wide variety of human diseases - including Parkinson's, diabetes and stroke - and specifically recommends an extension of the purposes for which human embryo research can be allowed to include 'the development of therapeutic treatments for diseased or damaged tissues and organs'. A copy of the report is available on the HGAC website: www.dti.gov.uk/hgac/.

Organisational statements/policies

American Medical Association. Council on Ethical and Judicial Affairs. *Opinions of the Council on Ethical and Judicial Affairs: Gene Therapy and Surrogate Mothers*. Report E (I-88). Chicago: The Association, 1988. 3 p.

The American Medical Association approves of the use of somatic and germ-line gene therapy provided: 1) that the research conforms to its Council on Ethical and Judicial Affairs' guidelines on clinical investigations; 2) that it adheres to stringent safety considerations; and 3) that gene therapy only be utilised for therapeutic purposes in the treatment of human disorders, and not for enhancement or eugenic purposes.

Catholic Health Association of the United States (CHA). Research Group on Ethical Issues in Early Human Development and Genetics. *Human Genetics: Ethical Issues in Genetic Testing, Counseling, and Therapy*. St. Louis, Mo.: Catholic Health Association of the United States; 1990. 58 pages.

The CHA focuses on germ-line gene therapy and research on gametes and pre-embryos. It sees the development of "gonadal cell" therapy as an "especially important good to be sought insofar as therapies will provide a positive solution to a negative diagnosis". Because such therapy helps to avoid selective abortion for genetic defects, the CHA supports it.

Council for International Organisations of Medical Sciences (CIOMS). **The Declaration of Inuyama and Reports of the Working Groups**. *Human Gene Therapy* 2(2): 123-129, Summer 1991.

At a 1990 conference held in Tokyo and Inuyama, Japan, the Council adopted a policy statement on human genetics. Somatic cell gene therapy should be evaluated like other innovative therapies. It requires independent review and interventions should only be limited to conditions that cause significant disability, and not enhance or suppress cosmetic, behavioral or cognitive defects unrelated to a disease. Before germ-line gene therapy is undertaken, its safety must be very well established.

Council for Responsible Genetics. **Position Paper on Human Germ Line Manipulation Presented by Council for Responsible Genetics, Human Genetics Committee Fall, 1992.** *Human Gene Therapy* 4(1): 35-37, February 1993.

The Council unconditionally opposes germ-line gene therapy. Problems of obligations to future generations and social discrimination against those who do not submit to genetic engineering make such therapy intolerable.

Council of Europe. Parliamentary Assembly. **Recommendation 934 (1982) on Genetic Engineering**. *Human Gene Therapy* 2(4) 327-328, Winter 1991.

Based on its support of the right to life and to human dignity, the Council rejects germ-line genetic engineering because it would violate the implied right to a inherit a genetic pattern which has not been artificially changed. Somatic cell therapy is acceptable provided researchers follow standard guidelines for informed consent and for oversight by research ethics committees.

European Medical Research Councils. **Gene Therapy in Man: Recommendations of European Medical Research Councils**. *Lancet* 2 (8597): 1271-1272, 4 June 1988.

The Medical Research Councils of Austria, Denmark, Finland, France, The Netherlands, Norway, Spain, Sweden, Switzerland, the United Kingdom and West Germany agreed not to allow germ-line gene therapy.

Glover, Jonathan, *et al*. *Ethics of New Reproductive Technologies: The Glover Report to the European Commission*. DeKalb: Northern Illinois University Press, 1989. 159 pages.

Somatic gene therapy does not raise ethical questions significantly different from those raised by organ transplantation; the patient, with relatively low risk, may gain significant benefit from the procedure. However germ-line gene therapy should not be undertaken at this time due to concerns over the safety and concerns regarding our obligations to future generations.

Great Britain. Committee on the Ethics of Gene Therapy (Chairman: Cecil Clothier). **Report of the Committee on the Ethics of Gene Therapy: Recommendations**. [partial report] *Human Gene Therapy* 3(5): 519-523, October 1992. [Full report available from: London: Her Majesty's Stationery Office, 1992 January. 41 pages. Command paper number: Cm 1788]

While the Clothier Committee recommended that germ-line gene therapy should not yet be undertaken, it approved continued study of somatic cell gene therapy. The Committee further recommended the establishment of a government supervisory body to provide scientific and medical advice on the safety and efficacy of human gene modification, and its use.

World Council of Churches. Sub-unit on Church and Society. *Biotechnology: Its Challenge to the Churches and the World*. Geneva: The Council, 1989. 34 pages.

The Council calls for a ban on germ-line gene therapy and recommends strict control over somatic cell gene therapy, bearing in mind the potential misuse of the technology to discriminate against those held to be defective.

World Medical Association. *World Medical Association Statement on Genetic Counseling and Genetic Engineering*. No. 17.S. Available from the World Medical Association, 28 Avenue des Alpes, 01210 Ferney-Voltaire, France. 1987 October. 2 pages.

The Association makes general recommendations regarding gene therapy. It suggests that such research on human subjects adhere to guidelines posed in the Declaration of Helsinki, and that full informed consent be obtained. No hazardous or unwanted virus can be inserted into patients. Evaluation of the effectiveness of the therapy should be made. Human gene therapy should not be performed if simpler or safer treatment exists for a disease.

Priorities for Ireland

Most of these have both medical and veterinary relevance:

> Identify priority human and animal diseases for Ireland. Take advantage of well developed pedigree studies for heritable disorders such as cystic fibrosis and spina bifida. Work with companies such as Affymetrix in US and LION Ag in Germany to develop analysis systems such as single-nucleotide polymorphisms Chips for genotyping and as measures of variation.

> Build on strength for health maintenance especially in the probiotic area for both humans and animals. The mechanisms of drug action be actively sought out and the knowledge gained should be used to guide applications and future developments across the pharmaceutical field. Validity of probiotic science will be derived by the same process where mechanisms can be linked directly to efficacy and applications. In this regard, funds to establish clinical efficacy should be increased to meet the promise of concept substantiation and label claims.

> Establish international collaborations with leading biomedical institutes and industries. Encourage establishment of subsidiaries in Ireland especially in the area of genomics and bioinformatics where complimentary capabilities should be attractive to these industries.

> Research areas should include identifying ideal DNA fragments for use as vaccines, improving vaccine delivery systems, and determining dosage-potency requirements.

Further reading

Beard, C.W. and Mason, P.W. (1998) Out on the farm with DNA vaccines. Nature Biotech. 16:1325 1328.

Gerdts V. *et al.* (1997). Protection of pigs against Aujeszky's disease by DNA vaccination. J. Gen. Virology 78:2139-2146.

Kodihalli S. *et al.* (1997). Cross-protection among lethal H5N2 influenza viruses induced by DNA vaccine to the hemagglutinin. J. Virology 71:3391-3396.

Collins M.L. *et al.* (1997). A branched DNA signal amplification assay for quantification of nucleic acid targets below 100 molecules/ml. Nucleic Acids Res. 25: 2979–2984.

Horn T. *et al.* (1997). An improved divergent synthesis of comb-type branched oligodeoxyribonucleotides (bDNA) containing multiple secondary sequences. Nucleic Acids Res. 25: 4835–4841.

Eigen M. and Rigler R. (1994). Sorting single molecules: application to diagnostics and evolutionary biotechnology. Proc Natl Acad Sci USA 91: 5740–5747

Castro A. and Brooks Shera E. (1995). Single-molecule electrophoresis. Anal Chem. 67: 3181–3186.

Mehrpouyan M. *et al.* (1997). A rapid and sensitive method for non-isotopic quantitation of HIV-1 RNA using thermophilic SDA and flow cytometry. Nucleic Acids Res. 25: 4842–4849.

Joshua Legerberg (2000) Infectious History. Science 288: 287-293.

Barbara R. Jasny and Pamela J. Hines (1999). Genome Prospecting, Science October 15; 286-443.

Eliot Marshall (2000) Human Genome: Rival Genome Sequencers Celebrate a Milestone Together. Science 2000 June 30; Science 288: 2294-2295.

Phillips, RL. *et al.* (2000). The Genetic Programme of Hematopoietic Stem Cells. Science 288: 1635-1640.

Chapter 7

REGULATIONS

REGULATIONS

Modern methods of biotechnology offer tremendous potential for addressing many pressing human and environmental needs. Implicit in the effective utilisation of these biotechnology applications are issues of concern with respect to safety, efficacy and environmental impact.

Current U.S. Regulations

The United States has been grappling with these regulatory issues considerably longer than most other countries. It also has the largest stake in the technology. Since regulations in other jurisdictions, including the EU and Ireland are still evolving, and likely to be influenced by the US experience, it is worth outlining the regulatory Framework for GMOs in the United States.

Three agencies share primary responsibility for regulating the organisms, products and processes of recombinant DNA technology, whether they be designed for closed systems or for environmental release: the Food and Drug Administration (FDA), the United States Department of Agriculture (USDA), and the Environmental Protection Agency (EPA). Regulations under the Occupational Safety and Health Administration (OSHA) cover those working with rDNA, while the Department of Health and Human Services (DHHS) oversees the health of the general public.

Many states and local authorities were not satisfied with existing oversight and some 14 states and several municipalities enacted their own biotechnology legislation. Agencies must also adhere to the umbrella National Environmental Policy Act (NEPA) which is binding on all federal agencies.

The move from the laboratory to the field proved a challenge for the relevant agencies. In the short time that elapsed between the initial development of the capabilities of recombinant DNA technology the controversy over this research shifted focus from the presumed risks associated with the possible escape of GMOs from research laboratories to the nature of the long-term environmental impact of GMOs that are intentionally released. The agencies base their analysis of oversight not principally on any presumed theoretical "exotic" risks but rather exploit the vast cache of accumulated knowledge that has been amassed over years of research using highly developed scientific procedures for assessing field tests and planned introductions. Using such a scientific approach deduced from first principles is probably the most effective mechanism regulatory bodies can take in crafting effective regulations.

The United States Department of Agriculture (USDA)

Scope for coverage is food and fibre products. While its authority is as equally applicable to genetically modified animals, plants, and microorganisms it is in one sense outside the circle of ecological safety, in that its primary concerns are the safety of crop plant and food animals, and the safety and wholesomeness of food products.

The USDA has nine divisions that deal with biotechnology:

▶ The Agricultural Research Service (ARS)

▶ The Food Safety and Inspection Service (FSIS)

▶ The Animal and Plant Health Inspection Service (APHIS)

▶ The Agricultural Marketing Service (AMS)

▶ The Cooperative State Research Service (CSRS)

▶ Extension Service

▶ The National Agricultural Library (NAL)

▶ The Forest Service (FS)

▶ The Economic Research Service (ERS)

The Committee on Biotechnology in Agriculture (CBA) is comprised of administrators of the USDA agencies with major activities involving biotechnology. ARS has formed the Agricultural Biotechnology Research Advisory Committee (ABRAC) to review proposals, provide guidance on matters of biosafety in the development and use of biotechnology in agriculture. APHIS is the watchdog that guards the licensing of veterinary biological material and issues permits for transport of biological material and field tests and commercialisation of genetically engineered plants and microorganisms. APHIS has formed the Biotechnology, Biologics and Environmental Protection Division (BBEPD) with responsibility for all biotechnology products. Under NEPA, the USDA has a responsibility for ensuring ecological safe utilisation of crops, livestock, and veterinary products produced both from traditional and recombinant DNA methods. FSIS assures the safety and wholesomeness of food products.

USDA policy on the regulation of biotechnology, consistent with the overall federal policy, does not view GMOs as fundamentally different from those produced using traditional methods. The USDA considered that the products of the new techniques of biotechnology were in principle covered by regulations that had been implemented for existing technologies. They did, however, consider that the assessment of the products of the new technologies in some instances required specific information that necessitated the introduction of some new regulations and the updating of some existing ones.

Since 1987 APHIS has approved or acknowledged over 6,000 field trials at over 15,000 field sites. The notification option, in effect since 1993 accounts for approximately 75 per cent of all current field-testing. Derivatives of 48 different plant species have been field tested to date, with a wide variety of modifications. Corn continues as the major crop being field tested under our regulations. In the past two years APHIS have seen the first field trials involving *Arabidopsis thaliana*, barley, broccoli, carrot, chicory, cranberry, creeping bentgrass, eggplant, gladiolus, grape, pea, pepper, raspberry, strawberry, sugarcane, sweetgum, sweet potato, watermelon, and wheat.

APHIS also issues licenses and permits for production, importation, sale and experimental use of various types of biological products. Specific information that must be submitted for GMOs and products includes detailed information on stability, genetic constructs and vectors, and the effects of any insertions and deletions on the organism.

FSIS' function is to assure the safety and wholesomeness of food products. FSIS is regulating the slaughter of animals derived from biotechnology experiments under the experimental animal regulations. In January 1993, FSIS petitioned ABRAC to address the scientific questions associated with the human food safety of products prepared from transgenic animals. In response, ABRAC formed a transgenic animal working group comprised of specialists in the field of animal biotechnology from industry, academia and government.

The Environmental Protection Agency (EPA)

Under NEPA, the EPA has broad jurisdiction over environmental impact. It mostly considers GMOs under the aegis of the "Toxic Substances Control Act" (TSCA) and the "Federal Insecticide, Fungicide, and Rodenticide Act" (FIFRA).

In general, TSCA will not be triggered if the microbes are used to produce foods, additives, drugs, vaccines, cosmetics or medical devices, if they are regulated by the FDA or USDA. Other than those listed exemptions, all other new or new use chemical end products from microorganisms, which themselves may be considered new, are subject to TSCA. Consent orders and negotiated agreements are used as the mechanisms to cover environmental introductions and sale. In order to test a product, an applicant must submit complete data. Product evaluation includes the equivalent to an Environmental Assessment or Environmental Impact Statements. Since 1984, notification of intent to field test GMOs and non-engineered non-indigenous pathogenic and non-pathogenic microorganisms was required, regardless of testing site size.

The EPA currently regulates chemical pesticides that are externally applied to plants. Now the agency wants to expand its federal regulatory powers over the characteristics of plants that help plants resist diseases and pests. The agency has coined a new term for these characteristics, calling them "plant-pesticides". All plants are able to prevent, destroy, repel or mitigate pests or diseases. That ability occurs naturally, and some crops have been bred for resistance to specific pests. EPA proposes to single out for regulation those pest-resistant qualities that were transferred to the plant through recombinant DNA technology.

Eleven Professional Scientific Societies took grave objection to the suggested regulations and they responded by developing a document entitled "Appropriate Oversight for Plants with Inherited Traits for Resistance to Pests: A Report". They determined that evaluation of the safety of substances in plants should be based on the toxicological and exposure characteristics of the substance and not on whether the substance confers protection against a plant pest. They asserted that the EPA proposal would:

▶ Erode public confidence in the safety of the food supply by sending the message that all plants contain "pesticides"

▶ Discourage the development of new pest-resistant crops, thereby prolonging the use of synthetic chemical pesticides

▶ Increase the regulatory burden for those developing pest-resistant varieties of crops, while also increasing federal and state bureaucracy

▶ Limit the use of rDNA technology for the development of pest-resistant plants to those applications that can pay the increased costs associated with additional regulation, and deny the benefit of this technology to applications for niche markets likely to be developed by small companies and public plant breeding programmes

▶ Handicap the United States in competition for international markets because of U.S. government policy that new pest-resistant varieties, or products from these varieties, be identified as containing their own "pesticides"

▶ Limit the use of valuable genetic resources and new technologies to improve crop protection from pests and disease.

Food and Drug Administration (FDA)

The FDA regulates biotechnology under the authority of the Food, Drug, and Cosmetic Act (FDCA) and the Public Health Services Act (PHSA). The agency has a mandate to ensure efficacy and safety of food and pharmaceutical products. The agency has a major responsibility in biotechnology in that 65 per cent of the current market share of biotechnology products passes through the agency for review and it has already reviewed thousands of biotechnology products.

Generally, whole foods, such as fruits, vegetables, and grains, are not subject to pre-market approval. The primary legal tool that FDA has successfully used to ensure the safety of foods is the adulteration provisions of Section 402(a)(1). The Act places a legal duty on developers to ensure that the foods they present to consumers are safe and comply with all legal requirements. FDA has authority to remove a food from the market if it poses a risk to public health. Foods derived from new plant varieties developed through genetic engineering are regulated under this authority.

A second section of the Act that FDA relies on is the food additive provision (Section 409). Under this section, substances that are intentionally added to food are food additives, unless the substance is generally recognised as safe (GRAS). Food additives are subject to review and approval by FDA before they may be used in food. When requested to do so, FDA also reviews and affirms the GRAS status of food ingredients.

In May 1992, the FDA issued a policy statement on regulating biotechnology food products. FDA requires pre-market review only for foods into which substances are intentionally introduced, significantly changing the structure, function or amount currently found in the food.

In May 2000, the FDA stated that they will publish a proposed rule mandating that developers of bioengineered foods and animal feeds notify the agency when they intend to market such products. The FDA also will require that specific information be submitted to help determine whether the foods or animal feeds pose any potential safety, labelling or adulteration issues.

On the "Labelling" Issue, FDA policy guidelines state that foods produced through biotechnology will be subject to the same labelling laws as all other foods and food ingredients. FDA requires that: labelling of a food or food ingredient, or additive, be truthful and not misleading, and that the product be declared by its common or usual name. In general the information on the label pertains to the composition and attributes of the food or food ingredients or additive but not to the details of agricultural practices or the manufacturing process.

Biomedical regulations

The greatest regulatory impact on pharmaceutical biotechnology is without question the FDA Modernisation Act of 1997. It presents an enormous task for a regulatory agency to implement the complex provisions of statutes and their amendments. There is a programme of user fees paid by the pharmaceutical and biotechnology firms that produce the candidate agents. Fast Track designations have led to competition among companies for the advantage of more expeditious approvals in marketing their products. There remain contreversial features, including the sensitive matter of prioritising both existing and new agents for trials in children, and the highly competitive matter of marketing to physicians unapproved uses of drugs, biologics, and medical devices based on peer-reviewed articles and possibly even manuscripts not yet published. A federal court has now ruled that FDA restrictions on company statements may violate First Amendment rights! The impression, overall, is that the FDA has done remarkably well to build and balance a sense of partnership with its several stakeholders: patient groups, pharmaceutical and biotech manufacturers, the research and clinical communities, and agency watchdog organisations.

All pharmaceutical companies are now eager to market their products globally, often through corporate alliances. Under the International Conference on Harmonisation, important efforts have been underway for several years to achieve nearly consistent criteria for toxicological studies and for clinical efficacy studies of therapeutic agents, and to reduce the often onerous documentation, requirements for duplicative research, delays in access for patients, and trade barriers long associated with disparate national policies and practices.

The regulatory status of diagnostic products and tests is entirely different from that for therapeutics. In many biotech companies, diagnostic tests are part of the business strategy along with therapies. The critical issue here is whether the company markets a laboratory service, covered by the Clinical Laboratories Improvement Act (CLIA) and administered by the Health Care Financing Administration, or a test kit, which is regulated by the FDA.

International Perspective

Biotechnology is a worldwide industry. In the case of genetically modified crops alone, field trials are being carried out in at least 22 countries, and cover a wide range of crops (see Figure.5 on page 209). Despite the fact that almost 80 per cent of these trials take place in the United States, the regulatory issues are of concern to all, and biotechnology issues are front and centre in many international fora. For instance several nations are working on the United Nations' Biosafety Protocol. The purpose of the protocol is to protect biological diversity from potential adverse effects resulting from the transboundary movement of living modified organisms, including those made through biotechnology. It will also address the needs of developing countries to develop the capacity to assess and manage potential risks. The CODEX Alimentarius Commission has established the CODEX Committee on Food Labelling to arrive at a common international position on labelling.

The Organisation for Economic Cooperation and Development and the World Health Organisation have embraced the concept of substantial equivalence as the cornerstone of safety assessment for genetically modified foods and crops. The most complex regulatory and political situation is in the European Community, especially with regard to labelling for consumers.

The OECD's Working Group on Harmonisation of Regulatory Oversight in Biotechnology decided at its first session, in June 1995, to focus its work on the development of consensus documents that are mutually recognised among member countries. These consensus documents contain information for use during the regulatory assessment of a particular product. The consensus documents comprise technical information for use during the regulatory assessment of products of biotechnology and are intended to be mutually recognised among OECD Member countries. These documents focus on the biology of organisms (such as plants, trees or microorganisms) or introduced novel traits.

Irish Regulations

History of GMO regulation in Ireland

By 1973, the techniques of gene cloning were developed. In 1974, the Medical Research Council (MRC) was requested by the Department of Health to report on any recombinant DNA research in Ireland. An expert group was then set up to study developments abroad and to monitor the situation in Ireland. In 1977, the MRC Committee was broadened to include representatives from the National Science Council (NSC) and the Agricultural Institute (AFT). The Royal Irish Academy (RIA) also set up a broadly based Committee to give advice in general terms on scientific, medical, legal, political or other problems that might arise. In 1978, the EEC proposed a Council directive on rDNA work. However, this proposal was replaced by a Council recommendation in 1980 specifying that each Member State should have a national authority for notification of experiments and that each national authority should be responsible for the classification and storage of such notifications.

In 1981, a National rDNA Committee was formed and the MRC and RIA Committees were disbanded. The Committee consisted of a Chairman and 14 members, including representatives from Government Departments (Agriculture, Health and Labour), Agencies (National Drugs Advisory Board, the Agriculture Institute, National Board for Science & Technology), research experts from the Higher Education sector, Trade Unions and the Confederation of Irish Industry. Functions included:

◗ **Considering and establishing national guidelines for all work on recombinant DNA in Ireland, and harmonising such guidelines with those of international organisations**

▶ Establishing and maintaining liaison with appropriate bodies in Ireland, with international organisations involved in rDNA activities, and also with appropriate national bodies in other countrie

▶ Providing advice to the appropriate bodies on matters relating to rDNA activities, at the request of such bodies or at the Committee's own initiative.

Figure 5a: Percentage breakdown of GMO field trials by species

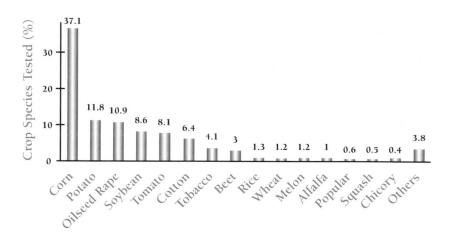

Figure 5b: Percentage breakdown of GMO field trials by country

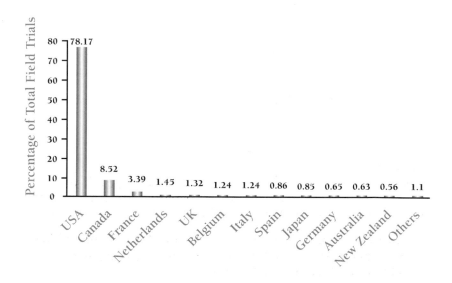

In 1990, EU Directives 90/219/EEC (contained use) and 90/220/EEC (deliberate release into the environment) were adopted. From 1991-1994, the Department of the Environment was nominated as provisional competent authority to regulate the use of GMOs in Ireland.

Adoption of legislation implementing the directives in Ireland

Section 111 of the Environmental Protection Agency Act of 1992, provides for the Minister for the Environment and Local Government to give full effect to the two EU Directives (90/219/EEC & 90/220/EEC) by means of statutory regulation, after consultation with any other Minister of the Government concerned. These Regulations are as follows:

- Genetically Modified Organisms Regulations, 1994, (S. I. No. 345 of 1994)

- S. I. No. 348 of 1996 (Genetically Modified Organisms (Amendment) Regulations, 1996 -concerning criteria for the classification of GMMs into Group I-Second Schedule and geographical distribution of an organism-Part II, Section A, para 3 of the Ninth schedule)

- S. I. No. 332 of 1997 (Genetically Modified Organisms (Amendment) Regulations, 1997-concerning labelling-Eight Schedule).

EU Directive 90/219/EEC covers only GMMs (Genetically Modified Micro-organisms). However, the Irish Regulations also covers GM animals and plants used in containment.

Nomination of a competent authority

Regulations (S. I. No. 345 of 1994) to implement the EU Directives, were made in November 1994, and the EPA was nominated as the competent authority to administer the Regulations in Ireland. The commencement date for implementation was 1 January, 1995. The Department of the Environment & Local Government (DELG) are responsible for the national policy in the GMO area and the DELG casts the Member State vote under Article 21 of Directive 90/220/EEC.

Advisory Committee on Genetically Modified Organisms

An Advisory Committee was set up in 1995, under Part VI of the Regulations. The Committee consists of 12 members nominated by both Government and non-Government organisations (NGO's). Nominating bodies include:

- EPA
- Minister for the Environment & Local Government
- Minister for Agriculture & Food
- Minister for Health & Children
- Minister for Enterprise and Employment
- Commissioners for Public Works in Ireland
- National Authority for Occupational Safety and Health
- Organisations which in the opinion of the EPA are representative of persons whose professions or occupations relate to biotechnology research or the biotechnology industry
- Organisations which in the opinion of the EPA are concerned with environmental protection.

The Committee is appointed for a three year term. The EPA can consult the Committee on any aspect of its functions under the Regulations. The Committee has met quarterly, has discussed relevant issues and has advised the EPA in relation to its functions under the Regulations.

Regulation of GMOs

Contained uses of GMOs in laboratories or in industry

This covers any GMO operation where organisms are genetically modified, or where GMOs are cultured, stored, used, transported, destroyed or disposed of. Containment is provided by physical barriers, or a combination of physical barriers, together with chemical and/or biological barriers. Containment is used to limit the contact of the GMO with the general population and the environment. For some Group II GMMs there is a requirement to prevent the release of the GMMs from the physical containment facility.

The main requirements of the Regulations in this area are:

- Human health and environmental risk assessment
- Categorising the GMO work, taking into account the nature of the organism and the type of activity
- Giving notice to the EPA of existing GMO work
- Making of a public Register of all GMO users in Ireland
- Provision for confidentiality

- Giving advance notice to the EPA of an intention to use an installation for the first time, for some activities consent must be given by the EPA before work can start

- Notification to the EPA of individual activities; involving GMOs, and consent is needed for some activities

- Power of the EPA to grant or refuse consent

- Principals of good microbiological practices (GMP)

- Establishment of Biological Safety Committees (BSC)

- Preparation of emergency plans, where necessary

- Site inspections

- Reporting accidents

- Fees for notifications

- Review of contained uses of GMOs

- Enforcement and Regulation

- Report to the EU Commission.

Deliberate release into the environment

This means any intentional release into the environment of a GMO without provisions for containment. There are two different types of release covered by the Regulations.

Deliberate Release for R&D purposes-Field Trials

The main requirements of the Regulations for deliberate release into the environment for R&D purposes are:

▶ A technical description of the proposed deliberate release-as outlined in the Seventh Schedule of the Regulations

▶ A statement evaluating the impacts and risks posed by the GMO to human health or environment

▶ Information on previous releases with the GMO either inside or outside the EU

▶ The notifier may reference data from another notifier

▶ A notifier can submit a notification for the release of a GMO on different trial sites

▶ The notifier must place an advertisement in a newspaper circulating in the area where the proposed field trial is to take place, giving the following:

(a)   the name & address of notifier
(b)   a description of the organism to be released
(c)   the location & purpose of the deliberate release
(d)   the date or dates of release.

▶ **The information on the location of the proposed deliberate release must be the same as that placed on the GMO Register by the EPA**

▶ **The notifier must send notice to:**

(a)   the owner of the site of the proposed deliberate release
(b)   the local authority where the release is intended to take place.

▶ **Any person or body may within 21 days of the publication of the notice of the deliberate release make representations in writing to the EPA in relation to the notification**

▶ **There is provision to submit an amended notification, if necessary**

▶ **The notifier must pay the appropriate fee**

▶ **The EPA may charge for site inspections & monitoring**

The duties of the EPA in relation to Field Trials are to:

(a)   acknowledge receipt of the notification in writing
(b)   make a decision on a request to keep information confidential
(c)   place the relevant information on the GMO Register
(d)   send a copy of SNIF (Ninth Schedule) to EU within 30 days of receipt of notification
(e)   examine the notification for compliance with the Regulations;
(f)   evaluate the risks posed by the deliberate release
(g)   consider any observation by another CA
(h)   consider any objections
(i)   record its conclusions in writing.

When the EPA makes its decision it must inform the following:

▶ **The owner of the site where the deliberate release is taking place**

▶ **The local authority where the deliberate release is taking place**

▶ **Each Member State of the EU**

▶ **EU Commission**

▶ Any person who made representations to the EPA within the prescribed period.

To date, one field trial took place during the 1997 growing season (two GM sugar beets) and five field trials (5 locations) took place during the 1998 growing season (one GM sugar beet) in Ireland. Four field trials were planted at four locations with a GM sugar beet in Ireland in 1999.

Placing GMO products on the market

In Ireland

A person cannot place a product on the market in Ireland which contains or consists of a GMO unless consent is given in writing under Part 1V of the Genetically Modified Organisms Regulations, 1994, or consent is obtained from the Competent Authority of another EU Member State in accordance with Part C of Directive 90/220/EEC. No notifications have been received by the EPA since the Directive was transposed into Irish law.

The main requirements for the placing on the market of plant products containing GMOs are:

▶ General information-name and address of notifier, including the name, qualifications and experience of the responsible scientists, etc.

▶ Information relating to the recipient-complete name, reproduction, survivability, dissemination, etc.

▶ Information relating to the genetic modification-methods used for transformation, type and source of the vector, etc.

▶ Information relating to the genetically modified plant - description of the trait (s), information about the gene sequence used, stability of the insert, information on any toxic or harmful effects on human health and the environment arising form the genetic modification, etc.

▶ Information on the potential environmental impact from the release of the genetically modified plants

▶ Information on data or results from previous releases

▶ An assessment of any risks for human health or the environment

▶ Name and address of the manufacturer or distributor

▶ Type of expected use

- Where the product will be used
- Information relating to the introduced genetic material, e.g., the nucleotide sequence which could be included in a register of modifications
- Measures to take in case of unintended release or misuse
- Storage and handling instructions
- Labelling requirements.

In the case of crop plants, it is only the 'live' seed (able to germinate or transfer its genetic material to other plants) that is regulated under Directive 90/220/EEC. Once the seed is processed (at certain temperatures) the DNA is denatured (non-viable) and therefore the product is not classified as a GMO, e.g., oil derived from genetically modified soybeans. Such products as well as 'live' GMOs to be used for human food consumption are regulated under EU Regulation 258/97 (Concerning Novel Foods and Novel Food Ingredients).

In the European Union

The manufacturer of a GMO product deals with the Competent Authority from a Member State where the product will be marketed for the first time. The Competent Authority carries out the main environmental risk assessment and adopts a favourable or unfavourable opinion on the product within a maximum of 90 days of receiving the dossier. If the opinion is favourable, it is then sent to the Commission who will send it to all the Authoritys in other Member States for review. Consent for the release will be given by the main evaluating Competent Authority within 60 days if no insurmountable difficulties or objections are raised by the authorities of the other Member States. However, if objections are raised by another Member State, consent can only be given if a qualified majority vote is obtained under Article 21 of Directive 90/220/EEC. If the qualified majority (at least 62 votes (71%) cast by not less than 10 Member States) is in favour of placing the product on the market, consent will be given to the notifier and the product can be marketed in the EU.

If a qualified majority is not achieved the Commission submits a proposal to the Council, who have three months to make a decision on the proposal. In the absence of a unanimous decision, the proposal is adopted by the European Commission in consultation with its Scientific Committees. This is the route by which the Ciba Maize was granted access to the EU markets after it failed to receive a qualified majority from the various competent authorities.

Table 7:   GMO products approved under Directive 90/220/EEC (Nov 1998)

1.   Vaccine against Aujeszky's disease

2.   Vaccine against rabies

3.   Tobacco-herbicide tolerant

4.   Vaccine against Aujeszky's disease (further uses)

5.   Hybrid oilseed rape-herbicide tolerant

6.   Soybeans-herbicide tolerant

7.   Male sterile chicory-herbicide tolerant

8.   GM maize-insect & herbicide tolerant

9.   Hybrid oilseed rape -herbicide tolerant

10.   Hybrid oilseed rape-herbicide tolerant (similar to No. 9)

11.   GMMs-test kit to detect antibiotic remnants in milk

12.   GM carnations

13.   GM maize-herbicide tolerant

14.   GM maize-insect tolerant

15.   GM maize-insect & herbicide tolerant

16.   GM oilseed rape-herbicide tolerant

17.   GM carnations

18.   GM carnations.

Eighteen GM products had been approved under Directive 90/220/EEC by November 1998, including a number of plants which have been modified for herbicide resistance (Table 8). It is anticipated that more plant products will be submitted under Part C of 90/220/EEC in future years.

Register of GMO users

The EPA has set up a Register of GMO users as required under Article 8 (1) of the Regulations. The Register contains information on the following:

▶ Name and address of the notifier

▶ Description of each GMO

▶ Purpose of the contained use, deliberate release, or placing on the market

▶ Other requirements.

The Register is available for inspection at the EPA headquarters by any member of the public during office hours. By the end of September 1999, 86 GMO users were listed on the GMO Register. Ninety two per cent (92%) are contained uses, 85 per cent are users in Type A operations (research & development purposes) and approximately 90 per cent of the users are working with Group I GMMs. This Register is updated on a regular basis.

EU novel foods legislation

EU Regulation 258/97 concerns the placing on the market of novel foods and novel food ingredients. A number of categories of novel foods are specifically mentioned, including:

▶ Foods and food ingredients containing or consisting of genetically modified organisms

▶ Foods and food ingredients produced from, but not containing, genetically modified organisms.

The Department of Health & Children were nominated as the Competent Authority to implement this regulation in Ireland.

An interpretative document was prepared by the EU Commission on the interplay between Regulation 258/97 and Directive 90/220/EEC.

The main features of this document are summarised as follows:

▶ Article 9 (1) of Regulation 258/97 states that Articles 11-18 of Directive 90/220/EEC shall not apply to foods or foods ingredients which contain or consist of GMOs. This means that a notifier must obtain consent under Regulation 258/97 for placing GMOs or products derived from GMOs on the market in the EU for food use

▶ Regulation 258/97 will not cover animal feed uses. This means that a product containing or consisting of GMOs which is to be placed on the market for both food & feed uses, will have to be assessed under both Regulation 258/97 and (in the absence of feed-specific legislation) under 90/220/EEC

▶ Article 9 (2) Regulation 258/97 states that in the case of foods or food ingredients containing or consisting of GMOs that an environmental Risk Assessment must be carried out as laid down in 90/220/EEC to ensure that all appropriate measures are taken to prevent adverse effects taken on human health & the environment which might arise from the deliberate release of GMOs into the environment.

▶ Human health aspects linked to the placing on the market of a GMO as food or food ingredient will be exclusively assessed under Regulation 258/97. Directive 90/220/EEC will only be concerned with human health aspects of feed and seed, for example, toxicity and allergenicity linked to the cultivation of plants

▶ Regulation 258/97 does not cover the placing on the market of seeds destined for cultivation. Therefore, in the absence of the necessary seed-specific legislation incorporating a similiar risk assessment to that in 90/220/EEC, the environmental and human health assessment for the cultivation of seed falls under 90/220/EEC. On the other hand, the placing on the market of foods and food ingredients resulting from those seeds, falls under Regulation 258/97.

With regard to the role of the EPA & the Department of Health & Children, the following modus operandi is in operation:

▶ Food products containing or consisting of GMOs or products derived from GMOs being placed on the market after May 1997 are regulated under Regulation 258/97 by the Department of Health & Children in Ireland

▶ Feed products containing or consisting of GMOs are regulated by the EPA under 90/220/EEC until there is specific EU feed legislation.

▶ environmental and human health assessment (toxicity & allergenicity linked to the cultivation of GM crops) are assessed under 90/220/EEC by the EPA

The Costs of Over-regulation

The purpose of regulations should be to insure safety and efficacy, to limit potential product risks while encouraging innovation and economic development. By raising the cost of biotechnology R&D over-regulation drains capital resources and slows the pace of research. This stalls innovation, which in turn, delays or blocks the entry of new products into the marketplace. This can sustain reliance on less efficient, less precise, less predictable and sometimes more hazardous alternative technologies and products.

Over-regulation leads to higher operating costs and extended development times, which raises investment risks and exacerbates concerns about long term prospects for company success. Less capital and higher "burn rates" jeopardise smaller firms.

Priorities

▶ Greater emphasis on generating the scientific knowledge and information needed to support biotechnology regulatory decisions

▶ Identify options to make the regulatory system more efficient, effective, responsive and predictable, using tools such as international benchmarking, performance standards and monitoring

▶ Improve international and domestic regulatory co-operation, harmonisation and related R&D programmes (for example, through mutual recognition agreements)

▶ Provide the general public with clear, timely information on regulatory processes, decisions

▶ Enforcement activities.

Chapter 8

INTELLECTUAL PROPERTY ISSUES

Intellectual Property Issues

General considerations

In the context of the World Trade Organisation's review of the Trade-Related Aspects of Intellectual Property (TRIPs) Agreement, many governments will be conducting consultations to develop National policies on the patenting of higher life forms. Biotechnology patent issues include, among others, whether and to what extent patent claims covering plants, animals and human body parts should be allowed, what exemptions and safeguards are needed to protect the public interest and whether or not ethical and moral aspects should be considered in granting patents. In 1997, the United Nations Educational, Social and Cultural Organisation (UNESCO) adopted the Universal Declaration on the Human Genome and Human Rights. Many nations are playing an active role in ensuring domestic and international implementation of the declaration and in addressing unresolved concerns shared by many countries.

Patent laws are founded on principles regarding reward, protection of property rights to immaterial products, and fair treatment of the inventor. Patents are granted as an incentive to promote development of new products and the creation of new jobs. Patents provide protection of inventions, demonstrating the three key characteristics of novelty, non-obviousness and utility. A patent is subject to limitations in time and place. The granting of a patent in itself does not give the right for the inventor/proprietor to use an invention, but it is a right to prevent others from exploiting that invention commercially. This means that it is possible to take out a patent on something which may be subsequently prohibited by, for example, environmental or health authorities.

Because biotech companies depend on private investments, patents are among the first and most important benchmarks of progress in developing a new biotechnology product. Patents offer limited protection against commercial use of a company's invention by a competitor. In biotechnology, patents are critical to raising capital to fund the research and development of products. Most biotechnology organisations advocate strong intellectual property protection for biotechnology inventions.

Patents on microorganisms have for years been granted in the US, Europe and Japan. Patents for genetically modified plants are available in the US, Japan and Europe. The first patents on transgenic animals have been granted in the US and by the European Patent Office. Patents on proteins, hormones, genes and cell lines, irrespective of their source of origin, are presently available in many countries in all fields of biotechnology.

There are a number of exceptions with regard to what can be patented.

These vary from country to country, but in most European countries inventions relating to: new discoveries (e.g. mathematical rules), diagnosis and treatment of disease (excluding technical apparatus)(Allowed in the US), inventions that are in conflict with normal decency and public order, plant and animal varieties (Allowed in the US and Japan) are not considered patentable. There are other rules concerning patent rights, which also vary from country to country, including whether the invention has been published, and the starting date and duration, etc of the patent. If there were no patents, the absence of a financial incentive to develop new products would make it difficult for companies to make large investments in research, since the results would be available for anybody to copy.

As an alternative companies could try to protect their inventions through secrecy, if possible. This would have the unfortunate consequence of impeding the exchange of information between scientists, and precluding society at large from insight into this research and development.

The costs of approving a new medical drug can easily exceed US$300 million and this would be a very risky investment without patent protection. The patent also ensures that the invention is publicly available, thus making it easier for others to undertake further development on the basis of the invention. The same principle applies to research in the agronomic sector where approval from environmental authorities for pesticides and fertilisers, and for new plant varieties, are lengthy and costly procedures, which may easily cost more than US$50 million. For these reasons the biotechnology and related industries support the view that patents should be available for all inventions having the potential for commercialisation.

Patenting Genes

Patents on genes, and particularly on human genes have been particularly controversial. Many of the critical voices tend to misunderstand what patents are and they often make contradictory statements. For example, in a followup memorandum after the Rio Summit in 1992 the WWF proposed that patents on genetic material from human beings, animals and plants should be prohibited, but it also believes that the developing countries' property rights to genetic material, including patents, must be safeguarded. Environmental organisations often fail to grasp that a patent does not amount to ownership of an object, but is a right to prevent others from making commercial use of an invention. Critics of patents also forget that patents do not give a right to use and that the development costs and expenditure related to approval of medical products would preclude development of new medical drugs if the products could not be patented.

The many resources invested in recent years in mapping the human genome have resulted in the discovery of an increasing number of new gene sequences and simultaneously the ensuing development of new medical and diagnostical applications based on this knowledge. Patenting of results from this research in the form of DNA sequences with unknown utility has been a controversial topic since the NIH in 1991 applied for patents on a number of cDNA sequences with unknown utility. The EU Commission's committee on human genome analysis made a general statement in 1992 against patents which only reveal DNA sequences but not their industrial utility, as such patents would decrease the free flow of DNA sequence data. An international agreement on patents on genes and living matter is still subject to debate. The NIH has now abandoned its applications and we will probably never know if it would have been possible to patent such DNA sequences under the present legislation.

Patenting Animals

Following Diamond vs Chakrabarty, in 1987, the US Patent and Trademark Office (PTO) considered all nonhuman, multicellular living organisms to be patentable.

The vital criteria embodied by a utility patent are novelty - biological material is new and has not previously been described; utility - the invention has a useful purpose; and non-obviousness - the invention is not a simple extension of the state of the art. Although not designed for protection of living organisms, utility patents now apply to plants, animals, and microorganisms. Some forms of property may also be protected as trade secrets, assuming that crucial information can be withheld from the public.

The first patent on a genetically manipulated animal, Harvard's OncoMouse, was granted in 1988. A nearly five-year hiatus in the issue of patents for animals followed, but now the PTO has issued patents for other transgenic mice, rabbits, goats, pigs and cattle. It remains true that most potentially patentable animals are transgenics, produced by some form of genetic manipulation.

Opponents of animal patents feared the broadness in Harvard's claim for the OncoMouse. It has been speculated that if granted a European patent, Harvard would be able to collect royalties on any non-human mammal developed with the same method (introduction of an oncogene into an embryo of the animal of choice). This sort of monopoly could be very costly in the entire scheme of research; only the intervention of a not-for-profit foundation has brought the OncoMouse into a cost position which allows its general use in cancer research.

Patent royalties on transgenic animals could be waived for farmers, but are not likely to be. There may be no way to strike a balance between farmers who want to lower costs and biological seedstock suppliers desiring maximum profit. But the issue may be irrelevant for traditional farmers if, as has been predicted, agriculture shifts from being an extensive effort to an intensive one and large companies retain ownership of transgenic animals.

Production groups point out a risk of inequality between genetic engineering and breeding, since genetic engineers may have greater access to animal varieties than breeders have to genes. Furthermore, genetic uniformity may increase. Patenting may increase the monopolisation of agriculture, as well as increase the dependency of farmers on biotechnology companies. A patent challenge can be a lengthy and expensive process, affordable only by large companies. Small companies may have no choice but to pay up. With a broad patent claim, entire market sectors could be closed to competition.

The concerns of some animal patent opponents extend to the possible lowering of social barriers which prevent maltreatment of living organisms, to say nothing of the issue of fairness. If domestic animals have evolved naturally through biological history, affected to a greater-or-lesser extent by human intervention, it seems ludicrous that engineering of a very small change in an animal's makeup should allow one to gain exploitative legal control over it and its descendants. Furthermore, there is valid concern that patents on living organisms could negatively alter society's perception of what constitutes life, blurring the line between animate and inanimate.

The Onco Mouse patent application was refused in Europe in 1989 due primarily to an established ban on animal patenting. The application was revised to make narrower claims, and the patent was granted in 1991. This has since been repeatedly challenged, primarily by groups objecting to the judgement that benefits to humans outweigh the suffering of the animal. Currently, the patent applicant is awaiting protestors' responses to a series of possible modifications to the application. Predictions are that agreement will not likely be forthcoming and that the legal wrangling will continue into the future.

For some companies, principally those working on transgenics whose intrinsic value is in the animal itself, rather than as a source of recombinant products, this appears to be a major concern. In many countries outside Europe, patenting of animals for xenotransplantation and recombinant product production is permitted, making the European market less interesting to at least some companies. The question of patentability also affects European researchers, whose work could be inhibited by lack of access to products not covered by European patents. At least some pharmaceutical and biologics companies do a significant proportion of their research and development outside Europe in order to access animal models. It has even been suggested that some countries are falling behind the US through inability to access animal models and protocols.

Biotechnology companies may be relatively unaffected by these proceedings, in that they can usually protect inventions in some manner other than direct claims on the animal itself. Included might be claims for medical uses (transplantation of organs from transgenic animals) or processes for protein production (by the so-called "pharming" companies). It may also be possible to receive patent protection through applications to individual European countries, rather than to the central European Patent Office.

EU Directive on the Protection of Biotechnological Inventions

The issue of patents on living organisms and parts of the human body has been the focus of discussions in the EU Parliament over a period of 11 years, since the Commission presented a proposal for a Directive on the protection of biotechnological inventions in October 1988. The proposal was introduced to harmonise the interpretation of the basically identical patent laws in the member states, thereby strengthening the competitiveness of the European biotechnological industry in relation to the same industries in the USA and Japan. The proposal would not have extended patent protection to anything that is presently not patentable.

In 1995, opponents of patents on genetic material exploited a loophole in the 1973 European Patent Convention to argue that transgenic plants can be considered a plant variety and, therefore, were not patentable.

The European Biotechnology Patent Directive (1997) sought to change this interpretation and in doing so to assist in clearing the backlog of around 1200 patent applications for plants, and 500-600 on animals that have built up. The Directive "explicitly allows patenting of life, including human genes, provided that a truly inventive step and industrial use can be proved and provided that the procedures involved are within defined ethical limits". A discovery of a gene in its natural state would thus not be patentable as some element of science is required. However, once the function of a gene is determined that gene could be patented. There would be no requirement for commercial applicability.

After about seven years work, the Directive has lapsed. Nothing in the present situation will therefore be required to change. Industrial circles generally are not dissatisfied, since for each change the wording of the Directive became less attractive to industry. The Greens and especially Greenpeace are wrongly claiming this to be a substantial victory. What they have achieved is to lose any influence the Parliament had obtained via the amendments introduced into the Directive. Comments in the press from a number of parliamentarians indicate that they see a need for regulation of the patent system in respect of biotechnology, and it has become known that the Commission is working on the drafting of a new proposal. The EU Parliament was especially opposed to those Articles relating to patenting parts of the human body, including genes, cell lines, etc, and to patenting animals.

The New Frontier for Patent Battles

DNA chips (see Chapter 1) are a pioneering technology used to identify genes by binding them onto a large array of sample sequences. The surge of competition between various companies to produce this technology, however, could be halted by current legal battles over patent rights.

Disputes have raged over patents on both the "hardware" (the chip technology) and the "software" (the actual genes that dot the arrays) involved in the innovative technology. Jeffrey Trent, who heads a DNA array project at the National Human Genome Research Institute in Bethesda, Maryland notes that the debate over patent disputes is really at a critical juncture right now and has the potential to limit access and availability of the technology.

In 1998, leading chip producer Affymetrix filed suit against two companies, Incyte Pharmaceuticals Inc. and Synteni Inc. of California (which have since merged) and is trading lawsuits with another chip maker, Hyseq Inc. of Sunnyvale, California. All three companies are countering each others' lawsuits. But all of them could be feeling some heat soon from University of Oxford Molecular Biologist, Edwin Southern, who was awarded a broad-ranging U.S. patent on a basic technology for laying short snippets of DNA in arrays. Southern has yet to try to enforce his patent with companies such as Hyseq and Affymetrix.

The picture is even more complicated on the "software" side. Patent offices already allow the patenting of newly discovered genes as long as a known function can be ascribed. Once genes are patented, DNA chip companies may be forced to obtain licenses before using portions of them on arrays.

The scale of the licensing problem may be overwhelming as each spot on the array involves a gene that potentially is patentable and an array of a 2.5-centimetre chip can contain up to 40,000 gene sequences. The current squabbles in the array community present serious concerns and run a risk of impeding the promise of what many are calling the "microchip of the 21st century". Perhaps the most devastating impact of this controversy may be felt by the genetic diagnostic companies. Their future products are being designed with the expectation that DNA array research can proceed with identifying the unique genetic expression patterns that could help predict the onset of prevalent diseases such as cancer, Alzheimer's, osteoporosis, and heart disease.

The OECD Position on Intellectual Property, Technology Transfer and Genetic Resources

An OECD Survey of Current Practices and Policies, reviews current practices and policies on intellectual property, technology transfer, and access to genetic resources, in an attempt to better understand the links between these topics that were highlighted by the adoption of the Convention on Biological Diversity (CBD). The analysis is based primarily on responses to an OECD Questionnaire, which complemented work done in other parts of the Organisation in relation to the Convention on Biological Diversity. Nineteen countries replied, which indicates considerable interest and commitment, even if the subject has been difficult for many respondents and required inter-agency, as well as public-private sector coordination.

Responses are heterogeneous as to structure and detailed content. However, a number of common conclusions emerged which point to the possibility of a common understanding of these complex issues.

Intellectual property

In public discussion of intellectual property, there are often misunderstandings of its nature and limitations. Intellectual property protection cannot be extended or enforced with regard to naturally occurring or socially maintained genetic resources, although patent, trade secret and other forms of protection can be enjoyed in products or information derived from such genetic resources and in genetic resources themselves where there has been the intervention of human ingenuity and the national laws allow. This distinction between the subject matter of intellectual property – which is invariably value-added subject matter in relation to subject matter existing in the public domain – is often confused with interests in physical property or cultural behaviour. Seen in this manner, intellectual property systems would not appear to have a clear role to play with regard to resolving concerns related to ownership or use of naturally occurring or socially maintained materials or information in the public domain. Only novel products and processes, including those derived from genetic resources and genetic resources themselves, where the technical intervention of humans has achieved a result which does not occur in nature, may claim some form of intellectual property protection, for a limited time.

The availability of such intellectual property protection, in both the "home" country and that to which technology is to be transferred, is seen as a fundamental prerequisite of co-operative activities that can lead to technology transfer agreements and to foreign investment in technology-importing countries. The overriding importance of strong intellectual property laws and enforcement procedures is underlined by nearly all national responses – this is one of their most emphasised areas of agreement.

Genetic resources

The Member countries of the OECD and many other countries continue to recognise and honour the principle of unrestricted access to genetic resources (in accordance with the International Undertaking on Plant Genetic Resources for Food and Agriculture), while also accepting the need to reconcile this with the sovereign rights of States over their own resources, and the resulting authority to determine access to genetic resources, as recognised in the Convention on Biological Diversity.

Conservation is fully consistent with the scientific exploration and technological exploitation of genetic diversity for the development of new products and processes. More than this, the application of modern science and technology to genetic resources is essential to achieving the most effective conservation of biodiversity. Conservation is also fully compatible with the principles of intellectual property protection for new products and processes.

Few of the responses identify specific projects related to the discovery or development of genetic resources. It is clear, however, that private and public agencies in some OECD Member countries (and also the European Commission) are very active in their exploration, and have accumulated considerable experience, taking into account the mutual needs and expectations of all the parties involved. So far, access to genetic resources has generally been arranged case by case. No response suggested that arrangements regarding access to and use of genetic resources have proven to be difficult to conclude or have led to unsatisfactory results for any project participants.

The principle of prior informed consent, regarding the handling and use of samples of genetic resources incident to the granting of access, is now widely accepted. Consent must be arranged between the interested parties and does not necessarily require state intervention. Universities and public R&D centres are developing and using "Material Transfer Agreements" (MTAs) which are strongly favoured by public germplasm collections. So far, consent has often been given freely, although industry expects that some sharing of benefits will be required in the future. "Codes of conduct" have been developed or are being developed. "Access legislation" would be a more formal type of legal instrument regulating the use of genetic resources. The Biodiversity Convention provides for access to genetic resources to be subject to national legislation. So far, no

OECD Member country has enacted access legislation, and only one or very few developing countries.

Equally, there is no European Union legislation covering access to genetic resources in the sense of the Biodiversity Convention. No initiative towards access legislation is reported in the responses. One apparent problem would be the identification of the entity having the necessary authority to grant access, or to authorise subsequent transfer of genetic materials.

Technology transfer

The transfer of technologies which use genetic resources, in favour of the providers of such resources, is expected to proceed on an *ad hoc* basis. No particular legal model or paradigm emerges from the responses; all traditional methods will be used, including disclosure of R&D results, licensing, information exchange, training, joint ventures, support of R&D and others. Also, no uniform idea has emerged on how to share in a fair and equitable way the benefits arising from the use of genetic resources with the indigenous populations concerned with the conservation of those resources. In order to give genetic resource providers due recognition and reward, various legal instruments have been mentioned. One successful example is the Letter of Collection Agreement (LOC) used by the US National Cancer Institute. A LOC is a contractual agreement providing financial reward to source countries and indigenous peoples through remuneration and technology transfer. LOCs have been negotiated with 19 developing countries.

Private sector

One of the main challenges to the implementation of international genetic resource conventions is that conventions are made among governments, but it is often the private sector that seeks access to genetic resources and that creates technology that can lead to commercial and other economic benefits. The measures required to induce the private sector to transfer technology will include the creation of conditions in the recipient country that encourage voluntary technology transfer from abroad.

In spite of strong interest in principle, some specific factors may inhibit the willingness of industrial or other sectors to conclude genetic resource agreements. One factor could be high transaction costs. Another is possible underestimation of the long timelags before R&D on a genetic resource may yield economic benefits, e.g. in the pharmaceutical sector. One should also consider the longer-term potential of "combinatorial" and other types of synthetic chemistry that can create and screen at low costs large numbers of diverse molecular structures of potential biological activity. Inhibitory conditions of access to the great storehouse of natural or socially maintained genetic resources could further encourage the ongoing search for chemical techniques which might reduce dependence on bioprospecting. A critical factor is whether a private sector company will be able to protect new technologies that are developed incident to a genetic resource development agreement, whether that protection comes through effective patent, plant variety, copyright or trade secret laws in the host country, or through reliance on effective contractual arrangements to protect trade secret information.

Economic and financial incentives and disincentives to encourage development of genetic resources can play a significant role in the decisional process preceding investment and technology transfer decisions. However, this role appears to be secondary to intellectual property protection and to the scientific and commercial assessment of genetic resource development. Marketing restrictions on products resulting from genetic resources are a significant complication for industry, but do not necessarily inhibit projects. Financial inducements to embark on projects are an encouragement but cannot be the main motivation for industry. The responses on the main future challenges facing the legal protection of biotechnology in general, show that there are many outstanding issues which need to be discussed in international fora. However, there is no "majority opinion" on the order of importance of these challenges. Comments are wide-ranging and extend to many fundamental issues: international harmonisation, restrictions of patent protection, patents considered to be "unduly broad", the interface between patents and plant variety rights, the impact of various lobbies, and others; a general question is the roles of bilateral and multilateral agreements and the combination thereof.

Conclusion

The religious coalition in the US postion on patents is "life should not be regarded solely as if chemical product subject to genetic alteration and patentable for economic benefit. Moral, social and spiritual issues should be considered". The industry view is that without patents, companies would be unwilling to invest in, or unable to attract capital for research that benefits humankind. They recognise that the ethical aspects of an invention must be considered in the procedure leading to the granting of a patent, but they do not believe that patent laws should be used to regulate ethical issues. It should be possible to patent the results of experiments which involve the genetic engineering of animals and plants permitted by the ethical councils, as these ethical questions have already been considered by such relevant public authorities.

However, it should be noted that the general requirements for patents should still be fulfilled. Patents on gene sequences with no proven utility do not fulfil the necessary requirements to be patentable and would possibly impede the open exchange of research results within this area if they were approved. In the end, the key to a balanced solution may be the integral involvement of scientists in decision-making processes, rather than making this a strictly legal or political debate.

For Ireland to have a well-articulated national strategy not only will help realise biotechnology's full benefits in terms of jobs, economic growth and quality of life, but also will allow it to participate responsibly and effectively in international negotiations and promote the country's position on these matters.

Priorities:

▶ Economic and financial incentives and disincentives to encourage development of genetic resources can play a significant role in the decisional process preceding investment and technology transfer decisions. However, this role appears to be secondary to intellectual property protection and to the scientific and commercial assessment of genetic resource development

▶ Marketing restrictions on products resulting from genetic resources are a significant complication for industry, but do not necessarily inhibit projects. Financial inducements to embark on projects are an encouragement but cannot be the main motivation for industry

▶ Fundamental issues must be addressed: international harmonisation, restrictions of patent protection, patents considered to be "unduly broad", the interface between patents and plant variety rights, the impact of various lobbies etc.; a general question is the roles of bilateral and multilateral agreements and the combination thereof

▶ For Ireland to have a well-articulated national intellectual property protection strategy not only will help realise biotechnology's full benefits in terms of jobs, economic growth and quality of life, but also will allow it to participate responsibly and effectively in international negotiations and promote the country's position on these matters.

Further Reading

Service, R.F. 1998. Will patent fights hold DNA chips hostage. *Science* 282:397.

Chapter 9

END OVERVIEW

END OVERVIEW

Responsibilities

The biotechnological revolution offers many promising avenues of research and technological development. As with any powerful technology there is potential for both great good and great harm. Harm may arise from the deliberate abuse of the technology or by the accidental deployment of technologies which, whilst supposedly benign, result in some kind of environmental damage. Recent history has shown that the price of a new technology in terms of environmental impact may take many years to be apparent, however even when that price is apparent the benefits may still outweigh the costs.

A particular aspect about the development of biotechnology is the amount of public debate which it has engendered, and the widespread concern that there has been about both the ethical and safety issues involved. It is important that scientists involved in this debate, and in the evaluation of safety criteria, ensure that there own objectivity is not compromised and that they are clear when they are offering calculable estimates of risk and when they are giving personal judgments about uncertainties.

When assessing risk and communicating the results it is important to be careful with the terminology used. Terms such as risk, hazard and uncertainty are often used in the public forum interchangeably. Risk is an empirically determined quantity based on measurements of occurrence. In a new technology, such as biotechnology, where the level of empirical knowledge is low it is inevitable that risk is not fully calculable and that various levels of uncertainty must be involved. It would be hoped that scientists would recognise this distinction and be making it in public pronouncements.

The Implications for Ireland

President Bill Clinton has stated that the past 50 years have been the age of physics, whereas the next will be "very likely characterised predominantly as the age of biology". The synthesis of this perspective is being realised today in the US and could be emulated in the high tech environment of Ireland.

The massive interest and commitment of resources in both the public and private sectors flows from the generally-held perception that genomics will be the single most fruitful approach to the acquisition of new information in basic and applied biology in the next several decades. If genomics were only to be a tool for the basic biologist, the benefits of this approach would be staggering, yielding new insights into fundamental processes such as cell division, differentiation, transformation, the development and reproduction of organisms and the diversity of populations. The rewards in applied biology, however, have clearly attracted the private sector and public interest. These include the promise of facile new approaches for drug discovery, new understanding of how cancers form, new approaches to the genetic engineering of plants for improved agronomic and qualitative traits such as disease resistance and improved nutrient content.

Ireland can take lessons from the growth of America's biotechnology industry which has resulted from a remarkable combination of entrepreneurship, innovative capital markets, and federal research investments. The United States leads the world in biotechnology, which is contributing to their strong economic growth and creating substantial improvements in quality of life.

These advances have been made possible by the twin strengths of federally-sponsored research carried out by the National Institutes of Health (NIH), National Science Foundation, US Department of Agriculture and other agencies, and the entrepreneurial leadership of about 1,300 U.S. biotech companies. In 1998, the industry generated revenues of about $19 billion, spent $10 billion on R&D, and employed about 150,000 highly-skilled workers. Most biotech companies are fairly small, with two-thirds of firms having fewer than 135 employees. The biotech industry survives on an inflow of funds from venture capitalists and proceeds from public share issues. These investment inflows are crucial because most biotech firms do not have substantial revenues, and the industry as a whole reports a net loss. Biotech investors often wait years to receive investment returns since it typically takes over seven years and $200-$350 million to bring a new biotech drug to market. Although the agriculture time line is shorter it still takes about six to seven years but costs much less. Therefore, the encouragement of risky and long-term capital inflows from investors is important to the continued health of the industry.

Priorities

Research priorities

▶ Expand research to discover, characterise, modify, and control the genetics and biochemical products and processes of a broad range of terrestrial and marine organisms for applications in biotechnology

▶ Apply the tools of modern biotechnology to problems in agriculture, the environment, and manufacturing to facilitate the development of new and improved products, processes, and test methods

▶ Strengthen and enhance facilities, repositories, databases, reference standards, and human resources to ensure the future vitality of the Irish biotechnology enterprise.

Recommendations to policymakers

▶ Support future policy dialogues that identify needs and mechanisms for follow-up regarding policy and managerial dimensions of biotechnology

▶ Raise awareness of the potential benefits and costs of using biotechnology to achieve National goals

▶ Assure relevant stakeholder and end-user participation in policy dialogues for identifying needs regarding biotechnology policy

▶ Develop mechanisms that help find funding for research by addressing issues of sustainability and user orientation

▶ Institute policy analysis on socioeconomic aspects of biotechnology, necessary legal reforms, and build regulatory capacity to deal with biotechnology and related agricultural policies

▶ Conduct regular studies to analyse trends in public and private investments and capacity development in biotechnology

▶ Initiate policies and programmes to encourage partnerships with the private sector that complement investments made in the public sector.

The Future

The practical effects of the genomics revolution will only be partially manifested during the next decade. During that time, the genomes of microbes, plants, and mammals will be sequenced, and much will be learned about the functions of genes and the means by which they are controlled. Today, humans employ the capabilities of only a few plants. A major challenge is to explore the opportunities inherent in some of the hundreds of thousands of them.

As noted to date, US investment in biotechnology has been focused primarily on the health field. The results of this research are having a profound impact on medicine and health care, providing improved approaches to the diagnosis, treatment, and prevention of disease. Ireland and Europe also has potential in this area and while health-related research must remain a priority, researchers are poised to build on the common foundation in basic science to bring the power of biotechnology to bear in other fields. Modest investments now in several rapidly developing areas of biotechnology research outlined above will lead to major economic and societal benefits, including foods that are more abundant and nutritious, a cleaner environment, and non- toxic biomanufacturing.

A coordinated effort to pursue these priorities can provide, over the next decade, the leverage needed to fulfill the broad promise of biotechnology, which may well play as pivotal a role in social and industrial advancement over the next 10 to 20 years as did physics and chemistry in the past century.

Biotechnology is poised to make major contributions to the economic growth of the European Union and Ireland in the 21st century. Coordinated implementation of these priorities will enable Ireland to stake its claim in this burgeoning field.

---- Appendix 1 ----

GENETICALLY MODIFIED PLANT
VARIETIES APPROVED UP TO EARLY 2000

Genetically Modified Plant Varieties

Firm	New Variety	Trait Gene & Source
2000		
Aventis	Male sterile corn.	The barnase gene from *Bacillus amyloliquefaciens.*
1999		
BASF AG Aspergillus	Phytaseed canola.	The phytase gene from niger var van Tieghem.
1998		
AgrEvo, Inc.	Glufosinate tolerant soybean.	Phosphinothricin acetyltransferase gene from Streptomyces viridochromogenes.
	Glufosinate tolerant sugar beet.	Phosphinothricin acetyltransferase gene from Streptomyces viridochromogenes.
	Insect protected and glufosinate tolerant maize.	The cry9C gene from Bacillus thuringiensis subsp. tolworthi and the bar gene from Strep. hygroscopicus.
	Male sterile or fertility restorer and glufosinate tolerant canola.	The male sterile canola contains the barnase gene and the fertility restorer canola contains the barstar gene from Bacillus amyloliquefaciens. Both lines have the phosphinothricin acetyltransferase gene from Streptomyces viridochromogenes.
Calgene Co.	Bromoxynil tolerant/insect protected cotton.	Nitrilase gene from Klebsiella pneumoniae and the cryIA(c) gene from *Bacillus thuringiensis subsp kurstaki.*

Firm	New Variety	Trait Gene & Source
	Insect protected tomato.	The cryIA(c) gene from *Bacillus thuringiensis subsp. kurstaki.*
	Glyphosate tolerant maize.	A modified enolpyruvylshikimate-3-phosphate synthase gene from maize.
Monsanto Co.	Insect and virus protected potato replicase gene.	The cryIIIA gene from Bacillus thuringiensis (Bt) sp. tenebrionis and the Potato Leafroll Virus.
	Insect and virus protected potato.	The cryIIIA gene from Bacillus thuringiensis (Bt) sp. tenebrionis and the Potato Virus Y coat protein gene.
Monsanto Co./Novartis	Glyphosate tolerant sugar Beet.	The enolpyruvylshikimate3-phosphate synthase gene from *Agrobacterium sp.* strain CP4, and a truncated lyphosate oxidoreductase gene from Ochrobactrum anthropi.
Pioneer Hi-Bred	Male sterile maize.	The DNA Adenine methylase gene from Escherichia coli.
University of Saskatchewan	Sulfonylurea tolerant flax.	Acetolactate synthase gene from Arabidopsis.
1997		
AgrEvo, Inc.	Glufosinate tolerant canola.	Phosphinothricin acetyltransferase gene from Streptomyces viridochromogenes.
Bejo Zaden BV	Male sterile radicchio rosso.	The barnase gene from Bacillus amyloliquefaciens.
Dekalb Genetics Corp.	Insect protected maize.	The cryIA(c) gene from Bacillus thuringiensis (Bt).

Genetically Modified Plant Varieties - contd...

FIRM	NEW VARIETY	TRAIT GENE & SOURCE
DuPont	High oleic acid Soybean.	Sense suppression of the Gm Fad2-1 gene which encodes a delta-12 desaturase enzyme.
Seminis Vegetable Seeds.	Virus resistant squash.	mosaic virus, zucchini yellow mosaic virus, and watermelon mosaic virus.
University of Hawaii/Cornell University.	Virus resistant papaya.	Coat protein gene of the papay a ringspot virus.
1996		
Agritope Inc.	Modified fruit ripening tomato.	S-adenosylmethionine hydrolasegene from E. coli bacteriophage T3.
Dekalb Genetics Corp.	Glufosinate tolerant maize.	Phosphinothricin acetyl transferase gene from Streptomyces hygroscopicus.
DuPont	Sufonylurea tolerant cotton.	Acetolactate synthase gene from tobacco, Nicotiana tabacum cv. Xanthi.
	Insect protected potato.	The cryIIIA gene from Bacillus thuringiensis
	Insect protected maize.	The cryIA(b) gene from Bacillus thuringiensis subsp. kurstaki.
	Insect protected maize.	The cryIA(b) gene from Bacillus thuringiensis subsp. kurstaki.
Monosanto Co.	Glyphosate tolerant/insect protected maize.	The enolpyruvylshikimate-3-phosphate synthase gene from *Agrobacterium sp.* strain CP4 and the glyphosate oxidoreductase gene from Ochrobactrum anthropi in the glyphosate tolerant lines. The CryIA(b) gene from B. thuringiensis.

Genetically Modified Plant Varieties - contd...

FIRM	NEW VARIETY	TRAIT GENE & SOURCE
Northrup King Co.	Insect protected maize.	The cryIA(b) gene from Bacillus thuringiensis (Bt) subsp. kurstaki.
Plant Genetic Systems NV.	Male sterile and fertility restorer oilseed rape.	The male sterile oilseed rape contains the barnase gene from Bacillus amyloliquefaciens; the fertility restorer lines express the barstar gene from Bacillus amyloliquefaciens.
	Male sterile maize.	The barnase gene from Bacillus Amyloliquefaciens.
1995		
AgrEvo Inc.	Glufosinate tolerant canola.	Phosphinothricin acetyltransferase gene from Streptomyces viridochromogenes.
	Glufosinate tolerant maize.	Phosphinothricin acetyltransferase gene from Streptomyces viridochromogenes.
Calgene Inc.	Laurate canola.	The 12:0 acyl carrier protein thioesterase gene from California bay, Umbellularia california.
Ciba-Geigy Corp.	Insect protected maize.	The cry1A(b) gene from Bacillus thuringiensis kurstaki.
	Glyphosate tolerant cotton.	Enolpyruvylshikimate-3-phosphate synthase gene from *Agrobacterium sp.* strain CP4.
Monsanto Co.	Glyphosate tolerant canola.	Enolpyruvylshikimate-3-phosphate synthase gene

FIRM	NEW VARIETY	TRAITGENE & SOURCE
		from *Agrobacterium sp.* strain CP4.
	Insect protected cotton.	The cryIA(c) from Bacillus thuringiensis (Bt) subsp. kurstaki.

1994

FIRM	NEW VARIETY	TRAITGENE & SOURCE
Asgrow Seed Co.	Virus resistant.	Coat protein genes of watermelon mosaic virus 2 and zucchini yellow squash mosaic virus.
	Flavr Savr™ tomato.	Antisense polygalacturonase gene from tomato.
Calgene Inc.	Bromoxynil tolerant cotton.	A nitrilase gene isolated from Klebsiella ozaenae.
DNA Plant Technology Corp.	Improved ripening tomato.	A fragment of the aminocyclopropane carboxylic acid synthase gene from tomato.
	Glyphosate tolerant soybean.	Enolpyruvylshikimate-3-phosphate synthase gene from *Agrobacterium sp.* strain CP4.
Monsanto Co.	Improved ripening tomato.	Aminocyclopropane carboxylic acid deaminase gene from Pseudomonas chloraphis strain 6G5.
	Insect protected potato.	The cryIIIA gene from Bacillus thuringiensis (Bt) sp. tenebrionis.
Zeneca Plant Science.	Delayed softening tomato.	A fragment of the polygalacturonase gene from tomato.

AGRICULTURAL BIO-TECH PRODUCTS ON THE MARKET

Agricultural Bio-tech Products on the Market - (Source: Bio Member Survey)

LibertyLink® Maize (Produced by AgrEvo) - Introduced in 1997 in the United States and 1998 in Canada, LibertyLink® Maize allows growers to apply Liberty® herbicide over the top during the growing season. Liberty herbicide kills over 100 grass and breadleaf weeds fast, with no crop injury. LibertyLink® Maize hybrids are offered by seed company partners like Pioneer, Novartis, Cargill, Garst and over 100 other seed companies. Liberty® herbicide is offered by AgrEvo.

LibertyLink® Canola (Produced by AgrEvo) - Introduced in 1995, LibertyLink® Canola allows growers to apply Liberty® herbicide over-the-top during the growing season. This results in weed control with no effect on crop performance or yield.

StarLink Maize (Produced by ArgEvo) - Introduced in 1998, these plants express a protein toxic to various lepidopteran pests, which allow less insecticide usage.

CLEARFIELD™ Maize (Produced by American Cyanamid) - Introduced in 1997 imidazolinone-tolerant and -resistant maize allows growers to apply the flexible and environmentally friendly imidazolinone herbicides to maize. Registration of LIGHTNING™ herbicide, a new imidazolinone specifically for use on CLEARFIELD Maize was approved by the EPA on March 31, 1997. One postemergence application of LIGHTNING™ herbicide provides both contact and residual control of broadleaf and grassy weeds resulting in maximum yield potential.

SMART® Canola Seed (Produced by American Cyanamid) - Introduced in 1995, imidazolinone-tolerant canola allows growers to apply environmentally friendly imidazolinone herbicides to canola. In Canada registration of ODYSSEY® herbicide, a new imidazolinone for use on imidazolinone-tolerant canola, was approved on April 4, 1997. One postemergence application of ODYSSEY® herbicide provides both contact and residual control of hard-to-control broadleaf and grassy weeds resulting in maximum yield potential.

Bollgard with BXN Cotton (Produced by Calgene, LLC, unit of Monsanto) - These cotton plants require less chemical herbicide and insecticide to lower grower input costs and to achieve greater crop yield.

Laurical® (Produced by Calgene, LLC) - A less- expensive source of high-quality raw materials for soaps, detergents and cocoa butter replacement fats. Rapeseed plants with more than 35 per cent laurate in oil have been produced.

DeKalBtTM Insect-Protected Hybrid Maize (Produced by DeKalb Genetics Corporation) - Approved in 1997, select DeKalb leader hybrids are now available with built-in protection against the European maize borer.

DeKalb Brand Roundup Ready® Maize (Developed by DeKalb Genetics Corporation) - Approved in 1998, DeKalb offers several elite hybrids with resistance to Roundup UltraTM herbicide.

DeKalb GR Hybrid Maize (Produced by DeKalb Genetics Corporation) - Approved in 1996, DeKalb GR hybrids provide growers the added weed control benefits of over-the-top glufosinate herbicide application during the growing season.

FreshWorld Farms® Tomato (Produced by DNAP Holding Corporation) - The FreshWorld Farms® tomato is a premium, fresh market tomato developed through somaclonal variation3 to have superior colour, taste and texture and a 10 to 14 day shelf life.

FreshWorld Farms Endless Summer® Tomato (Produced by DNAP Holding Corporation) - The Endless Summer® tomato is a genetically engineered version of the FreshWorld Farms® tomato on the market since April 1993 and shares its superior colour, taste and texture. What's new is its greatly extended shelf life of more than 30 to 40 days after harvest. Company scientists used Transwitch® technology to suppress production of ethylene, the hormone that causes tomatoes and other fruits to ripen. It is the company's first whole-food product developed through recombinant DNA technology.

FreshWorld Farms® Sweet Mini-Peppers (Produced by DNAP Holding Corporation) The FreshWorld Farms® sweet mini-pepper has a novel sweet taste, deep red colour and is nearly seedless. It was developed through anther culture, an advanced breeding technique that captures and stabilises preferred characteristics such as taste, texture and low seed count.

FreshWorld Farms® Cherry Tomatoes (Produced by DNAP Holding Corporation) - The FreshWorld Farms® cherry tomato is specially bred for superior taste, colour and texture. It is sold through distributors and supermarket chains in the Mid-Atlantic, Northwest and Midwest regions.

High pH Tolerant Maize **Hybrids** (Produced by Garst Seed Company) - These maize hybrids are capable of growing successfully on the severely alkaline soils that characterise the western U.S. maize belt.

Gray Leaf Spot Resistant Maize **Hybrids** (Produced by Garst Seed Company) - Maize hybrids tolerant to the disease Cercospora spp., which attacks maize hybrids in the Central and Southeastern maize belts.

G-Stac™ Maize **Hybrids** (Produced by Garst Seed Company) - Maize hybrids featuring "stacked" genes providing multitask capability. For example, hybrids that contain genes for the control of European maize borer (B.t.), genes for resistance to Liberty® herbicide and genes for resistance to imidazolinone herbicide all in the same maize hybrid.

Bollgard® Insect-Protected Cotton (Produced by Monsanto) - Introduced in 1996, cotton with Monsanto's Bollgard gene is protected against cotton bollworms, pink bollworms and tobacco budworms.

NewLeaf® Insect-Protected Potato (Produced by Monsanto) - Introduced in 1995, the NewLeaf® Potato is the first commercial crop to be protected against insect pests through biotechnology. Thanks to a gene from a variety of the B.t. bacteria, the NewLeaf® Potato is resistant to the Colourado potato beetle.

Roundup® Ready Cotton (Produced by Monsanto) - Approved in 1996,

Roundup Ready® cotton tolerates both topical and post-directed applications of Roundup® herbicide.

Roundup Ready® Soybeans (Produced by Monsanto) - Introduced in 1996, Roundup Ready® Soybeans allow growers to apply Roundup® herbicide over-the-top during growing season. The result is dependable, superior weed control with no effect on crop performance or yield.

Roundup Ready® Maize (Produced by Monsanto) - Approved in 1997 Roundup® Ready Maize allows over-the-top applications of Roundup® herbicide during the growing season for superior weed control.

YieldGard™ Insect-Protected Maize (Produced by Monsanto) - The YieldGard gene provides control of the European maize borer throughout the maize plant during the season.

NatureGard® Hybrid Seed Maize (Produced by Mycogen) - These maize plants express a protein toxic to European maize borer that reduces or eliminates the need for insecticides.

IMI-Maize **(Produced by Mycogen)** - Maize hybrid that can tolerate application of imidazolinone herbicides.

High Oleic Sunflower (Produced by Mycogen) - Sunflower plants modified by metagenesis to produce sunflower oil that is low in trans- fatty acids, does not require hydrogenation and has improved temperature stability.

High Oleic Peanut (Produced by Mycogen) - Peanut plants modified by metagenesis to produce nuts in high oleic acid results in longer life for nuts, candy and peanut butter.

NK Knockout™ Maize, **NK YieldGard™ Hybrid** Maize, **Attribute™** B.t. **Sweetcorn** (Produced by Novartis Seeds) - Novartis seeds has produced several maize varieties that have been modified to provide natural protection against certain pests.

Novartis Seeds Roundup Ready® Soybeans (Produced by Novartis Seeds)

High Oleic Acid Soybeans (Produced by Optimum Quality Grains, L.L.C.) - These soybeans produce an oil that contains a higher level of oleic acid than that found in currently available soybean oil and also contains lower levels of saturated fat. The oil will fit applications that require enhanced stability without the need for chemical hydrogenation, which generates trans-fatty acids.

Low Linolenic Soybean Oil (Produced by Optimum Quality Grains, L.L.C.) - With less than 3.5 per cent, linoleic is an enhanced stability oil that will reduce the need for chemical hydrogenation, therefore reducing trans-fatty acids.

Low Saturate Soybean Oils (Produced by Optimum Quality Grains, L.L.C.) - This oil is 50 per cent less saturated fat than commodity soybean oil (vegetable oil), or approximately 8 per cent total saturated fat. A 14-gram serving has just one gram of saturated fat - the same as canola oil. Zero saturated fat can be reached in many formulations when a low saturated soy is used in place of commodity soy.

High Oleic Sunflower Oil (Produced by Optimum Quality Grains, L.L.C.) - As an enhanced-stability oil, high oleic sunflower oil (less than 80 per cent oleic) is excellent for use as an ingredient, in cooking or as spray oil, without the need for chemical hydrogenation. New hybrids currently in production are expected to increase oleic acid content to around 85 per cent.

Chy Max® (fermentation-derived) (Produced by Pfizer, marketed by Chr. Hansen's) - Chy Max® is another version of chymosin, an enzyme that causes milk to coagulate. It is an advanced fermentation ingredient that is of higher purity, quality and activity than natural rennet.

Increased Pectin Tomatoes (Produced by Zeneca Plant Sciences) - Tomatoes that have been genetically modified using antisense technology to remain firm longer and retain pectin during processing into tomato paste.

Agricultural Biotechnology Products Expected on the Market Within Six Years

Genetically Engineered Cotton Fibre (Produced by Agracetus, unit of Monsanto Company) – This biotech product will enhance fibre performance, reduce dye-shop pollution and improve textile manufacturing efficiency.

LibertyLink® Rice (Produced by AgrEvo) - These LibertyLink® crops will be available in Canada and/or the United States. Like LibertyLink® Maize, when used together with Liberty® herbicide, they will allow farmers greater flexibility and environmental soundness in weed control.

SeedLink Maize (Produced by AgrEvo) - These plants provide a more reliable pollination control system for maize seed production. The use of the SeedLink System eliminates the need for hand or mechanical detasseling.

CLEARFIELD™ Wheat (Produced by American Cyanamid) - American Cyanamid is cooperating with universities, public and private laboratories and seed companies to develop wheat varieties tolerant to imidazolinone herbicides. Imidazolinone herbicides are flexible, environmentally friendly and provide contact and residual control of weeds common to wheat production, including ones not controlled by currently registered wheat herbicides.

CLEARFIELD™ Rice (Produced by American Cyanamid) - American Cyanamid is cooperating with universities and public and private seed companies to develop rice varieties tolerant to imidazolinone herbicides. Imidazolinone herbicides are flexible, environmentally friendly and provide superior contact and residual control of weeds.

CLEARFIELD™ Sugar Beets (Produced by American Cyanamid) - American Cyanamid is cooperating with universities and seed companies to develop sugar beet varieties tolerant to imidazolinone herbicides. Imidazolinone herbicides are flexible, environmentally friendly and provide superior contact and residual control of weeds.

High-Stearate Oil (Produced by the Calgene, LLC, unit of Monsanto Company) - High-stearate oil is an ingredient in margarine, shortenings and other food ingredients that would not require hydrogenation, thus reducing the expense.

Medium Chain Fatty Acids/Medium Chain Triglycerides (Produced by Calgene, LLC) - This will be a less-expensive source of raw materials for high-performance lubricants, nutritional formulas and high- energy foods.

Genetically Engineered Fruits and Vegetables with Longer Post-Harvest Shelf Life (Produced by Agritope, Inc., a wholly owned subsidiary of Epitope, Inc.) - Using ethylene-control technology, Agritope, Inc., has created delayed-ripening, longer-lasting tomatoes, raspberries and strawberries.

Ripening-Controlled Cherry Tomatoes (Produced by DNAP Holding Corporation) - Using the same technology as in its Endless Summer™ fresh market tomato, the company has developed cherry tomatoes with longer market life, improved flavour and better harvest traits through ripening control.

Firmer Peppers (Produced by DNAP Holding Corporation) - This sweet pepper has been modified using Transwitch® technology to remain firmer after harvest. Pepper plants are currently in field evaluations.

Sweeter Peppers (Produced by DNAP Holding Corporation) - This pepper has been modified to be sweeter and tastier by overexpressing a gene for sweetness. Pepper plants are in early stages of seed increase and field evaluation.

Ripening-Controlled Bananas and Pineapples (Produced by DNAP Holding Corporation) - Using the same ripening control technology as in its Endless Summer™ tomato, the company is developing banana and pineapple varieties with extended market life.

Strawberry (Produced by DNAP Holding Corporation) - The company is improving the market life of fresh strawberries by using Transwitch® technology to keep fruit firmer after harvest and adding genes to resist disease.

Messanger™ (Produced by EDEN Bioscience) - This is the first of a series of products based on the Harpin Protein technology. Harpin Proteins induce disease resistance and promote increased yield in a broad range of agriculture and horticulture crops. Harpin Proteins induce the natural disease immune system and growth pathways inherent within each plant.

High-Solids Potato (Produced by Monsanto) - Monsanto has developed a higher-solids (or starch content) potato by introducing a starch- producing gene from a soil bacteria into a potato plant. With the reduction in the percentage of water in the genetically improved potato, less oil is absorbed during processing, resulting in a reduction of cooking time and costs, better-tasting french fries and an economic benefit to the processor.

Roundup Ready® Canola (Produced by Monsanto) - Roundup Ready canola allows growers to apply Roundup® herbicide over-the-top of the crop during the growing season, for superior weed control with enhanced crop safety.

Roundup Ready® Sugar Beets (Produced by Monsanto) - Roundup Ready sugar beets are tolerant of Roundup® herbicide and provide growers with a new weed-control option while the crop is growing.

NewLeaf® Plus (Produced by Monsanto) - Insect- and virus-protected potatoes.

These potatoes are protecting themselves against Colourado potato beetles and potato leaf roll virus.

New-Leaf® Y Insect-and Virus-Protected Potatoes (Produced by Monsanto) - These potatoes protect themselves against the Colourado potato beetle and the potato virus Y.

Second-Generation Bollagard® Insect-Protected Cotton (Produced by Monsanto) - This cotton controls insect pests, like the original Bollagard cotton, but using a different mode of action to help growers manage insect resistance concerns.

High-Stearate Soy Oil (Produced by Monsanto) - This is a functional oil with healthier properties for margarines and shortenings. High-stearate oil requires no hydrogenation and contains no trans-fatty acids, which increase cholesterol.

B.t. Sunflower, Soybeans, Canola and Wheat (Produced by Mycogen Corp.) - These crops will express a   protein toxin providing protection against various caterpillar and beetle pests.

Fresh Market Tomato (Produced by Zeneca Plant Sciences) - Zeneca is modifying the tomatoes for enhanced flavour, colour and increased antioxidant vitamin content.

Banana (Produced by Zeneca Plant Sciences) - Zeneca is developing an inherent resistance to Black Sigatoka and modifying ripening characteristics in bananas. This will reduce the need for chemical fungicides, as well as improve the agronomics of production and the quality to the consumer.

Modified Lignin in Paper Pulp Trees (Produced by Zeneca Plant Sciences under separate agreements with Shell Forestry and Nippon Paper) - By making lignin easier to remove from cellulose - the primary   ingredient in paper - papermakers can make high-quality paper with less energy and bleaching, which benefits both the paper processor and the environment.

AquaAdvantage® Salmon, Tilapia, Trout, and Flounder (Produced by A/F Protein) - The AquaAdvantage® salmon, tilapia, trout and flounder have the capability of growing from egg to market size (8 to 10 lb.) in one to one-and-a-half years. Conventional fish breeding techniques require three years to bring a fish to market. This new salmon could make fish more plentiful, decrease overfishing of wild salmon and lower consumer costs. A/F Protein expects to introduce the AquaAdvantage® salmon within four to six years to a public for whom salmon is an increasingly popular food.

Appendix 3

SELECTED RECENT AGBIOTECH DEALS

Selected Recent Agbiotech Deals

COMPANIES	DATE	DEAL SIZE ($M)	AREA
Axys Pharmaceuticals (S. San Francisco, / Global Agro (Encinitas, CA)	4/99	N/A	Acquisition of Global Agro.
Novartis (Basel, Switzerland) / Diversa (San Diego, CA)	1/99	N/A	Crop enhancement.
Pioneer Hi-Bred (Des Moines, IA) Maxygen (Redwood City, CA).	1/99	$90	Genomics for agbiotech.
Novartis Crop Protection (Basel, Switzerland) Pharmacopeia (Princeton, NJ).	12/98	N/A	Combinatorial library generation and screening for agbiotech.
Bayer (Leverkusen, Germany) / Paradigm Genetics (Research Triangle Park, NC).	11/98	$40	Herbicide novel gene targets.
DuPont (Wilmington, DE) / Lynx Therapeutics (Hayward, CA).	11/98	$60	Genomics for agbiotech.
Pioneer Hi-Bred (Des Moines, IA) / Oxford GlycoSciences (Oxford, UK).	9/98	$27	Proteomics for agbiotech.
Hoechst Schering AgrEvo (Berlin, Germany) / GeneLogic (Gaithersburg, MD).	6/98	$45	Genomics for agbiotech.
Monsanto (St. Louis, MO) / DeKalb Genetics (DeKalb, IL).	5/98	$2,500	Acquisition of DeKalb.

Selected Recent Agbiotech Deals - contd...

COMPANIES	DATE	DEAL SIZE ($M)	AREA
Monsanto (St. Louis, MO) / Millennium (Cambridge, MA).	10/97	$343	Genomics for agbiotech.
Novartis Crop Protection (Basel, Switzerland) / Chiron (Emeryville, CA).	9/97	N/A	Combinatorial library generation and screening for crop protection.
Monsanto (St. Louis, MO) / ArQule (Medford, MA)	12/96	$65	Screening for agrochemicals by Directed Array.
AgrEvo (Berlin, Germany) / Plant Genetic Systems (Ghent, Belgium).	8/96	$500	Acquisition of PGS.

Source: Biovista (www.biovista.com).

BIO-TECH ENZYME
PRODUCTS ON THE MARKET

Genencor International, Inc.

Liquefying enzymes
Thermostable Alpha-Amylases
Liquefaction of starch at high temperature

GC 521	developmental acid-stable, low-calcium thermostable liquefying enzyme (food grade)*
GC 526	developmental acid-stable, low-calcium thermostable liquefying enzyme (food grade)*
GC 527	developmental acid-stable, low-calcium thermostable liquefying enzyme for alcohol production. *available as Chometz-free.
SPEZYME® DELTA AA	low-pH, thermostable liquefying enzyme**
SPEZYME DELTA AA-L	low p-H, thermostable liquefying enzyme** **available as technical grade, food grade and Chometz-free.
SPEZYME® AA	thermostable liquefying enzyme***
SPEZYME® AA-L	thermostable liquefying enzyme*** ***available as technical grade, food grade and Chometz-free.

Low-Temperature Alpha-Amylases
Liquefaction of starch at low temperature

DEX-LO® CL	low-temperature liquefying enzyme.
DEX-LO® S	low-temperature liquefying enzyme.

SACCHARIFYING ENZYMES
Glucoamylases
Hydrolysis of soluble starch to glucose

OPTIDEX™ l-400	saccharifying enzyme.
DISTILLASE®	saccharifying enzyme for alcohol L-400 production.
OPTIDEX™ L-300	saccharifying enzyme.

OPTIDEX™ L-300A	wheat-grade saccharifying enzyme.

Glucoamylases & Pullulanases
High-glucose and maltose syrup

OPTIMAX™ 7525 HP	saccharifying and debranching enzymes.
POTIMAX™ L-300	low-pH, thermostable debranching enzyme.

Glucoamylase & Protease
Soluble starch and protein hydrolysis

FERMENZYME® L-300	saccharifying and proteolytic enzymes for alcohol production.

ISOMERIZING ENZYMES
Glucose Isomerase
High-frutose syrup

SPEZYME® GI	soluble glucose isomerase for on-column immobilisation onto resin (also supplied).

MALTOGENIC ENZYMES
Barley Beta-Amylases
High-maltose syrup

SPEZYME® BBA	barley beta-amylase.
SPEZYME® DBA	diastatic beta-amylase.

Malt Enzyme
High-maltose syrup

GC 600	malt enzyme.

Fungal Alpha-Amylase
High-maltose syrup

CLARASE® L-40,000	fungal alpha-amylase.

PROTEIN HYDROLYZING ENZYMES
Proteases
Improved fermentation efficiency

SPEZYME® FAN	protease for alcohol production.
GC 106	developmental low-pH protease for alcohol production.

VISCOSITY-REDUCING & (HEMI-) CELLULOSE HYDROLYZING ENZYMES
Cellulases & Xylanase
Whole grain feedstock and biomass processing

SPEZYME® CP	starch separation/viscosity-reducing enzyme.
SPEZYME® CE	starch separation/viscosity-reducing enzyme.
GC 140	developmental xylanase for viscosity reduction.

Sources: The Biotechnology Industry Organisation 1998, Organisation for Economic Cooperation and Development (OECD) Report, "Biotechnology for Clean Industrial Products and Processes"

TEXTILE ENZYMES

IndiAge® Product Line: Liquid and granular enzyme formulations for cotton and denim garment washing and cellulosic fabric finishing.

IndiAge® Euro® Product Line: Liquid and granular enzyme formulations for high-contrast denim washing.

Primafast® Product Line: Liquid enzyme formulations for value-adding treatment of lyocell fabrics.

Genencor® Optisize™ Product Line: Liquid enzyme preparations for conventional and high-temperature desising.

Genencor® Catalase T100: Liquid fungal catalase for the removal of residual hydrogen peroxide after bleaching.

DETERGENT ENZYMES

Granular Products for Powdered Detergent Formulas: Purafect®: High-strength proteases with particular effectiveness against stains and soils containing proteins.

Purafect® Ox: Oxidatively stable protease for bleach-containing detergents.

Properase®: High-performance high-pH alkaline protease; especially active in low-temperature wash conditions.

Purafect® OxAm: Oxidatively stable high-performance-amylase.

Purastar™ ST 5000: Thermostable bacterial-amylase with particular effectiveness in removing starch-based stains.

Liquid Products for Liquid Detergent Formulations: Purafect® L: High-pH alkaline proteases with particular effectiveness in removing insoluble proteinaceous stains.

Purafect®Ox L: Oxidatively stable protease with improved stability in detergent formulations that contain bleach.

Properase® L: High-performance protease with particular effectiveness in removing insoluble proteinaceous stains.

Purastar™ St 1500L: Thermostable-amylase with particular effectiveness in removing starch- based stains.

BREWING AND MALTING ENZYMES

LAMINEX® BG: Concentrated liquid cellulase complex standardised for ß-glucanase activity for improved lautering and increased brew house efficiency, especially in barley or high-glucan mashes, contains significant activity on xylanase. Also used to improve modification in malting.

Multifect® B: Liquid cellulase complex standardised for ß-glucanase activity for improved lautering and increased brew house efficiency, especially in barley or high-glucan mashes.

BAKING ENZYMES

Multifect® CL: Liquid cellulase with high cellulase/xylanase ratio.

Multifect® CS G: Granular cellulase with high cellulase/xylanase ration.

Multifect® Cellulase 300: Granular cellulase with high xylanase level.

SPEZYME® GA 300: Liquid glucomylase.

SPEZYME® BBA 1500: Liquid barley ß-amylase.

ENZYMES FOR FOOD AND SPECIALTY APPLICATIONS

Multifect® GC: Liquid cellulase complex for improved ultrafiltration.

Multifect® XL: Liquid fungal cellulase complex with specified level of xylanase activity for reduction of viscosity in cereal grain-based food systems and extraction of plant materials.

Multifect® CL: Liquid cellulase complex.

OxyGo® I 1500: Liquid glucose oxidase for removal of dissolved oxygen.

OxyGo® M 1500: Liquid glucose oxidase with low levels of side activities, particularly effective in removing oxygen from mayonnaise and salad dressings.

OxyGo® HP L5000: Liquid glucose oxidase with high GO/CAT ratio.

Bio-Tech Enzyme Products on the Market - contd...

OxyGo® S75: Solid glucose oxidase with low GO/Cat ratio.

OxyGo® WS25: Solid glucose oxidase.

Fermcolase® 1000: Liquid catalase for breakdown of hydrogen peroxide or generation of oxygen.

CAT HP® L5000: Liquid high-purity catalase.

Multifect® Xylanase: Liquid xylanase especially designed to modify or degrade xylan polymers; can be used as processing aid in various applications.

PrimaTan®: Liquid proteolytic enzyme for leather processing.

Batinase®: Liquid enzymes for leather processing.

PRODUCTS BY PRODUCED WITH ENZYMES

Alpha-amylases: Clarase®: Fungal alpha-amylase for detoxing and saccharifying starch.

Tenase®: Bacterial alpha-amylase for starch liquefaction at temperatures up to 90° C.

Cellulases: Cellulase: Fungal cellulase system that is primarily active on soluble forms of cellulase.

Glucoamylase: Optimax™: Glucoamylase and pullulanase product for higher glucose yields from starch.

Fermenzyme®: A glucoamylase system specifically designed for use in fuel alcohol fermentations.

Proteases: HT-Proteolytic®: Bacterial proteases that effectively hydrolyse proteins over the neutral to alkaline-pH range.

Acid Fungal Protease: Acid fungal protease characterised by its ability to hydrolyse proteins under acidic conditions.

Fungal Protease: Fungal protease containing endo- and exo-peptidases with a broad substrate specificity.

Bromelain: A protease isolated from the pineapple plant that hydrolyses plant and animal proteins to peptides and amino acids.

Papain: A protease isolated from papaya latex. The enzyme extensively hydrolyses proteins and has excellent stability at elevated temperatures.

Opticlean®: Bacterial alkaline protease particularly effective in highly alkaline detergent formulations up to pH 11.

Protex®: Bacterial alkaline protease for hydrolysing proteins under alkaline conditions up to pH 10.

Novo Nordisk

DETERGENTS

Removal of protein stains: Alcalase®, Esperase®, Savinase®, Everlase™

Removal of fatty stains: Lipolase™, Lipolase Ultra, Lipoprime™

Removal of starch stains: Termamyl®, BAN, Duramyl™

Colour care and particulate soil removal: Celluzyme®, Carezyme®

TEXTILES

Desising: Aquazym®, DeniPrime™, Termamyl, Thermozyme™

Denim finishing: Denimax®

Denim bleaching: DeniLite™

Bio-polishing: Cellusoft®

Wool finishing: Novolan™

Bleach cleanup: Terminox®

Silk degumming: Alcalase

STARCH AND FUEL ALCOHOL

Starch liquefaction: Termamyl, Termamyl Type LS, BAN

Starch saccharification: AMG, Promozyme®, Dextrozyme®, Fungamyl®, Maltogenase®

Starch isomerisation: Sweetzyme™

Others: Fructozyme®, Toruzyme®

ANIMAL FEED

Enzyme supplementation: Ronozyme®

PROTEIN/ PET FOOD

Protein hydrolysis: Alcalase, Flavorzyme™, Neutrase, Pancreatic Trypsin Novo (PTN), Protamex™, NovoPro D

Polysaccharide degradation: Viscozyme®, Celluclast®

Hydrolysis of triglycerides: Novozym® 871

BAKING

Flour supplementation: Fungamyl

Improved crust colour: AMG

Chilled and frozen dough: Fungamyl, AMG, Pentopan Mono BG

Anti-staling: Novamyl®

Dough improvement: Pentopan Mono BG, Fungamyl Super MA

Gluten strengthening: Gluzyme®, Fungamyl Super BR

BREWING

Replacing malt with barley: Cereflo®, Ceremix®, Neutrase®, Ultraflo™

Brewing with up to 100 per cent unmalted cereals: Termamyl, Neutrase, Fungamyl, Cereflo, AMG, Ultraflo

Liquefaction of adjuncts: Termamyl

Increase in fermentability: Fungamyl, Promozyme

Filtration improvement of wort and beer: Cereflo, Viscozyme, Finizym®, Ultraflo

Nitrogen control: Neutrase

Low-calorie beer: AMG

Accelerated maturation: Maturex®

POTABLE ALCOHOL

Starch liquefaction:Termamyl, Termamyl Type S, BAN, Fungamyl

Starch saccharification: AMG, Spirizyme®, Fungamyl

Improved yeast growth: Neutrase

WINE AND FRUIT JUICE

Primarily pectolytic enzymes: Pectinex®, Pectinex Ultra SP-L, Pectinex AR, Ultrazym®, Vinozym®, Cellubrix, Novoferm 61

Removal of starch from juice: AMG, Fungamyl

Aroma enhancement: Novoferm® 12

Membrane cleaning: Bio-Cip® Membrane

Enzymatic peeling of fruit: Peelzym™

Citrus industry: Citropex®

SUGAR

Polysaccharide degradation: Termamyl, Dextranase

Sweet syrups and sugar processing: Invertase™

OILS AND FATS

Interesterification: Lipozyme® IM

Production of lyso-lecithin and degumming of oils: Lecitase™

PULP AND PAPER

Bleach boosting: Pulpzyme®

Pitch control: Resinase™

Deinking of mixed office waste: Novozym 342

Modified starch: BAN, Termamyl, Aquazym

LEATHER

Bating: Pyrase®

Soaking: Aquaderm™

Unhairing: NUE

Degreasing: Greasex™

PERSONAL CARE

Contact lens cleaning: Clear-Lens™ Pro, Clear-Lens Lipo

Denture cleaning: Everlase™

DAIRY

Lactose hydrolysis: Lactozym®

Cheese maturation: Palatase®

Milk protein modifications: Alcalase, Pancreatic Trypsin Novo (PTN), Flavorzyme

Milk and whey processing: Catazyme®

ANALYSIS AND MEDICINES

For analytical purposes, oral medication and digestive aid formulations: Pancreatic Trypsin Novo (PTN), Proteolytic Enzyme Mixture (PEM), Chymotrypsin, Crystalline Porcine Trypsin, Crystalline Bovine Trypsin, Novozym 234 cell wall lysing enzyme, Bacterial Uricase Novo, Subtilisin-A (note that these enzymes are food grade and not pharmaceutical grade)

Gist-Brocades

Marketed by the European Association of Manufacturers of Fermentation Enzyme Products.

List of commercial enzymes from genetically modified microorganisms to be used in food.

Optiren™:- Optiren™ is an aspartic proteinase enzyme preparation produced by pure culture fermentation of *Aspergillus oryzae*, genetically modified to contain the aspartic proteinase gene from *Rhizomucor miehei*. The enzyme is used as a milk-clotting enzyme in the production of cheese.

Maxiren®:- Maxiren® is the biotechnology-produced version of calf rennet (chymosin) and is used as a milk-clotting enzyme in the production of cheese. It is produced by pure culture fermentation of the yeast *Kluyveromyces lactis*, modified to contain the calf gene encoding for chymosin.

Natuphos®:- Natuphos® is a phytase enzyme preparation produced in pure culture fermentation by a genetically modified strain of *Aspergillus niger*. It is used as a supplement in animal diets resulting in a marked improvement of the bioavailability of phosphorus in pigs, poultry and fish. As a consequence, phosporus excretion in manure is decreased by about 30 per cent. The use of Natuphos® also shows favourable effects on amino acid digestibility and mineral availability. It also reduces phosphate excretion and thus diminishes environmental pollution and eutrophocation.

Natugrain® Blend:- This enzyme blend, optimised in endoxylanase activity, has a marked favourable effect on the feed conversion ratio in poultry grown on diets with a high inclusion rate of wheat, barley and rye. Its use results in a reduced occurrence of dirty eggs in layers. The endoxylanase enzyme is produced by pure culture fermentation of a genetically modified strain of *Aspergillus niger*.

Other Engineered Enzymes

PRINCIPAL ENZYMATIC ACTIVITY	HOST ORGANISM (PRODUCTION ORGANISM)	DONOR ORGANISM	APPLICATION EXAMPLES (NON-EXHAUSTIVE LIST)*
Acetolactate decarboxylase.	Bacillus amyloliquefaciens or subtilis.	Bacillus sp.	Bevr
Amylase	Bacillus amyloliquefaciens or subtilis/ Bacillus licheniformis.	Bacillus sp./ Bacillus sp.	Stch, Bevr Stch, Frut, Bevr, Sugr, Bake.
Catalase	Aspergillus niger	Aspergillus sp.	Milk, Egg.
Chymosin	Aspergillus niger var. awamori/ K.lactis.	Calf stomach/ Calf stomach	Ches
Cyclodextrin glucano-transferase.	Bacillus licheniformis.	Thermoanaero-bacter sp.	Stch.

Bio-Tech Enzyme Products on the Market - contd...

PRINCIPAL ENZYMATIC ACTIVITY	HOST ORGANISM (PRODUCTION ORGANISM)	DONOR ORGANISM	APPLICATION EXAMPLES (NON-EXHAUSTIVE LIST)*.
ß-Glucanase.	Bacillus amyloliquefaciens. or subtilis/ Trichoderma reesei or longibrachiatum.	Bacillus sp./ Trichoderma sp.	Stch., Bevr Stch., Diet.
Glucose isomerase.	Streptomyces lividans/ Streptomyces rubiginosus.	Actinoplanes sp/ Streptomyces sp.	Stch/ Stch.
Glucose oxidase.	Aspergillus niger.	Aspergillus sp.	Egg, Bevr, Bake, Sald.
Hemicellulase.	Bacillus amyloliquefaciens or subtilis.	Bacillus sp.	Bake.
Lipase, triacylglycerol.	Aspergillus oryzae.	Candida sp./ Rhizomucor sp./ Thermomyces sp.	Fats/ Fats/ Fats, Bake.
Maltogenic amylase.	Bacillus amyloliquefaciens or subtilis.	Bacillus sp	Stch, Bevr, Bake.
Protease	Aspergillus oryzae/ Bacillus amyloliquefaciens or subtilis/ Bacillus licheniformis.	Rhizomucor sp./ Bacillus sp./ Bacillus sp.	Ches/ Meat, Fish, Stch, Bevr, Bake, Sald/ Meat, Fish.
Pullulanase	Bacillus licheniformis/ Klebsiella planticola.	Bacillus sp./ Klebsiella sp.	Stch/ Stch, Bevr, Bake.
Xylanase	Aspergillus oryzae/ Aspergillus niger var. awamori/ Aspergillus niger/ Bacillus amyloliquefaciens or subtilis/ Bacillu licheniformis/ Trichoderma reesei or longibrachiatum.	Aspergillus sp., Thermomyces sp/ Aspergillus sp./ Aspergillus sp./ Bacillus sp./ Bacillus sp./ Trichoderma sp	Stch Stch/ Bake/ Stch, Bevr, Bake/ Stch/ Stch/ Stch, Bevr.

Bake=Bakery, Bevr=Beverages (soft drinks, beer, wine), Ches=Cheese , Diet=Dietary food
Fats=Fats and oils,Frut=Fruit/veg, Sald=Salads, Stch=Cereal/starch, Sugr=Sugar/ honey

---------- Appendix 5 ----------

APPROVED BIOTECHNOLOGY DRUGS
SPRING 1999

Approved Biotechnology Drugs Spring 1999

PRODUCT	COMPANY	APPLICATION (USE)	DATE
Abbott HTLV-I/ HTLV-II EIA.	Abbott Laboratories.	EIA for detection of HTLV-I/ HTLV-II antibodies in serum in serum or plasma.	Aug. 1997
Abelcet® (amphotericin B lipid-complex injection).	The Liposome Company.	Treatment of invasive fungal infections in patients who are refractory to or intolerant of conventional amphotericin B (lipid-complex drug delivery system).	Nov. 1995
Actimmune® (Interferon gamma-1b).	Genentech.	Treatment of chronic granulomatous disease.	Dec. 1990
Activase® (Alteplase recombinant).	Genentech.	Acute myocardial infarction/ acute massive pulmonary embolism/ acute ischemic stroke within first three hours of symptom onset.	Nov. 1987 June 1990 June 1996
Adagen® (adenosine deaminase).	Enzon.	Treatment of severe combined immunodeficiency disease (SCID).	Mar. 1990
Albutein® (human albumin).	Alpha Therapeutic Corp.	Treatment of hypovolmeic shock; an adjunct in hemodialysis; in cardiopulmonary bypass procedures.	Jan. 1986
Alferon N® (interferon alfa-N3, human leukocyte derived).	Interferon Sciences.	Genital warts.	Oct. 1989

Approved Biotechnology Drugs Spring 1999 - contd...

PRODUCT	COMPANY	APPLICATION (USE)	DATE
Alphanate® (human antihemophilic factor).	Alpha Therapeutic Corp.	Treatment of hemophilia A or acquired Factor VII deficiency.	Feb. 1997
AlphaNine® SD (virus-filtered human coagulation Factor IX).	Alpha Therapeutic Corp.	To prevent and control bleeding in patients with Factor IX deficiency due to hemophilia B.	July 1996
AmBisome® (liposomal amphoteri B).	NeXstar Pharmaceuticals Inc.	Primary treatment for presumed fungal infections in patients with depressed immune function and fevers of unknown origin (FUO).	Aug. 1997
AMPHOTEC® (lipid-based colloidal dispersion of amphotericin B).	SEQUUS Pharmaceuticals Inc.	Second-line treatment of invasive aspergillosis infections.	Nov. 1996
Apligraf® (graftskin).	Organogenesis.	For treatment of venous leg ulcers.	May 1998
Avonex® (recombinant interferon beta 1-alpha).	Biogen.	Relapsing forms of multiple sclerosis.	May 1996
BeneFix™ Coagulation Factor IX (recombinant).	Genetics Institute.	Treatment of hemophilia B.	Feb. 1997
Betaseron® (recombinant interferon beta 1-B).	Berlex Laboratories/ Chiron.	Relapsing, remitting multiple sclerosis.	Aug. 1993

Approved Biotechnology Drugs Spring 1999 - contd...

PRODUCT	COMPANY	APPLICATION (USE)	DATE
Bioclate™/ Helixate® (recombinant antihemophilic factor).	Centeon.	Blood-clotting factor VIII for the treatment of hemophilia A.	Dec. 1993 Feb. 1994
BioTropin™	Biotech General.	Human growth hormone deficiency in children.	May 1995
Carticel™ (autologous cultured chondrocytes).	Genzyme	Knee cartilage damage.	Aug. 1997
Ceredase®/ Cerezyme® (alglucerase/ recombinant alglucerase).	Genzyme	Type 1 Gaucher's disease.	April 1991 May 1994
CytoGam® (CMV immune globulin IV).	MedImmune Inc.	Prevention of cytomegalovirus (CMV) in kidney transplant patients/ for prophylaxis against CMV disease associated with kidney, lung, liver, pancreas and heart transplants.	April 1990 Dec. 1998
DaunoXome® (liposomal form of the chemotherapeutic agent daunorubicin).	NeXstar Pharmaceuticals Inc.	First-line treatment for HIV-related Kaposi's sarcoma (liposomal drug delivery system).	April 1996
DOXIL® (STEALTH® [pegylated] liposomal formulation of doxorubicin hydrochloride).	SEQUUS Pharmaceuticals Inc.	Second-line therapy for Kaposi's sarcoma in AIDSpatients patients (liposomal drug delivery system).	Nov. 1995

Approved Biotechnology Drugs Spring 1999 - contd...

PRODUCT	COMPANY	APPLICATION (USE)	DATE
Enbrel (etanercept).	Immunex Corporation.	Reduction in signs and symptoms of moderately to severely active rheumatoid arthiritis in patients who have had an inadequate response to one or more disease-modifying antirheumatic drugs (DMARDS).	Dec. 1998 Feb. 1999
Engerix-B® (recombinant Hepatitis B vaccine).	SmithKline Beecham.	Hepatitis B vaccine/ adults with chronic Hepatitis C infection.	Sept.1989 Aug.1998
Epogen® (epoetin alfa).	Amgen	Treatment of anemia associated with chronic renal failure and anemia. in Retrovir® -treated HIV-infected patients.	June 1989
Fertinex™	Serono Laboratories Inc.	Female infertility to stimulate ovulation in women with ovulatory disorders and in women undergoing assisted reproductive technologies treatment.	Aug. 1996
Follistim™ (follitropin beta for injection).	Organon Inc.	Recombinant follicle-stimulating hormone for treatment of infertility.	Sept. 1997
Geref®	Serono Laboratories Inc.	Growth hormone deficiency in children with growth failure.	Oct. 1997

Approved Biotechnology Drugs Spring 1999 - contd...

PRODUCT	COMPANY	APPLICATION (USE)	DATE
GenoTropin®	Pharmacia & Upjohn.	Human growth hormone deficiency in children/ human growth hormone deficiency in adults.	Aug. 1995 Nov. 1997
Gonal-F (follitropin alfa).	Serono Laboratories Inc.	Functional infertility not due to primary ovarian failure. Treatment of patients with metastatic breast cancer whose tumours over express the HER2 protein.	Sept. 1998
Herceptin® (trastuzumab).	Genentech, Inc.	Treatment of patients with metastatic breast cancer whose tumours over express the HER2 protein.	Sept. 1998
Humalog® (recombinant insulin).	Eli Lilly.	Diabetes.	June 1996
Humatrope®	Eli Lilly.	Human growth hormone deficiency in children/ somatotropin deficiency syndrome in adults.	Mar. 1997 Aug. 1996
Humulin® (recombinant human insulin).	Eli Lilly.	Diabetes.	Oct. 1982
Integrelin™ (eptifibatide for injection).	COR Therapeutics, Inc./Schering -Plough Corp.	Treatment of patients with acute coronary syndrome and angioplasty.	May 1998
Infergen® (interferon alfacon-1).	Amgen.	Hepatitis C.	Oct. 1997

PRODUCT	COMPANY	APPLICATION (USE)	DATE
Intron A® (alpha-interferon).	Schering-Plough.	Hairy cell leukemia/ genital warts/ AIDS-related Kaposi's sarcoma/ non-A, non-B hepatitis/ hepatitis. B/ Chronic malignant melanoma/ extended therapy for chronic viral hepatitis. C/ Treatment for follicular lymphoma in conjunction with chemotherapy/treatment of hepatitis B in pediatric patients.	June 1986 June 1988 Nov. 1988 Feb. 1991 July 1992 Dec. 1995 Mar. 1997 Nov.1997 Aug. 1998
Kogenate® (recombinant antihemophilic factor).	Bayer.	Replaces blood clotting factor VIII for the treatment of hemophilia A.	Sept. 1989
Leukine® (yeast-derived GM- CSF)/ Leukine Liquid.	Immunex.	Autologous bone marrow transplantation/ to treat white blood cell toxicities following induction chemotherapy in older patients with acute myelogenous leukemia/for use following allogenic bone marrow transplantation from HLA- matched related donors/ for use mobilising peripheral blood progenitor cells and for use after PBPC transplantation/ (Leukine Liquid) ready to use formulation multidose vial.	Mar. 1991 Sept. 1995 Nov. 1995 Dec. 1995 Nov. 1996
Luestatin™ (cladribine or 2-CDA).	Ortho Biotech.	First-line treatment of hairy cell leukemia.	Mar 1993

Approved Biotechnology Drugs Spring 1999 - contd...

PRODUCT	COMPANY	APPLICATION (USE)	DATE
LYMErix™ (recombinant OspaA).	SmithKline Beecham Biologicals.	Prevention of Lyme disease.	Dec. 1998
Neupogen® (Filgrastim).	Amgen.	Chemotherapy-induced neutropenia/ bone marrow transplant accompanied neutropenia/ severe chronic neutropenia/ autologous bone marrow transplant engraftment. or failure/ mobilisation of autologous PBPCs post-chemotherapy.	Feb. 1991 June 1994 Dec. 1994 Dec. 1995 April 1998
Neumega® (Oprelvekin).	Genetics Institute.	Prevention of severe chemotherapy-induced thrombocytopenia in cancer patients.	Nov. 1997
Norditropin®	Novo Nordisk.	Human growth hormone deficiency in children.	May 1995
Novolin® (recombinant human insulin).	Novo Nordisk.	Diabetes.	Oct. 1982
Nutropin®/ Nutropin AQ® (somatropin rDNA).	Genentech	Growth hormone deficiency in children/ growth hormone deficiency in adults/ growth failure associated with chronic renal insufficiency prior to kidney transplantation/ short stature associated with Turner Syndrome.	Nov. 1993 Jan. 1994 Jan. 1996 Dec. 1996
Oncaspar® (pegaspargase).	Enzon/ Rhone-Poulenc Rorer.	Acute lymphoblastic leukemia.	Feb. 1994

Approved Biotechnology Drugs Spring 1999 - contd...

PRODUCT	COMPANY	APPLICATION (USE)	DATE
Orthoclone OKT3® (Muromonab -CD3).	Ortho Biotech.	Reversal of acute kidney transplant rejection.	June 1986
Photofrin® (Porfimer sodium).	Ligand Pharmaceuticals (licensed QLT Phototherapeutic.	Palliative treatment of totally and partially obstructing cancers of esophagus.	Nov. 1995
Prandin™ (repaglinide).	Novo Nordisk.	Anti-diabetic agent for treatment of Type 2 diabetes.	Dec. 1997
Procrit®	Ortho Biotech.	Treatment of anemia in AZT- treated HIV- infected patients/ anemia in cancer patients on chemotherapy/for use in anemic patients scheduled to undergo elective noncardiac, nonvascular surgery.	Dec. 1990 April 1993 Dec. 1996
Proleukin, IL-2® (Aldesleukin).	Chiron.	Treatment of kidney (renal) carcinoma/. treatment of metastatic melanoma.	May 1992 Jan. 1998
Protropin® (somatrem).	Genentech.	Growth hormone deficiency in children.	Oct. 1985
PROVIGIL® (modafinil) Tablets.	Cephalon, Inc.	To improve wakefulness in patients with excessive daytime sleepiness (EDS) associated with narcolepsy.	Dec. 1998
Pulmozyme® (dornase, alfa recombinant).	Genentech.	Mild to moderate cystic fibrosis/ advanced cystic fibrosis/ pediatricuse in infants 3 months to 2 years and children 2 to 4 years old.	Dec. 1993 Dec. 1996 Mar. 1998

Approved Biotechnology Drugs Spring 1999 - contd...

Product	Company	Application (use)	Date
Rebetron®	Schering-Plough Corp.	Combination therapy for treatment of chronic hepatitis C in patients with compensated liver disease who have relapsed following alpha-interferon treatment/ treatment of chronic hepatitis C in patients with compensated liver disease previously untreated with alpha interferon therapy.	June 1998 Dec. 1998
Recombinate® rAHF/ (recombinant antihemophilic factor).	Baxter Healthcare (Genetics Institute).	Blood-clotting Factor VIII for the treatment of hemophilia A.	July 1986
Recombivax -HB® (recombinant hepatitis B vaccine).	Merck	Hepatitis B vaccine for adolescents and high-risk infants/ adults/ dialysis/ pediatrics.	Jan. 1987 Jan. 1987 Jan. 1989 June 1993
Refludan® (lepirudin (rDNA) for injection).	Hoechst Marion Roussel	For anticoagulation in patients with heparin-induced thrombocytopenia and associated thromboembolic disease in order to prevent further thromboembolic complications.	Mar. 1998
Regranex® Gel (gel becaplermin).	Ortho -McNeil/ Chiron	Platelet-derived growth factor treatment of diabetic foot ulcers.	Dec. 1997
Remicade® (infliximab).	Centocor, Inc.	Short-term management of moderately to severely active Crohn's disease including those patients with fistula.	Aug. 1998

PRODUCT	COMPANY	APPLICATION (USE)	DATE
Renagel® Capsules (sevelamer hydrochloride).	GelTex Pharmaceuticals, Inc./ Genzyme General.	Reduction of serum phosphorus in patients with end-stage renal disease.	Nov. 1998
ReoPro™ (Abciximab).	Centocor, Inc./ Eli Lilly	Reduce acute blood clot-related complications for high-risk angioplasty patients/reduce acute blood clot complications for all patients undergoing any coronary intervention/ treatment of unstable angina not responding to conventional medical therapy when percutaneous coronary intervention is planned within 24 hours.	Dec. 1994 Dec. 1997
Retavase™ (reteplase recombinant plasminogen activator).	Centocor, Inc.	Management of acute myocardial infarction in adults.	Oct. 1996
RespiGam® (immune globulin enriched in antibodies against respiratory synctytial virus [RSV]).	MedImmune, Inc.	Prevention of respiratory synctytial virus in infants under 2 with bronchopulmonary dysplasia or history of prematurity.	Jan. 1996
Rituxan™ (Rituximab).	IDEC Pharmaceuticals /Genentech.	Relapsed or refractory low-grade or follicular, CD20-positive B-cell non-Hodgkin's lymphoma.	Nov. 1997

PRODUCT	COMPANY	APPLICATION (USE)	DATE
Roferon-A® (recombinant interferon alfa-2a).	Hoffmann-La Roche Inc.	Hairy cell leukemia/ AIDS-related Kaposi sarcoma/ chronic phase Philadelphia chromosome positive chronic myelogenous leukemia/ hepatitis C.	June 1986 Nov. 1988 Oct. 1995 Nov. 1995
Saizen® (recombinant human growth hormone).	Serono Laboratories Inc.	Growth hormone deficiency in children.	Oct. 1996
Serostim®	Serono Laboratories Inc.	Cachexia (AIDS-wasting).	Aug. 1996
Simulect (basiliximab).	Novartis Pharm Corporation/ Ligand Pharma.	For the prevention of acute rejection episodes in kidney transplant recipients.	May 1998
SYNAGIS™ (palivizumab).	MedImmune, Inc.	Prevention of lower respiratory tract disease caused by respiratory syncytial virus (RSV) in pediatric patients at high risk of RSV disease.	June 1998
Tamiflu™ (oseltamivir phosphate).	Hoffmann -La Roche/ Gilead Sciences.	Treatment of the most common strains of influenza (A & B).	Oct. 1999
Targetin™ (bexarotene)	Ligand Pharma.	Cutaneous manifestations of T-cell lymphoma.	Dec. 1999
Thyrogen® (thyrotropin alfa for injection).	Genzyme General.	Adjunctive diagnostic tool for serum thyroglobulin (Tg) testing with or without radioiodine imaging in	Dec. 1998

PRODUCT	COMPANY	APPLICATION (USE)	DATE
		the follow up of patients with thyroid cancer.	
Tripedia®	Pasteur Merieux Connaught	Vaccination of infants 2, 4 and 6 months of age and first booster at 15-18 months/primarily for whooping cough.	July 1996 Nov. 1992
TriHIBit™	Pasteur Merieux Connaught.	Childhood immunisation between 15-18 months for acellular pertussis, diphtheria, tetanus and HIB disease.	Sept. 1996
Venoglobulin® -S (human immune globulin intravenous 5 % and 10 % solutions).	Alpha Therapeutic. Corp.	Primary immunodeficiencies; idiopathic hrombocytopenic purpurea (ITP); kawasaki disease.	Jan. 1995 Nov. 1991
VISTIDE® (cidofovir injection).	Gilead. Sciences Inc.	Treatment of cytomegalovirus (CMV) retinitis in AIDS patients.	June 1996
Vitravene™ (fomivirsen sodium, injectable).	Isis Pharmaceuticals, Inc./ CIBA Vision Corp.	Treatment of cytomegalovirus (CMV) retinitis in patients with AIDS.	Aug. 1998
WinRho SDF®	Nabi	Prevention of Rh isoimmunisation in pregnant women and the treatment of thrombocytopenic purpurea (TP) (a platelet disorder that can cause uncontrolled bleeding).	Mar. 1995
Zenapax (Daclizumab).	Hoffmann- La Roche Inc.	Humanised monoclonal antibody for prevention of kidney transplant rejection.	Dec. 1997

The medicines and vaccines included on this list are produced and/or developed by companies involved in recombinant DNA research or other biotechnology applications.

Sources: The Biotechnology Industry Organisation
            Biotechnology State of the Industry Report 1998, BioWorld Publishing Group
            BioCentury, BioCentury Publications®

TERMS COMMONLY USED
IN BIOTECHNOLOGY

The following glossary is not complete. We have tried to include the most commonly used terms that appear in reports on biotechnology and genetic engineering. The explanations are kept as simple as possible.

Acclimatisation
Adaptation of an organism to a new environment.

Active immunity
A type of acquired immunity whereby resistance to a disease is built up by either having the disease or receiving a vaccine against it.

Active site
The part of a protein that must be maintained in a specific shape if the protein is to be functional, for example, the part to which the substrate binds in an enzyme. The part of an enzyme where the actual enzymatic function is performed.

Adaptation
In the evolutionary sense, some heritable feature of an individual's phenotype that improves its chances of survival and reproduction in the existing environment.

Adjuvant
Insoluble material that increases the formation and persistence of antibodies when injected with an immunogen.

Additive genetic variance
Genetic variance associated with the average effects of substituting one allele for another.

Aerobic
Needing oxygen for growth.

Affinity chromatography
A technique used in bioprocess engineering and analytical bio chemistry for separation and purification of almost any biomolecule, but typically a protein, on the basis of its biological function or chemical structure. The molecule to be purified is specifically and reversibly adsorbed by a complementary binding substance (ligand) that is immobilised on a matrix, the matrix usually being in the form of beads. The matrix then is washed to remove contaminants, and the molecule of interest is dissociated from the ligand and is recovered from the matrix in purified form by changing the experimental conditions.

Agglutinin
An antibody that, is capable of recognising and binding to an immunological determinant on the surface of bacteria or other cells and causing them to clump... (agglutination)

Agrobacterium
A bacterium normally responsible for production of crown gall disease in a variety of plants. A plasmid has been isolated from this bacterium that is useful in plant genetic engineering. This plasmid, called the Ti plasmid, has been modified so that it does not cause disease but can carry foreign DNA into susceptible plant cells.

Allelle
Any of several alternative forms of a given gene.

Allele frequency
Often called gene frequency. A measure of how common an allele is in a population; the proportion of all alleles at one gene locus that are of one specific type in a population.

Allelic exclusion
A process whereby only one immunoglobulin light chain and one heavy chain gene are transcribed in any one cell; the other genes are repressed.

Allogenic

Of the same species, but with a different genotype.

Allopolyploid

Polyploid produced by the hybridisation of two species.

Allotype

The protein product (or the result of its activity) of an allele which may be detected as an antigen in another member of the same species.
(e.g. Histocompatibility antigens, immunoglobulins), obeying the rules of simple Mendelian inheritance.

Alternative splicing

Various ways of splicing out introns in eukaryotic pre-mRNAs resulting in one gene producing several different mRNAs and protein products.

Alu family

A dispersed intermediately repetitive DNA sequence found in the human genome in about three hundred thousand copies. The sequence is about 300 bp long. The name Alu comes from the restriction endonuclease AluI that cleaves it.

Ames test

A widely used test to detect possible chemical carcinogens; based on muta-genicity in the bacterium Salmonella.

Amino acids

Building blocks of proteins. There are twenty common amino acids: alanine, arginine, asparagine, aspartic acid, cysteine, glutamic acid, glutamine, glycine, histidine, isoleucine, leucine, lysine, methionine, phenylalanine, proline, serine, threonine, tryptophan, tyrosine, and valine.

Amplification

The process of increasing the number of copies of a particular gene or chromosomal sequence. This can also include amplification of the signal to improve detection as an alternative to amplification of the sequence.

Anaerobic

Growing in the absence of oxygen.

Aneuploidy

The condition of a cell or of an organism that has additions or deletions of a small number of whole chromosomes from the expected balanced diploid number of chromosomes.

Annealing

Spontaneous alignment of two complementary single polynucleotide (RNA, or DNA, or RNA and DNA) strands to form a double helix.

Anti-oncogene

A gene that prevents malignant (cancerous) growth and whose absence, by mutation, results in malignancy (e.g retinoblastoma).

Antibiotic

Chemical substance formed as a metabolic byproduct in bacteria or fungi and used to treat bacterial infections. Antibiotics can be produced naturally, using microorganisms, or synthetically.

Antibody

Protein produced by humans and higher animals in response to the presence of a specific antigen.

Anticodon

Triplet of nucleotide cases (codon) in transfer RNA that pairs with (is complementary to) a triplet in messenger RNA. For example, if the codon is UCG, the anticodon might be AGC.

Antigen

A substance to which an antibody will bind specifically.

Antigenic determinant

See Hapten.

Antihemophilic factors

A family of whole blood proteins that initiate blood clotting, such as Factor VIII and kidney plasminogen activator.

Antisense RNA

RNA produced by copying and reversing a portion of an RNA-encoding DNA, usually including a protein-specifying region, and placing it next to a transcription control sequence. This cassette can be delivered to the target cell, resulting in genetic transformation and production of RNA that is complementary to the RNA that is produced from the original, not reversed, DNA segment. This complementary, or antisense, RNA is able to bind to the complementary sequences of the target RNA, resulting in inhibition of expression of the target gene.

Antiserum

Blood serum containing specific antibodies against an antigen. Antisera are used to confer passive immunity to many diseases and as analytical and preparative reagents for antigens.

Assay

Technique for measuring a biological response.

Attenuated

Weakened; with reference to vaccines, made from pathogenic organisms that have been treated so as to render them avirulent.

Autoimmune disease

A disease in which the body produces antibodies against its own tissues.

Autoimmunity

A condition in which the body mounts an immune response against one of its own organs or tissues.

Autosome

Any chromosome other than a sex chromosome.

Avirulent

Unable to cause disease.

Bacillus subtilis

A bacterium commonly used as a host in recombinant DNA experiments.

Important because of its ability to secrete proteins.

Bactericide

An agent that kills bacteria. Also called biocide or germicide.

Bacteriophage

Virus that reproduces in and kills bacteria. Also called phage.

Bacterium

Any of a large group of microscopic, single-cell organisms with a very simple cell structure. Some manufacture their own food from inorganic precursors alone, some live as parasites on other organisms, and some live on decaying matter.

Base

On the DNA molecule, one of the four chemical units that, according to their order, represent the different amino acids. The four bases are: adenine (A), cytosine(C), gua-nine (G), and thymine (T). In RNA, uracil (U) substitutes for thymine.

Base pair

Two nucleotide bases on different strands of a nucleic acid molecule that bond together. The bases generally pair in only two combinations; adenine with thymine (DNA) or uracil (RNA), and guanine with cytosine.

Batch processing

Growth in a closed system with a specific amount of nutrient medium. In bioprocessing, defined amounts of nutrient material and living matter are placed in a bioreactor and removed when the process is completed. *Cf.* Continuous processing.

Bioassay

Determination of the effectiveness of a compound by measuring its effect on animals, tissues, or organisms, usually in comparison with a standard preparation.

Biocatalyst
In bioprocessing, an enzyme that activates or speeds up a biochemical reaction.

Biochemical
The product of a chemical reaction in a living organism.

Biochip
Electronic device that uses biologically derived or related organic molecules to form a semiconductor.

Biocide
An agent capable of killing almost any type of cell.

Bioconversion
Chemical restructuring of raw materials by using a biocatalyst.

Biodegradable
Capable of being broken down by the action of microorganisms found under conditions generally in the environment.

Biological oxygen demand (BOD)
The amount of oxygen used for growth by organisms in water that contains organic matter, in the process of degrading that matter.

Biologic response modulator
A substance that alters the growth or functioning of a cell. Includes hormones and compounds that affect the nervous and immune systems.

Biomass
The totality of biological matter in a given area. As commonly used in biotechnology, refers to the use of cellulose, a renewable resource, for the production of chemicals that can be used to generate energy or as alternative feed-stocks for the chemical industry to reduce dependence on non-renewable fossil fuels.

Bioprocess
A process in which living cells, or components thereof, are used to produce a desired end product.

Bioreactor
Vessel used for bioprocessing.

Biosynthesis
Production of a chemical by a living organism.

Biotechnology
Development of products by a biological process. Production may be carried out by using intact organisms, such as yeasts and bacteria, or by using natural substances (e.g.enzymes) from organisms.

B lymphocytes (B-cells)
A class of lymphocytes, released from the bone marrow and which produce antibodies.

Bovine somatotropin
(also called bovine growth hormone.) A hormone secreted by the bovine pituitary gland. It has been used to increase milk production by improving the feed efficiency in dairy cattle.

Callus
A cluster of undifferentiated plant cells that can, for some species, be induced to form the whole plant.

Carcinogen
Cancer-causing agent.

Catalyst
An agent (such as an enzyme or a metallic complex) that facilitates a reaction but is not itself changed at completion of the reaction.

Cell
The smallest structural unit of living organisms that is able to grow and reproduce independently.

Cell culture
Growth of a collection of cells, usually of just one genotype, under laboratory conditions.

Cell fusion
See Fusion.

Cell line

Cells which grow and replicate continuously in cell culture outside the living organism.

Cell-mediated immunity

Acquired immunity in which T lymphocytes play a predominant role. Development of the thymus in early life is critical to the proper development and functioning of cell-mediated immunity.

Chemostat

Growth chamber that keeps a bacterial or other cell culture at a specific volume and rate of growth by continually adding fresh nutrient medium while removing spent culture.

Chimera

An individual (animal, plant, or lower multicellular organism) composed of cells of more than one genotype. Chimeras are produced, for example, by grafting an embryonic part of one species onto an embryo of either the same or a different species.

Chromosomes

Threadlike components in the cell that contain DNA and proteins. Genes are carried on the chromosomes.

Cistron

A length of chromosomal DNA representing the smallest functional unit of heredity, essentially identical to a gene.

Clone

A group of genes, cells, or organisms derived from a common ancestor. Because there is no combining of genetic material (as in sexual reproduction), the members of the clone are genetically identical or nearly identical to the parent.

Codon

A sequence of three nucleotide bases that in the process of protein synthesis specifies an amino acid or provides a signal to stop or start protein synthesis (translation).

Coenzyme

An organic compound that is necessary for the functioning of an enzyme. Coenzymes are smaller than the enzymes themselves and may be tightly or loosely attached to the enzyme protein molecule.

Cofactor

A nonprotein substance required for certain enzymes to function. Cofactors can be coenzymes or metallic ions.

Colony-stimulating factors

A group of lymphokines which induce the maturation and proliferation of white blood cells from the primitive cell types present in bone marrow.

Complementarity

The relationship of the nucleotide bases on two different strands of DNA or RNA. When the bases are paired properly (adenine with thymine [DNA] or uracil [RNA] and guanine with cytosine), the strands are said to be "complementary."

Complementary DNA (cDNA)

DNA synthesised from an RNA template rather than from a DNA template. This type of DNA is used for cloning or as a DNA probe for locating specific genes in DNA hybridisation studies.

Conjugation

Sexual reproduction of bacterial cells in which there is a one-way exchange of genetic material between the cells in contact.

Continuous processing

A method of bioprocessing in which new materials are added and products removed continuously at a rate that maintains the volume at a specific level and usually maintain the composition of the mixture as well. Cf. Batch processing and chemostat.

Crossing over

Exchange of genes between two paired chromosomes.

Culture

As a noun, cultivation of living organism in prepared medium; as a verb, to grow in prepared medium.

Culture medium

Any nutrient system for the artificial cultivation of bacteria or other cells; usually a complex mixture of organic and inorganic materials.

Cyto

A prefix referring to cell or cell plasm.

Cytogenetics

Study of the cell and its heredity related components, especially the study of chromosomes as they occur in their "condensed" state, when not replicating.

Cytokines

Intercellular signals, usually protein or glycoprotein, involved in the regulation of cellular proliferation and function.

Cytoplasm

Cellular material that is within the cell membrane and surround the nucleus.

Cytotoxic

Able to cause cell death A cytotoxic substance usually is more subtle in its action than is a biocide.

Defensin

A natural defence protein isolated from cattle. It may prove effective against shipping fever, a viral disease that attacks cattle during transport, causing an estimated US$250 million in losses each year.

Deoxyribonucleic acid (DNA)

The molecule that carries the genetic information for most living systems. The DNA molecule consists of four bases (adenine, cytosine, guanine, and thymine) and a sugar-phosphate backbone, arranged in two connected strands to form a double helix. See also Complementary DNA; Double helix; Recombinant DNA; Base pair.

Diagnostic

A product used for the diagnosis of disease or medical condition. Both monoclonal antibodies and DNA probes are useful diagnostic products.

Differentiation

The process of biochemical and structural changes by which cells become specialised in form and function as the organism develops.

Diploid

A cell with two complete sets of chromosomes. Cf. Haploid.

DNA

See Deoxyribonucleic acid.

DNA probe

A molecule (usually a nucleic acid) that has been labelled with a radioactive isotope, dye, or enzyme and is used to locate a particular nucleotide sequence or gene on a DNA or RNA molecule.

Double helix

A term often used to describe the configuration of the DNA molecule. The helix consists of two spiraling strands of nucleotides (a sugar, phosphate, and base), joined crosswise by specific pairing of the bases. See also Deoxyribonucleic acid; Base; Base pair.

Downstream processing

The stages of processing that take place after the fermentation or bioconversion stage, includes separation, purification, and packaging of the product.

Drug Delivery

The process by which a formulated drug is administered to the patient. Traditional routes have been orally or by intravenous perfusion. New methods that are being developed are through the skin by application of a transdermal patch or across the nasal membrane by administration of a specially formulated aerosol spray.

Electrophoresis

A technique for separating different types of molecules in a gel (or liquid), ion-conducting medium, based on their differential movement in an applied electrical field.

Endonuclease

An enzyme that breaks nucleic acids at specific interior bonding sites; thus producing nucleic acid fragments of various lengths. *Cf.* Exonuclease.

Enzyme

A protein catalyst that facilitates specific chemical or metabolic reactions necessary for cell growth and reproduction. *Cf* Catalyst.

Epitope

A site on the surface of a macro-molecule capable of being recognised by an antibody. An epitope may consist of just a few amino-acid residues in a protein or a few sugar residues in a polysaccharide. A synonym is "immunological determinant."

Erythropoietin

(also abbreviate EPO) A protein that boosts production of red blood cells. It is clinically useful in treating certain types of anemias.

Escherichia coli (*E. coli*)

A bacterium that inhabits the intestinal tract of most vertebrates. Much of the work using recombinant DNA techniques has been carried out with this organism because it has been genetically very well characterised.

Eukaryote

A cell or organism containing a true nucleus, with a well-defined membrane surrounding the nucleus. All organisms except bacteria, archebacteria, viruses, and blue-green algae are eukaryotic. *Cf.* Prokaryote.

Exon

In eukaryotic cells, the part of the gene that is transcribed into messenger RNA and encodes a protein. *See also* Intron; Splicing.

Exonuclease

An enzyme that breaks down nucleic acids only at the ends of poly-nucleotide chains, thus releasing one nucleotide at a time, in sequential order. *Cf.* Endonuclease.

Expression

In genetics, manifestation of a characteristic that is specified by a gene. With hereditary diseases, for example, a person can carry the gene for the disease but not actually have the disease. In this case, the gene is present but not expressed. In molecular biology and industrial biotechnology, the term is often used to mean the production of a protein by a gene that has been inserted into a new host organism.

Expressed sequence tags (ESTs)

A unique DNA sequence derived from a cDNA library (therefore from a sequence which has been transcribed in some tissue or at some stage of development). The EST can be mapped, by a combination of genetic mapping procedures, to a unique locus in the genome and serves to identify that gene locus.

Factor VIII

A large, complex protein that aids in blood clotting and is used to treat hemophilia. *See also* Antihemophilic factors.

Feedstock

The raw material used in chemical or biological processes.

Fermentation

An anaerobic process of growing microorganisms for the production of various chemical or pharmaceutical compounds. Microbes are normally incubated under specific conditions in the presence of nutrients in large tanks called fermentors.

Frameshift

Insertion or deletion of one or more nucleotide bases such that incorrect triplets of bases are read as codons.

Fusion

Joining of the membrane of two cells, thus creating a new, fused cell that contains at least some of the nuclear material from both parent cells. Used in making hybridomas.

Fusion protein

A protein with a polypeptide chain derived from two or more proteins. A fusion protein is expressed from a gene prepared by recombinant DNA methods from the portions of genes encoding two or more proteins.

Gene

A segment of chromosome that encodes the necessary regulatory and sequence information to direct the synthesis of a protein or RNA product. *See also* Operator; Regulatory gene; Structural gene, Suppressor gene.

"Gene machine"

A computer controlled, solid-state chemistry device for synthesising oligodeoxyribonucleotides by combining chemically activated precursors of deoxyribonucleotides (bases) sequentially in the proper order.

Gene mapping

Determination of the relative locations of genes on a chromosome.

Gene sequencing

Determination of the sequence of nucleotide bases in a strand of DNA.

Gene therapy

The replacement of a defective gene in an organism suffering from a genetic disease. Recombinant DNA techniques are used to isolate the functioning gene and insert it into cells. Over three hundred single gene genetic disorders have been identified in humans. A significant percentage of these may be amenable to gene therapy.

Gene Code

The mechanism by which genetic information is stored in living organisms. The code uses sets of three nucleotide bases (codons) to make the amino aids that, in turn, constitute proteins.

Genetic engineering

A technology used to alter the genetic material of living cells in order to make them capable of producing new substances or performing new functions.

Genetic screening

The use of a specific biological test to screen for inherited diseases or medical conditions. Testing can be conducted prenatally to check for metabolic defects and congenital disorders in the developing foetus as well as postnatally to screen for carriers of hereditary diseases.

Genetic map

A linear designation of sites within a chromosome or genome, based upon the various frequencies of recombination between genetic markers. *See* Linkage map.

Genome

The total hereditary material of a cell, comprising the entire chromosomal set found in each nucleus of a given species.

Genotype

Genetic make-up of an individual or group. *Cf.* Phenotype.

Germ cell

Reproductive cell (sperm or egg). Also called gamete or sex cell.

Germicide

See Bactericide.

Germplasm

The total genetic variability, represented by germ cells or seeds, available within a particular population of organisms.

Gene pool

The total genetic information contained within a given population.

Growth hormone

(Also called somatotropin) A protein produced by the pituitary gland that is involved in cell growth. Human growth hormone is clinically used to treat dwarfism. Various animal growth hormones can be used to improve milk production as well as producing a leaner variety of meat.

Haploid

A cell with half the usual number of chromosomes, or only one chromosome set. Sex cells are haploid. *Cf.* Diploid.

Hapten

A small molecule which, when chemically-coupled to a protein, acts as an immunogen and stimulates the formation of antibodies not only against the two-molecule complex but also against the hapten alone.

Hemagglutination

Clumping (agglutination) of red blood cells, for example by antibody molecules or virus particles.

Hereditary

Capable of being transferred as genetic information from parent cells to progeny.

Histocompatibility

Immunologic similarity of tissues such that grafting can be done without tissue rejection.

Histocompatibility antigen

An antigen that causes the rejection of grafted material from an animal different in genotype from that of the host animal.

Homologous

Corresponding or alike in structure, position, or origin.

Hormone

A chemical that acts as a messenger or stimulatory signal, relaying instructions to stop or start certain physiological activities. Hormones are synthesised in one type of cell and then released to direct the function of other cell types.

Host

A cell or organism used for growth of a virus, plasmid, or other form of foreign DNA, or for the production of cloned substances.

Host-vector system

Combination of DNA-receiving cells (host) and DNA-transporting substance (vector) used for introducing foreign DNA into a cell.

Humoral immunity

Immunity resulting from circulating antibodies in plasma protein.

Hybridisation

Production of offspring, or hybrids, from genetically dissimilar parents. The process can be used to produce hybrid plants (by cross-breeding two different varieties) or hybridomas (hybrid cells formed by fusing two unlike cells, used in producing monoclonal antibodies). The term is also used to refer to the binding of complementary strands of DNA or RNA.

Hybridoma

The cell produced by fusing two cells of different origin. In monoclonal antibody technology, hybridomas are formed by fusing an immortal cell (one that divides continuously) and an antibody-producing cell. *See also* Monoclonal antibody; Myeloma.

Immune serum

Blood serum containing antibodies.

Immune system

The aggregation of cells, biological substances (such as antibodies), and cellular activities that work together to provide resistance to disease.

Immunity

Nonsusceptibility to a disease or to the toxic effects of antigenic material. *See also* Active i., Cell-mediated i.; Humoral i.; Natural active i.; Natural passive.; Passive i.

Immunoassay

Technique for identifying substances based on the use of antibodies.

Immunodiagnostics

The use of specific antibodies to measure a substance. This tool is useful in diagnosing infectious diseases and the presence of foreign substances in a variety of human and animal fluids (blood, urine, etc.) It is currently being investigated as a way of locating tumour cells in the body.

Immunofluorescence

Technique for identifying antigenic material that uses antibody labelled with fluorescent material. Specific binding of the antibody and antigen can be seen under a microscope by applying ultraviolet light rays and noting the visible light that is produced.

Immunogen

Any substance that can elicit an immune response, especially specific antibody production... An immunogen that reacts with the elicited antibody may be called an antigen.

Immunoglobulin

General name for proteins that function as antibodies. These proteins differ somewhat in structure, and are grouped into five categories on the basis of these differences: immunoglobulin G (IgG) IgM, IgA, IgD and IgE.

Immunology

Study of all phenomena related to the body's response to antigenic challenge (i.e., immunity, sensitivity, and allergy).

Immunomodulators

A diverse class of proteins that boost the immune system. Many are cell growth factors that accelerate the production of specific cells that are important in mounting an immune response in the body. These proteins are being investigated for use in possible cures for cancer.

Immunotoxins

Specific monoclonal antibodies that have a protein toxin molecule attached. The monoclonal antibody is targeted against a tumour cell and the toxin is designed to kill that cell when the antibody binds to it. Immunotoxins have also been termed "magic bullets."

Inducer

A molecule or substance that increases the rate of enzyme synthesis, usually by blocking the action of the corresponding repressor.

Interferon

A class of lymphokine proteins important in the immune response. The are three major types of interferon: alpha (leukocyte), beta (fibroblast), and gamma (immune). Interferons inhibit viral infections and may have anticancer properties.

Interleukin

A type of lymphokine whose role in the immune system is being extensively studied. Two types of interleukin have been identified. Interleukin 1 (IL-1), derived from macrophages, is produced during inflammation and amplifies the production of other lymphokines, notably interleukin 2 (IL-2). IL-2 regulates the maturation and replication of T lymphocytes.

Intron

In eukaryotic cells, a sequence of DNA that is contained in the gene but does not encode for protein. The presence of introns divides the coding region of the gene into segments called exons. *See also* Exon; Splicing.

In vitro

Literally, "in glass." Performed in a test tube or other laboratory apparatus.

In vivo

In the living organism.

Isoenzyme (isozyme)

One of the several forms that a given enzyme can take. The forms may differ in certain physical properties, but function similarly as biocatalysts.

Isogenic

Of the same genotype.

Kidney plasminogen activator

A precursor to the enzyme urokinase that has bloodclotting properties.

Leukocyte

A colourless cell in the blood, lymph, and tissues that is an important component of the body's immune system; also called white blood cell.

Library

A set of cloned DNA fragments.

Ligase

An enzyme used to join DNA or RNA segments together. They are called DNA ligase of RNA ligase, respectively.

Linkage

The tendency for certain genes to be inherited together due to their physical proximity on the chromosome.

Linkage map

An abstract map of chromosomal loci, based on recombinant frequencies.

Linkage group

A group of gene loci known to be linked; a chromosome. There are as many linkage groups as there are homologous pairs of chromosomes. *See* Synteny.

Linker

A fragment of DNA with a restriction site that can be used to join DNA strands.

Lipoproteins

A class of serum proteins that transport lipids and cholesterol in the blood stream. Abnormalities in lipoprotein metabolism have been implicated in certain heart diseases.

Locus(Plural loci)

The position of a gene, DNA marker or genetic marker on a chromosome. *See* Gene locus.

Lymphocyte

A type of leukocyte found in lymphatic tissue in the blood, lymph nodes, and organs. Lymphocytes are continuously made in the bone marrow and mature into antibody-forming cells. *See also* B lymphocytes; T lymphocytes.

Lymphokine

A class of soluble proteins produced by white blood cells that play a role, as yet not fully understood, in the immune response. *See also* Interferon; Interleukin.

Lymphoma

Form of cancer that affects the lymph tissue.

Lysis

Breaking apart of cells.

Lysozyme

An enzyme present in, for example, tears, saliva, egg whites and some plant tissues that destroys the cells of certain bacteria.

Macrophage

A type of white blood cell produced in blood vessels and loose connective tissues that can ingest dead tissue and cells and is involved in producing interleukin 1. When exposed to the lymphokine "macrophage-activating factor," macrophages also kill tumour cells. *See also* Phagocyte.

Marker

Any genetic element (locus, allele, DNA sequence or chromosome feature) which can be readily detected by phenotype, cytological or molecular techniques, and used to follow a chromosome or chromosomal segment during genetic analysis. *See* Centromere marker; chromosome marker; DNA marker; genetic marker; inside marker; outside marker.

Macrophage-activating factor

An agent that stimulates macrophages to attack and ingest cancer cells.

Medium

A liquid or solid (gel) substance containing nutrients needed for cell growth.

Meiosis

Process of cell reproduction whereby the daughter cells have half the chromosome number of the parent cells. Sex cells are formed by meiosis. *Cf.* Mitosis.

Messenger RNA (mRNA)

Nucleic acid that carries instructions to a ribosome for the synthesis of a particular protein.

Metabolism

All biochemical activities carried out by an organism to maintain life.

Microbial herbicides/pesticides

Microorganisms that are toxic to specific plant/insects. Because of their narrow host range and limited toxicity, these microorganisms may be preferable to their chemical counterparts for certain pest control applications.

Microbiology

Study of living organisms and viruses, which can be seen only under a microscope.

Microorganism

Any organism that can be seen only with the aid of a microscope. Also called microbe.

Mitosis

Process of cell reproduction whereby the daughter cells are identical in chromosome number to the parent cells. *Cf.* Meiosis.

Molecular genetics

Study of how genes function to control cellular activities.

Monoclonal antibody

Highly specific, purified antibody that is derived from only one clone of cells and recognises only one antigen. *See also* Hybridoma; Myeloma.

mRNA

Messenger RNA.

Multigenic

Of hereditary characteristics, one that is specified by several genes.

Mutagen

A substance that induces mutations.

Mutant

A cell that manifests new characteristics due to a change in its DNA.

Mutation

A change in the genetic material of a cell.

Muton

The smallest element of a chromosome whose alteration can result in a mutation or a mutant organism.

Myeloma

A type of tumour cell that uses monoclonal antibody technology to form hybridomas.

Natural active immunity

Immunity that is established after the occurrence of a disease.

Natural killer (NK) cell

A type of leukocyte that attacks cancerous or virus-infected cells without previous exposure to the antigen. NK cell activity is stimulated by interferon.

Natural passive immunity

Immunity conferred by the mother on the foetus or new-born.

Nitrogen fixation

A biological process (usually associated with plants) whereby certain bacteria convert nitrogen in the air to ammonia, thus forming a nutrient essential for growth.

Nuclease

An enzyme that, by cleaving chemical bonds, breaks down nucleic acids into their constituent nucleotides. *See also* Exonuclease.

Nueic acid

Large molecules, generally found in the cell's nucleus and/or cytoplasm, that are made up of nucleotide bases. The two kinds of nucleic acid are DNA and RNA.

Nucleotide base
See Base.

Nucleotides
The building blocks of nucleic acids. Each nucleotide is composed of sugar, phosphate, and one of four nitrogen bases. If the sugar is ribose, the nucleotide is termed a "riboucleotide," whereas deoxyribonucleotides have deoxyribose as the sugar component. The sequence of the nucleotides within the nucleic acid determines, for example, the amino acid sequence of an encoded protein.

Nucleus
The structure within eukaryotic cells that contains chromosomal DNA.

Oligodeoxyribonucleotide
A molecule consisting of a small number (about two to a few tens) of nucleotides linked by sugar to phosphate in a linear chain.

Oncogene
Any of a family of cellular DNA sequences which possess the potential to become malignant by undergoing alteration. There are 4 groups of viral and non-viral oncogenes: protein kinases, GTPases, nuclear proteins, and growth factors.

Oncogenic
Cancer causing.

Oncology
Study of tumours.

Open reading frame
A nucleotide sequence beginning with a start (AUG) codon, continuing in register with amino acid-encoding codons, and ending with a stop codon.

Operator
A region of the chromosome, adjacent to the sequences encoding the gene product, where a repressor protein binds to prevent transcription.

Operon
Sequence of genes responsible for synthesising the enzymes needed for biosynthesis of a molecule. An operon is controlled by an operator gene and a repressor gene.

Opsonin
An antibody that renders bacteria and other antigenic material susceptible to destruction by phagocytes.

Organic compound
A compound containing carbon.

Passive immunity
Immunity acquired from receiving preformed antibodies.

Pathogen
Disease-causing organism.

Peptide
Two or more amino acids joined by a linkage called a peptide bond.

Phage
See Bacteriophage.

Phagocyte
A type of white blood cell that can ingest invading microorganisms and other foreign material. *See also* Macrophage.

Phenotype
Observable characteristics, resulting from interaction between an organism's genetic make-up and the environment. *Cf.* Genotype

Photosynthesis
Conversion by plants of light energy into chemical energy, which is then used to support the plants' biological processes.

Plasma
The fluid (non-cellular) fraction of blood.

Plasmapheresis
A technique used to separate useful factors from blood.

Plasmid

A small circular form of DNA that carries certain genes and is capable of replicating independently in a host cell.

Pleiotropic

Genes or mutations that result in the production of multiple effects at the phenotypic level. It is the consequence of the fact that biochemical pathways starting from different genes intersect in many places, inhibiting, deflecting, and variously modifying each other. Introduced genes may also insert into sites that effect phenotypic changes other than the one desired.

Polyclonal

Derived from different types of cells.

Polymer

A long molecule of repeated subunits

Polymerase

General term for enzymes that carry out the synthesis of nucleic acids.

Polymerase chain reaction (PCR)

A technique used for enzymatic *in vitro* amplification of specific DNA sequences without utilising conventional procedures of molecular cloning. It allows the amplification of a DNA region situated between two convergent primers and utilises oligonucleotide primers that hybridise to opposite strands. Primer extension proceeds inward across the region between the two primers. The product of DNA synthesis of one primer serves as a template for the other primer; repeated cycles of DNA denaturation, annealing of primers, and extension result in an exponential increase in the number of copies of the region bounded by the primers.

Polypeptide

Long chain of amino acids joined by peptide bonds.

Probe

See DNA probe.

Prokaryote

A cellular organism (e.g., bacterium, blue-green algae) whose DNA is not enclosed within a nuclear membrane. *Cf.* Eukaryote.

Promoter

A DNA sequence that is located near or even partially within encoding nucleotide sequences and which controls gene expression. Promoters are required for binding of RNA polymerase to initiate transcription.

Prophage

Phage nucleic acid that is incorporated into the host's chromosome but does not cause cell lysis.

Protein

A molecule composed of amino acids. There are many types of proteins, most carrying out functions essential for cell growth.

Protein A

A protein produced by the bacterium *Staphylococcus aureus* that specifically binds antibodies. It is useful in the purification of monoclonal antibodies.

Protoplast

The cellular material that remains after the cell wall has been removed.

Pure culture

In vitro growth of only one type of microorganism.

Radioimmunoassay

A technique for quantifying a substance by measuring the reactivity of radioactively labelled forms of the substance with antibodies.

Reagent

Substance used in a chemical reaction, often for analytical purposes.

Recombinant DNA (rDNA)

The DNA formed by combining segments of DNA from two or more different sources or different regions of a genome.

Regeneration

Laboratory technique for forming a new plant from a clump of plant cells.

Regulatory gene

A gene that acts to control the protein-synthesising activity of other genes.

Replication

Reproduction or duplication, as of an exact copy of a strand of DNA.

Replicon

A segment of DNA (e.g., chromosome or plasmid) that can replicate independently.

Repressor

A protein that binds to an operator adjacent to a structural gene, inhibiting transcription of the gene.

Restriction enzyme

An enzyme that recognises a specific DNA nucleotide sequence, usually symmetrical, and cuts the DNA within or near the recognised sequence. This may create a gap into which new genes can be inserted.

Reticuloendothelial system

The system of macrophages, which serves as an important defence system against disease.

Retrovirus

An animal virus that contains the enzyme reverse transcriptase. This enzyme converts the viral RNA into DNA which can combine with the DNA of the host cell and produce more viral particles.

Rheology

Study of the flow of matter such as fermentation liquids.

Rhizobium

A class of microorganisms that converts atmospheric nitrogen into a form that plants can utilise for growth. Species of this microorganism grow symbiotically on the roots of certain legumes such as peas, beans, and alfalfa.

RIA (Radioimmunoassay)

A diagnostic test using antibodies to detect trace amounts of substances. Such tests are useful in biomedical research to study how drugs interact with their receptors.

Ribonucleic acid (RNA)

A molecule similar to DNA that functions primarily to decode the instructions for protein synthesis that are carried by genes. *See also* Messenger RNA; Transfer RNA.

Ribosome

A cellular component, containing protein and RNA, that is involved in protein sythesis.

Ribozyme

Any of the RNA molecules possessing catalytic activity and acting as biological catalysts.

RNA

Ribonucleic acid.

Scale-up

Transition from small-scale production to production of large industrial quantities.

Selective medium

Nutrient material constituted such that it will support the growth of specific organisms while inhibiting the growth of others.

Sequence tagged site (STS):

Short (200 to 500 base pairs) DNA sequence that has a single occurrence in the human genome and whose location and base sequence are known. Detectable by polymerase chain reaction, STSs are useful for localising and orienting the mapping and sequence data reported from many different laboratories and serve as landmarks on the developing physical map of the human genome. Expressed sequence tags (ESTs) are STSs derived from cDNAs.

Serology

Study of blood serum and reaction between the antibodies and antigens therein.

Signal sequence

The N-terminal sequence of a secreted protein, which is required for transport through the cell membrane.

Single-cell protein

Cells or protein extracts from micro-organisms, grown in large quantities for use as protein supplements. Single cell protein is expected to have a nutritionally favourable balance of amino acids.

Site-specific recombination

A crossover event, such as the integration of phage lambda, that requires homology of only a very short region and uses an enzyme specific for that recombination. Recombination occurring between two specific sequences that need not be homologous; mediated by a specific recombination system.

snRNP

Small nuclear ribonucleoprotein (RNA plus protein) particle. Component of the spliceosome, the intron-removing apparatus in eukaryotic nuclei .

Somatic cells

Cells other than sex or germ cells.

Splicing

The removal of introns and joining of exons to form a continuous coding sequence in RNA.

Strain

A pure-breeding lineage, usually of haploid organisms, bacteria, or viruses.

Stringent response

A translational control mechanism of prokaryotes that represses tRNA and rRNA synthesis during amino acid starvation.

Structural gene

A gene that codes for a protein, such as an enzyme.

Substrate

Material acted on by an enzyme.

Suppressor gene

A gene that can reverse the effect of a mutation in other genes.

Synteny

All loci on one chromosome are said to be syntenic (literally on the same ribbon). Loci may appear to be unlinked by conventional genetic tests for linkage but still be syntenic.

Synteny test

A test that determines whether two loci belong to the same linkage group (i.e. are syntenic) by observing concordance (occurrence of markers together) in hybrid cell lines.

Template

A molecule that serves as the pattern for synthesising another molecule.

Therapeutics

Compounds that are used to treat specific diseases or medical conditions.

Thymus

A lymphoid organ in the lower neck, the proper functioning of which in early life is necessary for development of the immune system.

Tissue culture

In vitro growth in nutrient medium of cells isolated from tissue.

Tissue plasminogen activator (tPA)

A protein produced in small amounts in the body that aids in dissolving blood clots.

T lymphocytes (T-cells)

White blood cells that are produced in the bone marrow but mature in the thymus. They are important in the body's defence against certain bacteria and fungi, help B lymphocytes make antibodies, and help in the recognition and rejection of foreign tissues. T lymphocytes may also be important in the body's defence against cancers.

Toxin

A poisonous substance produced by certain microorganisms.

Transcription

Synthesis of messenger (or any other) RNA on a DNA template.

Transduction

Transfer of genetic material from one cell to another by means of a virus or phage vector.

Transfection

Infection of a cell with nucleic acid from a virus, resulting in replication of the complete virus.

Transfer RNA (tRNA)

RNA molecules that carry amino acids to sites on ribosomes where proteins are synthesised.

Transformation

Change in the genetic structure of an organism by the incorporation of foreign DNA.

Transgenic organism

An organism formed by the insertion of foreign genetic material into the germ line cells of organisms. Recombinant DNA techniques are commonly used to produce transgenic organisms.

Translation

Process by which the information on a messenger RNA molecule is used to direct the synthesis of a protein.

Transposon

A segment of DNA that can move around and be inserted at several sites in the genome of a cell possibly altering expression. The first to be described was the Ac/Ds system in maize shown by McClintock to cause unstable mutations.

tRNA

See transfer RNA.

Tumour necrosis factor

A cytokine with many actions including the destruction of some types of tumour cells without affecting healthy cells. However, hopes for their usefulness in cancer therapy have been dampened by toxic effects of the treatment. They are now being engineered for selective toxicity for cancer cells.

Tumour suppressor gene

Any of a category of genes that can suppress transformation or tumour-igenicity (probably ordinarily involved in normal control of cell growth and division.

Vaccine

A preparation that contains an antigen consisting of whole disease-causing organisms (killed or weakened), or parts of such organisms, and is used to confer immunity against the disease that the organism cause. Vaccine preparation can be natural, synthetic, or derived by recombinant DNA technology.

Vector

The agent (e.g., plasmid or virus) used to carry new DNA into a cell.

Virion

An elementary viral particle consisting of genetic material and a protein covering.

Virology

Study of viruses.

Virulence

Ability to infect or cause disease.

Virus

A submicroscopic organism that contains genetic information but cannot reproduce itself. To replicate, it must invade another cell and use parts of that cell's reproductive machinery.

White blood cells

See Leukocytes.

Wild type

The form of an organism that occurs most frequently in nature.

Yeast

A general term for single-celled fungi that reproduce by budding. Some yeasts can ferment carbohydrates (starches and sugars), and thus are important in brewing and baking.

Index